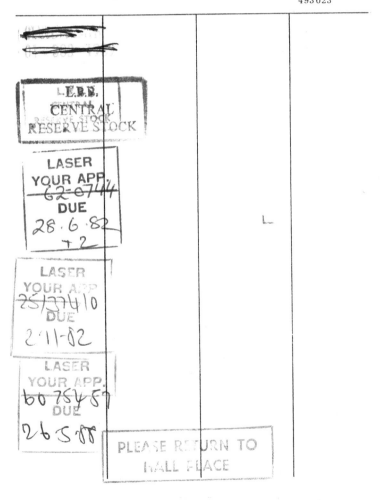

THE HISTORY AND TRADITIONS OF THE MOORFIELDS EYE HOSPITAL

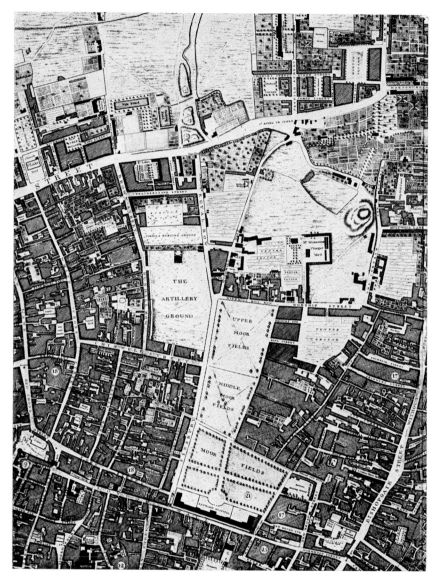

Map of London covering two of the Hospital's sites

The map section is taken from John Rocque's 1746 "Plan of the Cities of London and Westminster and Borough of Southwark", in 24 sheets to a scale of 26 inches to one mile, published in facsimile by Harry Margary of Lympne Castle, Kent, and is reproduced with his permission.

THE HISTORY AND TRADITIONS
OF THE
MOORFIELDS EYE HOSPITAL

VOLUME II

BEING A CONTINUATION OF TREACHER COLLINS' HISTORY OF THE FIRST HUNDRED YEARS

By

Frank W. Law

Consulting Surgeon; Member of the House Committee; formerly Member of the Committee of Management, the Board of Governors and the Finance Committee, and Chairman of the Medical Board; House Surgeon, Chief Clinical Assistant, Curator and Librarian, and Consultant Surgeon

WITH 69 ILLUSTRATIONS
and one coloured plate

LONDON
H. K. LEWIS AND CO. LTD.
1975

ISBN 0 7186 0404 0

PRINTED IN GREAT BRITAIN BY HEADLEY BROTHERS LTD
109 KINGSWAY LONDON WC2B 6PX AND ASHFORD KENT

To the memory of
the Author of Volume I
EDWARD TREACHER COLLINS
—and for Tommy

"*Nowhere is the temptation to write a romance instead of an historical study more compelling than here and it is for that reason that the greatest care has been taken in the use of all (these) documents.*"

WALTHER WOLF

(*Zwei Beiträge zur Geschichte der achtzehnten Dynastie*)

v

PREFACE

THE invitation to bring the history of Moorfields Eye Hospital up to date caused certain misgivings on realising that inevitable comparisons would be made between the first volume by Collins and this second volume. Collins' work was a masterpiece; the research involved in its compilation must have been prodigious, and after this interval of time—it was published in 1929 and recorded history of up to 160 years before that date—one is compelled to wonder how its author came by the mass of detailed information which it contains. Treacher Collins was elected to the staff in 1895, retired in 1922 and died in 1932—nonetheless I knew him, and well recall his visits to the Pathological Laboratory at the time when I was Curator. The fact that it is likely that the bulk of the work on his volume was done after release from his stressful and demanding hospital duties in no way detracts from its merit; it is a formidable and impressive achievement, and courage and considerable self-persuasion were surely necessary in order to be more stimulated than daunted by the task. In his preface he says that in early life a man has to learn history, in middle life to make it, and in his later years he becomes best qualified to write it; he goes on to quote "when a medical man begins to write on the history of his subject it is a sure sign of senility". Like him I can claim no exception to this rule, and merely cry "touché", adding in some extenuation that at least one was commissioned for the task.

Collins points out that he endeavoured to give his account of events in chronological order. A consideration of the manner in which to present the material in this volume gave one furiously to think. If one takes a subject and gives its history from beginning to end, one will at that end be talking of a period scores of years after the date of the next subject. On the other hand a truly chronological account would result in separate, constantly repeated references to one subject, with a result

vii

inconsequent and fragmentary. An attempt at compromise between these two extremes has been made, and each subject treated in the manner best suited to the record. Again, consideration of the very varied public for whom one was writing and the many different interests which it was desirable to serve made the question of selection or omission of subjects, and the placing of emphasis, a most difficult task. An endeavour has been made to cover the ground for all those who one thought might be gracious enough to become one's readers, and consolation drawn from the reflection that what is written without effort is in general read without pleasure. Reference to one's reading public reminds one of a further passage in Collins' preface, in which he says that, so intimately associated had the hospital been with scientific advances, that it was not possible to write a history of Moorfields without giving an account of them also. He hoped that such a course of action would increase his circle of readers. This action was not taken on the boastful assumption that a history of Moorfields is a history of Ophthalmology; it derives rather from the state of affairs as regards publication of matter in those days. The *British Journal of Ophthalmology* dates from 1917, having absorbed the *Ophthalmic Review* (1882) and the *Ophthalmoscope* (1903). There were certainly continental journals in circulation before that time, such as the *Annales d'Oculistique* (1838), the *Klinische Monatsblätter* (1863), Von Graefe's *Archiv* (1854), the *Archiv für Augenheilkunde* (1869), and in the same year the *American Archives;* but it is true that the majority of the journals which we know today came into being, like the Review, in the last two decades of the nineteenth century. Publication abroad was much less common then than it is today. It follows that for the greater part of the period covered by Collins' book there was no English publication to which one could submit an article. In 1857 the *Royal London Ophthalmic Hospital Reports* came into existence, but its contents were largely (though not exclusively) contributed by members of the staff; there were no book reviews nor correspondence, and the circulation was very limited, there being 195 subscribers a year after its appearance. This state of affairs justified and indeed perhaps compelled Collins' decision. On the other hand, while references to scientific progress are made throughout this present volume, it was thought that in these days of extensive travel, multiplicity of publications, freedom of communication, and world-wide publicity the need to adopt a similar course was removed. I hope that this decision in no way detracts from the interest or value of the book, nor alienates potential readers.

I am deeply conscious of the honour done to me by the authorities in inviting me to write this history, and the trust therein implied. Reference has been made to the diversity of people who may be inclined to read it, and the effort that has been made to provide for them all; but one is very aware that all too often an endeavour to please everybody results in pleasing nobody. Nonetheless the decision had to be made; I can but add that my pride in the commission is equalled only by my hope that I have in some measure fulfilled its object.

FRANK W. LAW

Chipperfield
May 1974

ACKNOWLEDGEMENTS

My main sources of information have been the Annual Reports of the Hospital and Institute and the Minute Books of the Committee of Management, the Board of Governors, the House Committees, Medical Committees, Finance Committee, Nursing Committee, and other Committees and Sub-Committees, all of which, covering the period concerned, I have read. Standard reference books such as the *Dictionary of National Biography*, *Who's Who*, *Who Was Who*, and the *Medical Directory* have been consulted, as have medical journals such as the *Ophthalmic Review*, the *Ophthalmoscope*, and the *British Journal of Ophthalmology* in this country. For the illustrations I have gone to the above Journals, to the collection of photographs at both branches of the Hospital, to Harry Margary (for the frontispiece) and to private sources.

I acknowledge gratefully the co-operation of Eustace Cornelius, Librarian, and R. S. Johnson-Gilbert, Secretary, at the Royal College of Surgeons, and of Mary Morris at the Secretariat there; and of Geoffrey Davenport, Assistant Librarian of the Royal College of Physicians. Personal comments, reminiscences, and suggestions have been gracefully provided by Maurice Whiting, Consulting Surgeon to the Hospital, Arthur Tarrant, one-time Secretary and House Governor, and by Sir Arthur Bryant; and I thank Sir Stewart Duke-Elder for writing a biographical note which I could hardly have written myself. At the Hospital I have enjoyed the willing and unfailing help of John Barber, Deputy House Governor, Arthur Gray, House Governor, and Brian Sharp, Secretary at High Holborn; of Miss Hopkins, personal assistant to the House Governor, Miss Mead, Administrative Assistant, and Miss Hartigan, Head Medical Social Worker, in the form of access to material and in tolerating and acceding to my many demands; and similarly, at the Institute, of Clifford Seath the Secretary. My thanks go to the Rev. Gordon Taylor, RNVR, for detailed information concerning the Chaplain's departments. I am most grateful to the Department of Audio-visual Communication at the Institute (Director, Dr. Peter Hansell) for the reproduction of the bulk of the illustrations. And I thank those who have have undertaken the typing of this work—Mrs Neata Brown, formerly my secretary, who typed most of the first copy; Mrs Allen; and Miss Hailey, who typed the final copy.

My colleague Charles Cook has provided helpful comment and criticism; I thank him for this and particularly for his undertaking the task of reading the proofs. Lastly, my wife has been a patient and tolerant help and critic throughout; she also prepared the Index, a task which has added yet one more item to the multitude for which I already have the privilege of thanking her.

F.W.L.

CONTENTS

CHAPTER 1

Treacher Collins – Early History
Move to Moorfields – Move to City Road

No more appropriate opening for the second volume of the History of Moorfields could be found than a tribute to the author of the first volume, in the form of a biographical note.

Edward Treacher Collins[1] was born in 1862, son of Dr W. J. Collins, in London; his mother, daughter of Mr Edouard Treacher, came of Huguenot stock. Educated at University College School and the Middlesex Hospital, he became house surgeon at Moorfields in 1884, and three years later became Curator and Pathologist, a post which he held for seven years. The list of his hospital appointments is formidable, and includes Moorfields, Charing Cross, Belgrave, Westminster Ophthalmic, and the Oxford Eye Hospital; he was lecturer to the London School of Tropical Medicine, Charing Cross Hospital, and the Oxford Postgraduate School. He was Bowman Lecturer in 1921, and MacKenzie Lecturer in 1931; he had been awarded the Nettleship Medal in 1915. Holding in turn the offices of Councillor, Secretary, and Vice-President of the Ophthalmological Society of the United Kingdom, he became President in 1917, and while President took a leading part in the formation of the Council of British Ophthalmologists, the precursor of the present Faculty; he was President of the former body for three years.

In the early 1920's Collins found himself faced with a problem which repeated itself for the more senior of today's ophthalmologists at the end of the second world war—that of restarting the International Congresses which war had interrupted. In 1922 an American ophthalmological congress had been held, which Collins had attended as the official British representative, but the resumption of International Congresses nearer the area of recent conflict was more difficult. A convention of English-speaking ophthalmologists was held in London in 1925 for which event Collins was elected President of the

[1] Vol. I, p. 179 et alibi.

I

Ophthalmological Society for a second time—an occurrence unique in its history. Between six and seven hundred delegates attended; the programme included a visit to Moorfields, of which many, especially those who had been connected with the hospital in the past, availed themselves. Collins presided over the Congress with great distinction and took the opportunity of getting together a small Committee of five who were to try to arrange an International Congress. Some of us know the amount of work which such a venture entails; the Committee succeeded in its efforts, and a meeting was held at Scheveningen in 1927 which 50 delegates, representing 25 nationalities, attended. This meeting saw the foundation of the International Council of Ophthalmology, and Collins was made Honorary President of the Council. The series of International Congresses proper was resumed by the holding of the XIII Congress in Amsterdam in 1929. Later, in this milieu he conceived the foundation of an International Federation of Ophthalmological Societies whose function was to facilitate intercourse and exchange ideas between the national societies, and elect the International Council; this body was in active session by the time of the 1937 Congress in Cairo.

In 1894 the Royal Oculist was asked to select a surgeon to go to Persia to operate on the Shah's eldest son, and nominated Collins. This successful trip was rewarded by the award of the Order of the Lion and the Sun, and recorded by Collins in a book entitled *In the Kingdom of the Shah*. Mention of a book brings us to a consideration of Collins' writings as a whole, and it is difficult to do justice to the value of this prodigious output. While Curator at Moorfields he amassed the material for a series of Hunterian lectures which, revised and enlarged, appeared in book form in 1896 under the title *Researches into the Anatomy and Pathology of the Eye*, which gained the Middlemore Prize. His interest in research never abated. Throughout his life, and in spite of his many clinical and administrative responsibilities, he never ceased to inquire, and the field covered by his inquiries was vast. He rarely failed to take part in a discussion, whether international or in the more limited national or even local field; and of his remarks it was once said that they were frequently of more value than the paper that provoked them. There are more than 20 papers in the *Royal London*

Ophthalmic Hospital Reports, and over 100 in the *Transactions of the Ophthalmological Society of the United Kingdom*, while his name as author appears in many other journals and periodicals. It has been said that at that stage of our speciality one had only to look down a microscope to discover something new and worthy of report; while there is a basis of truth in the statement, a study of Collins' writings reveals a scientific acumen and sincerity which completely exclude the trivial, even considering that half of them date from the last century.

Collins died in 1932. He was blessed with the ability to combine a scientific interest and administrative facility with a charm of manner and social flair which endeared him to all and enabled him to give such valuable service in the field of international collaboration and liaison. All the comments one reads testify to his generosity in deed and thought; his characteristics were energy, application, sincerity, and versatility. At the risk of a cliché, one may justifiably call him the doyen of British ophthalmologists of his time.

In 1933 it was reported that about eighty bound volumes and 700 unbound volumes of the Collins History were unsold. Mrs Collins offered to buy these and sell them to anyone interested for the benefit of the hospital, a proposition which the Committee of Management gratefully accepted. It is not recorded how many were sold; but it is a fact that when attempts, by advertising and other means, were made to obtain a few necessary copies at the time of the production of this volume and the proposed reprinting of Vol. 1, no success whatever was achieved. There were but three copies available; two in the House Governor's Office and one in the possession of the writer. Apparently all the volumes purchased in 1933 were stored in the Hospital; their fate was, and remains, a mystery.

Though the first volume of this history took some parts of the tale well into the present century it did not do so in any detail. Collins gave a full account of the opening of the Hospital on its new site, and a description of its layout and administration. He described the setting up of a separate refraction department for school children, and added some philosophical remarks about hospitals, hospital activities in general, and special hospitals in particular, together with biographical details of some senior members of the Staff. He states, however, that his history commences with the foundation of the hospital in 1804 and ends with the celebration of its centenary, and the natural break in the Hospital's history occurs at about that time, roughly when it commenced its new life in its new situation. It is therefore proposed that this history shall take up the tale from about the date of the Hospital's centenary. In the interests of continuity and for the benefit of those not familiar with the early history, a brief summary of its first hundred years would be appropriate.

British soldiers were landed in Egypt in 1800 following Nelson's defeat of the French Fleet at the Battle of the Nile; they returned home in 1803 with large numbers of them suffering from "Egyptian Ophthalmia"[2], a mixed infection of trachoma and purulent ophthalmia. It was largely the presence in the country of these unfortunate men in such numbers that stimulated John Cunningham Saunders, sponsored by other physicians and surgeons from St Thomas' and Guy's Hospitals, to found the London Dispensary for curing Diseases of the Eye and Ear. Trachoma of course continued to constitute a serious menace for many years after the foundation of the Hospital, to wane in the third and fourth decades of this century almost to extinction, and to show signs of returning with the upsurge of immigration after the last war. As mentioned elsewhere, the third house surgeon, between the wars, spent considerable time each morning treating trachoma. In 1904 Holmes Spicer was asked whether a patient could go to America—a not infrequent question, doubtless raised by reason of possible trachomatous infection. He maintained that the Hospital was "being made use of" and firmly refused to answer the question. Eye disease in the early nineteenth century was dealt with by general surgeons and physicians with no special training, or else, far worse, was in the hands of quacks, self-styled oculists, with no medical training at all. This latter fact undoubtedly prevented many medical men from specialising in Ophthalmology.

[2] See Meyerhof, Max (1932), *Br. J. Ophthal.*, **16**, 129, and Law, F. W. (1939), *Ibid.*, **23**, 81.

The Hospital started in Charterhouse Square and opened on 25 March, 1805. Three years later it became exclusively an eye Hospital, the first of its kind in the world, with the revised title "The London Infirmary for Curing Diseases of the Eye". The need for expansion soon became evident, and a site was acquired in Moorfields. In this context the map reproduced as the frontispiece to this volume makes a fascinating study. Many landmarks remain to this day, *e.g.* London Wall, the Moor Gate, the Artillery Ground and the south part of City Road, though called at this time Royal Row and provided with a turnpike at its Old Street crossing. On reaching Old Street, City Road ceases; its northwesterly extension to the west end had not yet been made. The Moor Fields were divided into three; upper, middle, and lower. The site of upper Moorfields became Finsbury Square, and Lower Moorfields became Finsbury Circus. The track running northwards up the east side of Lower Moorfields became Blomfield Street; that running east and west along the north side, formerly Broker Row, became Eldon Street. At the junction of these two tracks, at the north east corner of Lower Moorfields, the new Hospital was erected in 1822 and once again re-named, this time "The London Ophthalmic Infirmary". Doubtless its familiar nickname "Moorfields" soon became current; it certainly persisted, though it did not become the official title until 1956, when a happy piece of legislation altered the clumsy "Moorfields, Westminster and Central Eye Hospital" to "Moorfields Eye Hospital". However, there was, in fact, from 1675 until after this time, a "Moorfields Hospital", and anyone claiming to have been an inmate there would have been reckoned an escaped lunatic; the Hospital appears on the plan under its official title of the Bethlem Hospital. It moved to Lambeth in 1815.

To mark the agreement of the Duchess of Kent and of the Princess Victoria to become Patronesses of the Ophthalmic Infirmary in 1836, the Hospital was once again renamed, and assumed the title Royal London Ophthalmic Hospital.

By 1888 the need for more room had again become urgent. Negotiations were in hand for the acquisition of more land adjacent to the Hospital; presumably with a view to increasing the prestige of the Hospital and improving its negotiating

5

power, a petition for a Charter of Incorporation was presented in 1890, and the Charter was granted in December of that year. Negotiations for an extended site were complicated and prolonged, and in the end broke down; a blessing in disguise, for the new site acquired in City Road soon after (1894) offered many advantages and far greater potential than the project of expansion at Blomfield Street. The new site for the hospital will also be found on the map. The "Perilous Pond", which gave its name to Peerless Street, had been transformed into "the completest swimming bath in the whole world" by William Kemp in 1743; it is seen on the map just north of Old Street, together with the "noble fish pond", also constructed by Kemp, just beside it. Between 1850 and 1860 the pool and pond were built over; it is exactly on this site that the hospital stands. The familiar bend on the City Road is already forecast by the 18th century footpath. The locality would appear to have retained its partiality for the provision of ablutionary facilities; does not nearby Ironmonger Row do so to this day? And again, if one walks today west along Old Street from the hospital, past the block which has replaced the old and famous—or infamous— lunatic asylum, whose buildings became St Luke's Printing Works and were still standing in the writer's time, does not one come at once to Bath Street, doubtless named in reference to the facilities offered in the neighbourhood? From the map one sees that this was the result of a re-naming, the previous title (of less salubrious connotation) being Pesthouse Row. Many other names on the map provoke interest and would repay research if one had the time—Mr Witanoom's Vinegar Yard and the Lord Mayor's Dog House, to name but two.

The foundation stone was laid in 1897 by H.R.H. The Prince of Wales, and the new hospital opened in 1899 by T.R.H. The Duke and Duchess of York, afterwards King George V and Queen Mary. All these activities are admirably described in the Collins volume, and a reprint of *The Times* account of the opening ceremony appears in the hospital report for 1900.

Soon after the Hospital was established on its new site a joint Committee was set up to consider the naming of wards and the commemoration of benefactors. It recommended that one ward should be named "Bowman"; another "Edward VII", with a tablet to indicate that the opening of the ward was

6

made possible by a grant from the King Edward's Hospital Fund. It recommended also that the names of those non-medical gentlemen whose names had been given to wards in the old Hospital be placed in the Board Room. It further enacted that the names of the Physicians, Surgeons and Assistant Surgeons, past and present, be recorded in the entrance hall. This latter suggestion was carried out, and the boards bearing these names decorated the walls of the hall for many years. They were taken down in 1963 when the hall was re-designed and re-decorated; a recent suggestion is that the names should be indited on smaller boards to be hung in the alcoves on the main ground floor corridor, where they would surely be more suitable. Amongst other considerations, that of expense has so far post-poned the implementation of this design.

The hospital had not occupied its new site in City Road for more than a few years when the area immediately on its south east side, lying in the angle between City Road and Peerless Street, came into the market. The Hospital authorities went deeply into the matter of purchase. It would seem likely that they were more interested in preventing the acquisition of the site for purposes which would not be agreeable to the Hospital than in its purchase for extension purposes, financially embar-rassed as they were, and still unable to utilise all the beds in the Hospital. The ground rent of the Hospital was calculated at 7½d (3p) per foot; the Peerless Street site was offered at 1/- (5p) a foot, which was mainly frontage. The hospital adviser started by saying that the price asked was excessive—but later com-pletely reversed his opinion. On being approached, King Edward's Fund gave it as their opinion that the Hospital was already too worried over matters of rent to incur further res-ponsibilities in that direction. Presumably through the Fund, the Central London Ophthalmic Hospital became interested—not primarily in the site, but in the question of possible amal-gamation if the site were acquired. Their advances were fruitless, Moorfields replying, with some hauteur, that they "entertained no idea of amalgamation". We shall see how this attitude became modified twenty, and again forty, years later.

7

CHAPTER 2

*Financial difficulties – Ladies' Guild
Collins' address – The Friends of Moorfields*

IN studying the history of the hospital at the turn of the century
one cannot but sense on all hands a feeling of relief and achievement following the great adventure of the move to City Road.
Nonetheless this sense of achievement did not justify or induce
any relaxation of effort; nor was the situation entirely satisfactory from the financial aspect. Indeed, the history of the
Hospital ever since the move to City Road is dominated by the
record of financial difficulties, unfortunate restrictions, economies and appeals for funds. There were serious worries over the
cost of maintenance, which in the old building had been some
£8000 a year, and which was expected to be in the new building
"as much as £11,000 a year". A heavy burden was that of rates,
which in 1904 amounted to just under a thousand pounds per
annum, a figure exceeded by no other London Hospital except
Guy's and St Thomas'. The annual ground rent called for an
additional £1210 and a start was made to raise a fund of £50,000
to guarantee this charge. Though the hospital opened free of
debt to the builders, it was not possible, for financial reason,
to utilise all its facilities, and 5 wards containing 68 beds were
not opened—half the accommodation of the new hospital. In
1901 the financial situation caused "grave anxiety";[1] a grant
of £2150 from the Prince of Wales Fund (as it then was), of
which £900 was an annual grant made on the condition that
18 more beds were opened, relieved the situation to some extent,
but the Committee earnestly appealed for £5169, the sum
required to clear the hospital from debt, and for further annual
subscriptions amounting to £8000 for maintenance—this in
addition to the projected £50,000 "Rent Fund". In 1902
negotiations for the sale of the old site in Moorfields were
completed; the resultant sum of £78,500 enabled the repayment
of the loan and mortgage, the closing of the Building Fund

---

[1] "Only by a loan of £5000", says the report for that year, were the authorities
able to keep the Hospital open.

Accounts, and the transfer of the balance of £578 to the Rent Fund, all bills for the building, furnishing, and equipment of the new Hospital having been paid. Fifty beds were still reported closed in 1902; a further £4500 came from the newly-named King Edward Hospital Fund in December of that year. £2500 of this was a special donation on condition that 30 more beds were opened in 1903; and the remaining £2000 was an annual grant towards the cost of maintaining the 30 additional beds, which were duly opened in February 1903 by the Lord Mayor and Lady Mayoress, "attended by the Sheriffs". The King Edward's fund buttressed their generosity with the admonition "We consider this hospital should receive more support from the public."

The unfortunate story of closed beds continues, it would seem almost indefinitely. Twenty remained idle up to 1913, and 18 in 1914; from that date there is little reference to closed beds in the records, doubtless because of the allocation of part of the hospital's space to the Service departments for the use of troops. Thus, in 1914, 20 were allocated to the Army, and 10 to the Admiralty; the Army allocation was increased in 1916 to 30. These beds reverted to civilian use in 1919, from which date one finds fewer references to the subject in the records, though 18 closed beds are referred to in 1926. The annual subscriptions rose from £1096 in 1900 to £1710 in 1904; donations fell from £4385 in the former year to £2503 in the latter. In that year King Edward's Hospital Fund gave £2000 as an annual grant towards maintaining the beds opened by the Fund, and a special donation of £2000; the Hospital Saturday Fund gave £248 and the Hospital Sunday Fund £1006. These two Funds both arose in the year 1873 as a result of the growing concern amongst responsible citizens of the inadequacy of hospital accommodation and the lack of availability of specialist opinion. Indeed the medical and hospital services in general were very poor; for example, there were fewer than 30 general hospitals in all London. The Hospital Saturday Fund started at Speakers' Corner in Hyde Park, of all unlikely places; there a Captain Mercier succeeded in launching the idea of the collection of small regular contributions from employed people each Saturday. The scheme prospered; organisations supported it and provided facilities for the collection of contributions; and

9

from this interesting if humble origin grew the important and valuable Fund of today.

The Metropolitan Hospital Sunday Fund was started by the Rev. J. C. Muller, Vicar of Greenwich, at a public meeting held at the Mansion House; churches of all denominations were to give their collections on a certain Sunday to help the sick. Since then Hospital Sunday has generally been held on or near the first Sunday after Trinity. The Fund soon gathered widespread and influential support; each Lord Mayor of London since its inception has been President and Treasurer of the Fund, and Her Majesty the Queen is Patron. Grants are made to hospitals, homes, District Nursing Associations and many medical charities, largely but not exclusively those which have not been taken over by the State. Much of the income comes from wisely invested legacies, and in addition to the "Sunday" income house-to-house collections, Flag days and individual contributions augment the resources. Up to date the Fund has disbursed $5\frac{1}{2}$ million pounds.

The year 1904 began with a deficit of £6900; by the end of it the committee was proud to announce the reduction of this discrepancy by some £250. A special committee was now appointed to arrange for the Centenary Appeal; this task was rendered more difficult because it corresponded in time with rebuilding appeals by two large General Hospitals and a special Hospital. A centenary festival Dinner was held at the Hotel Cecil in May; Sir Charles Wyndham presided and the sum of £2270 was raised. The anxiety of the authorities may be measured by its appointment of a special Drug Committee, later constituted into a permanent sub-committee, to examine every item under the heading of Surgery and Dispensary with a view to economy. An interesting item of extraordinary expenditure in this year consisted of £112 spent on the installation, for the first time, of electric fire alarms and fire appliances. Four years later the figure for subscriptions had risen by £100, and the donations had fallen a further £400; the authorities pointed out reluctantly that they were using legacies for current expenses; that, though they did not wish to close more beds, they would do that in preference to selling investments; and that the 20 beds so often referred to remained closed for lack of funds. An unfortunate step dictated by the serious financial situation was taken in 1909; it was decided to divert the dividends of the Centenary Fund (as the Rent Fund was renamed in the Centenary year) from investment to annual income. This increased the latter by £200 but stopped the automatic increase of the Fund, which, intended to reach £50,000, at the end of the year stood at the humbling figure of £6545.

The Hospital appeared to receive financial support from a faithful band, exemplary in constancy but relatively few in numbers. The list of annual subscriptions and donations appeared in each annual report. In 1914 the entries, though over 1200, may be thought few when one considers the wide appeal the Hospital should have had; further, the majority of the names appear year after year. The annual report for 1919 contains this sentence: "It is not right that the national work of this Hospital should be supported only by some 1500 persons." An interesting and remarkable feature is the support given by the Corporation of London and the City Companies; regular and generous donations are recorded and the Companies listed as supporting the Hospital in 1914 numbered no less than 29. Life Governorship was conferred on anyone giving ten guineas or more in any one year; in this year the list of "Life Governors since 1899" contains 600 names.

Support came sometimes from unexpected sources and in unexpected ways. In November 1912 the Hospital received a cheque for £20.12.4 from Sir Thomas Crosby on behalf of the Town Council of Ischl in Austria; this was a souvenir of a recent visit of a deputation from the Council to London. On 7 December of that year Miss Florence Taylor, from Westcliff on Sea, called on the Secretary and handed him a sealed packet. Presumably to ensure rapid benefit, she then went to Woking and committed suicide. The packet was found to contain her Will in which all her estate was left to the Hospital.

Financial worries were unabated throughout the war period. In 1915 it was reported that expenditure had exceeded income for five years leaving a total deficiency of £2196. Income from legacies continued to fall; the situation was aggravated by the fact that the site in City Road was leasehold, whereas that in Moorfields had been freehold. The year 1920 saw a large increase in the number of patients. Although the annual subscriptions remained fairly steady, donations to the Hospital fell off seriously, causing increased worry to those trying to balance the budget. The work of the Hospital increased, and expanded in many directions. A special Appeal Committee was set up to deal with finance; a Lady Almoner was appointed for the first time, and a Samaritan Fund started. A scheme was instituted to enable in-patients to contribute towards their maintenance by weekly payments not exceeding £2 per week. The V.D. Department was started under a Ministry of Health and L.C.C. grant; an assistant organiser was appointed to the L.C.C. school children's department, and new arrangements were instituted in the general out-patient department in an endeavour to cope with the ever increasing number of patients attending.

In this year at a time of "crisis" represented by a debt to the bankers of £5000, a debit balance for the year of over £2000, and a sale of investments for £5500 whose book value was £8000, two benefactors sent a joint donation of £5000 intended to be used to start an ophthalmic convalescent home. In the circumstances they consented to its temporary use in relieving the immediate necessities of the Hospital, and the bank loan was repaid. With this concession they stipulated that should the Hospital again become solvent, and the scheme for starting a convalescent home materialise, the donation should be paid back and used for that purpose. The anonymity of the donors is preserved in the annual report; they were, in fact, a surgeon on the staff and his wife. The idea of a convalescent home, once raised, obviously had a considerable appeal to other potential subscribers, and contributions continued to come in; a further £6100 was thus received by the end of the year.

However, in 1922 the Committee of Management were able to announce that the income had met the expenditure "for the first time since 1917". The fact that this had occurred in 1917 had been tactfully and tactically omitted from the relevant Report! 1922 saw the accomplishment of a scheme of combination and co-operation amongst the London hospitals, for which previous attempts had met with no success. The King Edward's Hospital Fund organised a combined appeal, from which Moorfields benefited to the tune of £2740. Nonetheless, efforts by the Hospital authorities to continue to balance their budget were unremitting; receipts from both in-patients and out-patients increased, and reductions in expenditure were effected on provisions, surgery and dispensing, domestic matters and establishment. A bank loan was paid off; an outstanding loan of £6000 from the Convalescent Home Fund continued to worry the authorities, who reported a loss of £4425 on the year's working again in 1924.

A supreme effort to raise funds was made in 1925. By permission of the Lord Mayor a Festival Dinner was held in the Mansion House, chaired by the President, H.R.H. Prince Arthur of Connaught. The financial result was that nearly £6000 was raised towards the liquidation of the debt, and for the Nurses' Home Fund. An important side result was that 56 new annual subscribers were enrolled. The moving figure in the scheme was Lady Cooper, a member of the Committee and wife of a former Lord Mayor of London. Her name is commemorated in the Lady Cooper Memorial Chapel. In 1926 a full-time appeal secretary was appointed in the person of Arthur Cowell.

Evidence of the interest of the Ladies in the welfare of the Hospital, and the raising of funds for the provision of amenities, appears early in its history. We read that in 1828 there was a sale of Ladies Fancy Work in the Egyptian Hall of the Mansion House, which lasted for 3 days and produced what must have been the astonishingly gratifying sum of £2200 for "the nearly exhausted funds of the Infirmary". There were 34 Lady patronesses of the Sale, headed by the Duchess of Kent, of whom a dozen or so bear names suggesting relationship to a member of the Hospital Staff, medical or lay. They were all made Honorary Life Governors.

This assistance became more organised soon after the Hospital moved to City Road, for in 1900 we read of the formation of the Royal London Ophthalmic Hospital Guild. Its first main concern was the provision of clothing for the patients while in Hospital, and of household linen, though there was also a subscription and donation list which provided funds for the Guild to hand over for Hospital expenses. It would appear that before long the Guild was covering all the needs of the

Hospital in the way of linen. The task of brightening and furnishing the in-patients' sitting rooms was undertaken; when the New Private Wards, and Nurses' and Maids' quarters, came into use the Guild provided bedspreads and blankets. Funds were raised by Sales of Work, and monetary gifts to various departments of the hospital were made; a cot was endowed, and money provided for the maintenance of beds and cots.

In the Annual Report for 1913 there appears a report of "An address delivered at the fourteenth Annual Meeting of the Royal London Ophthalmic Hospital Guild by E.T.C., 24th February, 1914". Even without this clue to its authorship there would have been no difficulty in attribution; the style is so clear and characteristic that one recognises it at once. The address is worth quoting in full.

"In proposing the adoption of the Annual Report I notice that there is one important function performed by this Guild to which no reference has been made, that is the creation of an atmosphere of interest in the hospital and its work.

The hospital is situated in the centre of a poor and populous district, eminently suitable for the purpose for which it is designed, viz., the treatment of disease of the eyes in the indigent poor, but not well suited to attract the notice of the rich and benevolent upon whose subscriptions and support it so largely depends. It is, therefore, very desirable that meetings of this Ladies' Guild should from time to time be held at the hospital, so that its members may see for themselves the good work which is being done and on leaving be able to recount what they have seen to anyone who will listen.

In order to help in the diffusion of this atmosphere of interest in the hospital, I propose this afternoon to tell you something of its upgrowth and progress.

The great scientist, Alfred Russell Wallace, who died last year, towards the close of his life wrote a book in which he described some of the remarkable developments which he had seen take place during the nineteenth century. He called the book "The Wonderful Century", he might well have included in it a chapter on the upgrowth of our knowledge of diseases of the eye, for it is full of interest and romance. Of that upgrowth this hospital is today the outward and visible sign, and the pictures on these walls are the portraits of the men who worked the wonders.

For the origin of this hospital we must go to Napoleon; to

14

Napoleon's ambition to emulate Alexander the Great and found an Eastern Empire. With this object in view, he, towards the end of the eighteenth century, took a large army to Egypt. The British troops followed under Sir Ralph Abercrombie, and while in Egypt contracted a contagious form of ophthalmia, which had been prevalent in that country for many generations. On the return of the British troops to this country in 1801 and 1802, many of them were incapacitated from further military duties on account of their damaged eyesight, and discharged from the Army.

They then went to their homes in the towns and villages of England carrying with them this contagious eye disease throughout the length and breadth of the land. The result was that at the beginning of the nineteenth century ophthalmia became exceedingly prevalent. At that time there was in this country no organised effort for the treatment of infections of the eye; they were mostly left to the mercy of quacks and other unqualified persons. John Cunningham Saunders, a young, able and highly-trained surgeon, recognised this, and in the year 1804 proposed the foundation of this hospital. He lived but till 1810, but during the few years he was attached to the hospital he invented a method of operating on children born blind with cataract which we still employ.

Associated with Saunders in the foundation of the hospital was Dr J. R. Farre, whose full-length portrait of considerable artistic merit, painted by Thomas Phillips, R.A., you see on my right. For 50 years he held the post of physician to the hospital, and continued to take the greatest interest in it up to the time of his death.

When Saunders died, two surgeons of the first rank came forward to take on this work, Benjamin Travers and Thomas Lawrence (afterwards Sir Thomas Lawrence, Bart.). Both were men of the highest scientific attainments: both became Fellows of the Royal Society. Both were general hospital surgeons: Travers at St Thomas' and Lawrence at St Bartholomew's. Both, as the outcome of their experience at this hospital, wrote text books on diseases of the eye, and by their writings, teaching and example, served to raise the treatment of eye diseases out of the hands of quacks and make it a recognised branch of medical practice.

I now pass to the year 1851, a year which will always be known as the golden year of ophthalmology, for in it a physicist and physiologist in Königsberg named v. Helmholtz discovered the possibility of looking into the back of the eye and seeing the optic nerve, the blood vessels emerging from it, and the retina, inventing for us the instrument we call the ophthalmoscope.

The year 1851 was the year of the first great exhibition in

15

London and numbers of people flocked here from the Continent; among them came from Holland a young physiologist and ophthalmologist named Donders, and from Germany a young man fresh from studying in all the eye clinics of the continent, named v. Graefe. On the staff of the Moorfields Hospital at that time was William Bowman. These three great men, destined by their work to revolutionise our knowledge of eye disease, met for the first time that year here at Moorfields Hospital, and ever after remained firm and devoted friends.

Donders has left it on record how after he and Graefe had taken their modest breakfast in Oxford Street amongst the working men they went on to Moorfields and spent the rest of the day until late at night with Bowman discussing matters of mutual interest. Now what was the chief topic of discussion between them? Why, the wonderful discovery, which Graefe had to tell, of his fellow countryman's in Königsberg; the possibility of seeing into the back of the eye.

It seems possible that Helmholtz at first did not fully realise all the possibilities of his great discovery, but Graefe, who was more of a practical surgeon, recognised them at once. It is stated that when Graefe looked into the eye with the ophthalmoscope and saw for the first time the optic nerve, the retina and its blood vessels, his cheeks reddened and he jumped up and cried out in an excited manner: "Helmholtz has discovered for us a new world. What is there left to be done?"

It was true Helmholtz had discovered a new world. A new world of far more interest to my mind, and certainly of far more importance to mankind than any tracts of ice and snow which we choose to call the polar regions. It was not true, however, that nothing further was left to be done. The exploration of that new world and the interpretation of the changes met within it have ever since occupied, and still occupy, many able minds. In that new world Graefe himself made discoveries of the greatest importance.

If after leaving this meeting to inspect the hospital you walk down to the end of the passage, you will come to "the Dark Room". A large room with its walls painted black, and in it a number of separate compartments each lit with an electric lamp. Throughout the morning each of these compartments is occupied by a patient and a doctor, the latter looking into the back of the former's eyes in the manner first taught us by Helmholtz.

If then you will pass on into the large out-patient consulting room, you will come to a number of boards with letters on them, or test types, and see a number of cases full of trial lenses. Here during the morning you would find a number of people having their sight tested for spectacles, in accordance with the laws and directions first laid down for us with scientific accuracy and precision by the great Dutchman Donders.

If next you pass up a narrow staircase by the side of the library, you will come to the museum and pathological laboratory, a part of the institution established at the instigation of Bowman himself, where are carried out microscopical investigations of the tissues of the eyes which have to be removed, a line of research in which he made such great discoveries.

If from there you pass on to the second floor, you will come to the operating theatre, where almost daily operations are performed for the relief of the disease called "glaucoma", an affection which, until Graefe first showed us how to deal with it, inevitably ended in blindness.

In speaking of the operating theatre at Moorfields, I must not omit to mention the name of George Critchett, who was a contemporary of Bowman's on the staff of this hospital. His remarkable skill and ingenuity as an operator helped largely to enhance the fame and reputation of the institution, both amongst the general public and his professional brethren. Many came from abroad to witness his dexterity, and when surrounded by a most critical audience he always remained cool and unperturbed.

There is one other picture in this collection to which I wish to direct your attention, and that is the portrait of Harry Sedgwick; the legend attached to the frame states that he was a munificent benefactor. It is the only picture in this room with which I have found the legend associated. Though the walls may appear somewhat crowded, I feel quite sure that space could be found by the Committee of Management for a portrait of equal size to that of Sedgwick's if a benefactor of equal munificence was forthcoming. Harry Sedgwick was for several years Chairman of this hospital, and on his death left a sum of £20,000, with the provision that it was always to be kept intact, the interest on it only being used for the expenses of the institution.

Having made a jump from the beginning of the century to 1851, I now proceed from 1851 to the present time. How does this hospital stand today? One thing is certain, it is not standing still. Ever since I have known it the course of this hospital has been one of progress.

I have seen it move from the old building opposite Broad Street Station, where we were cramped for light, air and space, to the present up-to-date establishment.

Last year in London there was held a large International

17

Medical Congress. I was one of the Secretaries of the Section of Ophthalmology, and the one question which I was constantly being asked by the members of that section, who came from all parts of the world, was how they could arrange a visit to the Moorfields Hospital. It is still a centre of pilgrimage for all those interested in the study of eye diseases.

I have seen established in this hospital an X-ray department. Formerly when a working man had received an injury to the eye with a piece of metal, it was often impossible to say whether or not the foreign body had lodged in the eye. Now by means of the X-rays we can not only tell if a piece of metal is located in the eye, but also estimate its exact size and position, even though it is completely hidden from view.

I have seen also the introduction of powerful electro-magnets by means of which we are able to draw out pieces of iron which have become lodged in the eye, and so save many eyes which would otherwise have been lost.

Another department which has been established of recent years is the bacteriological laboratory, where we are able to differentiate and recognise the minute foes with which we are in constant combat.

A great change and improvement in the nursing arrangements of the hospital has been effected since first I knew it. Dickens' "Sarah Gamp" would probably have felt insulted if asked to undertake anything so trivial as the nursing of a case of eye disease. At one time it was thought that any good woman could be a good nurse. Now we know that three years' training in a general hospital is essential. There are, however, many nurses who have been so trained who have never had anything to do with a case of eye disease.

The necessity for some special training in this subject has been recognised by the Queen Victoria's Jubilee district nurses, and they now all attend here for a short course of instruction. We might, however, do much more in the way of giving instruction in ophthalmic nursing had we more accommodation for probationers. At present we cannot even find room for all the nurses that are required to carry on the work of the hospital, and are unable to open any more beds because we have not space for more nurses. The next line of progress must be establishment of a nurses' home, and this will afford an excellent chance for someone to come forward and have his portrait hung as a companion to Harry Sedgwick's.

The last progressive movement in connection with this hospital to which I have to refer, is the establishment of this Ladies' Guild, an account of the fourteenth year of whose useful work you have just had read to you."

Not unnaturally the activities of the Guild fade, at least from the records, during the war years 1940–1946. Unfortunately this interval and the abnormal conditions prevailing after the war caused the virtual disintegration of the Guild, which remained in abeyance until it was resuscitated in 1948 under the title of the Ladies' Association; a similar but joint organisation catered for the Westminster and Central Branches, as they were then called. In 1957 we read of the disintegration of the Ladies' Association "as there seemed insufficient need for their services". Already the idea of a League of Friends of Moorfields had been mooted, which makes the reason given above read rather strangely; equally strange is it that the Association did not form the nucleus of the new body, as had been hoped. The members of the Association requested that the remaining funds be placed at the disposal of the Chief Executive Officer for investment, and that the interest therefrom be used, at the discretion of the Nursing Committee, for the purpose of providing annually a silver medal and a progress prize, while any surplus was to be applied for the benefit of the nurses.

In 1963 the organisation called the Friends of Moorfields was launched at a public meeting held at City Road, followed by a wine and cheese party; the Duchess of Fife was elected President and Lady Hoare Chairman. Its avowed objects were "the raising of money to be spent on increasing the comfort of patients and the nursing staff, outside the allocation provided by the Ministry of Health, and the recruitment of volunteers to help in the many ways which are of infinite importance to the happiness and general welfare of the patients, many of whom for shorter or longer periods are unable to see". There were 200 members and the Committee raised £2300 in the first year, part from a film Gala performance attended by H.R.H. the Duchess of Gloucester. The activities of the Friends included reading to and writing letters for patients, and escorting patients to and from hospital; mobile telephones, bed tables, a talking book Library, and many other amenities were provided. The Second Annual General Meeting on this and other occasions was held at the Mansion House and was attended by the Lord Mayor and Lady Mayoress; a successful Peacock Dinner Dance was held at Quaglino's. In 1967 a Hospital Shop was opened, and £1000 earmarked for a research project; in the next year the Friends took over the Out-Patients Canteen. The organisation goes from strength to strength and if one may judge by its donations to hospital projects, gathers an ever increasing number of supporters. Many of the gifts are devoted to objects which would not be reasonably covered by State funds, though that is not by any means always so; the Friends have supported research projects and purchased apparatus. In 1973 they provided half the £12,000 cost of the Argon Laser, then the only one in Europe, for the new Retinal Function Unit at City Road. Later in the year they contributed £10,000 towards the development of the Children's Ward at City Road, promising a further £8000 per annum over the next five years; this £83,000 project received £20,000 from the Hayward Trust, which a few years previously had financed the building of the new Theatre Suite. The balance was made up in a manner so appropriate that it is pleasing in its tidiness. The House Governor approached the Ulverscroft Foundation—a charitable Trust, founded on an enterprise concerned with the production of large-print books for the benefit of the partially sighted. They had, in fact, provided the actual hymn-books which, as recorded elsewhere, the Friends gave for use in the Hospital Chapel. The Foundation responded to the approach with enthusiasm and made a donation of £20,000.

An indication of the vitality of the organisation is given by the fact that in this year it received £4000 in subscriptions and donations, but earned £10,000 by fund raising activities. It is difficult to say exactly how much the Friends have given the hospital *in toto*, but it is a formidable sum; in the last three years it amounts to £23,000, and it should be noted that their contribution in personal service, though not comparably measurable, is of equal value and importance in a different way. The supporters connected with the hospital, and the administrative staff, have done and are doing a magnificent job, rendering a most valuable service to the hospital. Sir Frederick and Lady Hoare, who were both concerned with the creation of the Friends, retired in 1970, the one from the Treasurership and the other from the Chairmanship. Mr M. W. Jacomb succeeded as Treasurer and the Viscountess Ward as Chairman.

CHAPTER 3

Appointment of Surgeons – A. S. Morton
W. I. Hancock – Royal Patronage – Lay Support
Presidents – Chairmen – Secretaries – Lady
Almoners – Chaplains – Pathologist and Curator

SOON after the move to City Road the load of out-patient work assumed such serious proportions that consideration had to be given to increasing the surgical staff. In 1900 a Joint Committee of the Medical Board and Committee of Management was elected with this object. As a result of their recommendation it was decided to increase the number of Honorary Staff at the Hospital; this entailed three new appointments, and Percy Flemming,[1] J. H. Fisher,[2] and Arnold Lawson[3] were all elected on 7 May, 1900. Devereux Marshall[4] also succeeded John Tweedy[5] who resigned this year. In December of 1904 the death occurred of A. Quarry Silcock[6] after 18 years on the staff. He was the last member of the Staff who combined the practice of Ophthalmology with general surgery. He was succeeded by J. Herbert Parsons[7] who was appointed to the staff in 1905, in which year Sir Stephen Mackenzie[8] retired as Physician. In 1905 also W. T. Lister[9] retired after but a year on the Staff; he had filled the vacancy caused by the retirement of Waren Tay.[10] Lister was succeeded by Claud Worth. Interestingly enough, however, Lister returned to the fold in 1919 to serve as surgeon for another ten years.

The resolution of the Committee was to the effect that there should be six surgeons and six assistant surgeons, the latter to have charge of out-patients only except in the absence of the Surgeon of the day. This was a reversion to a former plan, but it broke down after a while and each member of the staff assumed charge of both in-patients and out-patients. It is difficult to discover, from the records, what the distinction between the

---

[1] Vol. 1, p. 199 et alibi.
[2] Vol. 1, p. 200.
[3] Vol. 1, p. 200.
[4] Vol. 1, p. 156 et alibi.
[5] Vol. 1, p. 202 et alibi.
[6] Vol. 1, p. 167 et alibi.
[7] Vol. 1, p. 206.
[8] Vol. 1, p. 160.
[9] Vol. 1, p. 206.
[10] Vol. 1, p. 148 et alibi.

two posts had been in the past; promotion to surgeon from assistant surgeon appears to have been practically automatic at the end of a period which was usually five years, but varied by a little from case to case. To arrange a balance of six each between surgeons and assistant surgeons would naturally require the passage of time; the balance was achieved in 1904 and held till 1907.

An entry relevant to staff appointments appears in 1900 in the Minutes of the General Committee, which incidentally at this time changed its title to Committee of Management. (The year before, the Medical Council underwent a similar change of title and became the Medical Board.) On 24 April is recorded a proposal that Rule XXIV, which stated that "an assistant surgeon who has served as such for 5 years shall if the Committee thinks fit, be elected full surgeon" be abrogated, and on 22 May the proposition was "sealed". There must have been some causal connection between this resolution and the deliberations of the Joint Committee, though the coincidental timing is difficult to explain. However that may be, seven years later the *status quo* was practically restored, for on 10 December, 1907 the Election Committee passed a resolution to the effect that an Assistant Surgeon should be eligible for appointment as Surgeon at the end of four years service, the Committee to meet "at once" and decide whether the promotion should be made. Flemming, Fisher, Lawson and Marshall were then all appointed surgeons, which made 10 surgeons and 2 assistant surgeons, and the even balance of six does not appear again on the list of Hospital Staff. At some indeterminate point in time between the resolution of the Election Committee in 1900 and the third decade of that century the practical distinction between surgeon and assistant surgeon ceased to exist as described above, and the newly appointed man had charge of beds from the outset. Arthur Lister was promoted surgeon after five years as assistant surgeon in 1944; in 1947 the Amalgamation brought the number of surgeons on the staff of the reorganised Hospital to 19, with two assistant surgeons appointed later in the year in the persons of A. G. Cross and A. G. Leigh; at the same time H. B. Stallard was appointed surgeon "in respect of his previous services to the Hospital as Honorary Assistant Surgeon from 1933 to 1938". In 1948 their names appear in the list of full

23

Surgeons, and the title assistant surgeon is not found again—
all are equal under the new regime, with the title Consultant
Surgeon.

Andrew Stanford Morton[11] retired in 1909. Educated at
Edinburgh and University College, London, he qualified from
Edinburgh in 1874, but did not take his Fellowship until 1888,
so that he was forty-eight years of age when appointed to the
staff of Moorfields, after serving as House Surgeon and clinical
assistant. He had previously been on the staff of the Royal Eye
and the Great Northern Hospitals. Generous tribute to his

A. Stanford Morton

[11] Vol. 1, p. 153 et alibi.

operative dexterity and his beautiful coloured drawings of ophthalmoscopic conditions has been paid in Volume 1 of the History. He made an important analysis of the results of Cataract Extraction at Moorfields while House Surgeon. His name will certainly not be forgotten as long as his ophthalmoscope remains in use; the design of this has apparently remained virtually unaltered since the first model was produced. Morton died in retirement at Clifton in 1927; he had been succeeded on the staff by William Ilbert Hancock—"Bertie" to his friends —whose lamentably short career terminated with his death 9 months afterwards; an embolism following an operation for appendicitis carried him off at thirty-six years of age. He qualified from Guy's Hospital, and was an outstanding athlete as a

W. Ilbert Hancock

student; a county player of tennis, cricket, and football, it is said that only a troublesome semilunar cartilage robbed him of an England Rugby Cap. Nonetheless he was devoted to his work, and held appointments at Moorfields, the Bolingbroke Hospital and East London Hospital for Children; his close application and high accomplishments are all the more creditable because he had no need to consider their pecuniary potentialities. He was an exceptionally dexterous operator, and had a retiring highly self-critical disposition; it is characteristic of him that his last published paper was entitled "Three cases of post-operative infection". They reflected no discredit upon himself, but he had the moral courage to publish, for the benefit of others, an account of catastrophes which many would have suppressed and perhaps even forgotten.

Malcolm Hepburn was elected to fill the vacancy on the staff caused by Hancock's death. This year also saw the death of Sir Stephen Mackenzie, consulting physician to the Hospital since his retirement from the active staff in 1905, and the resignation through illhealth of Marcus Gunn[12] in October, sadly followed by his death in the following month. He had succeeded Wordsworth in 1883 and thus was on the Staff for 26 years, having previously been House Surgeon; he was in fact the first officer who had so served the Hospital to be elected to the Honorary Staff. He was succeeded by George Coats.

In 1910 the Hospital lost one of its royal patrons in the person of the reigning monarch, King Edward the Seventh. A Loyal and Dutiful Resolution, signed by the President and Chairman of the Hospital, was sent to the Home Secretary, then Winston Churchill, who replied "at the Command of the King". A fund was opened to receive special donations to endow a bed in perpetuity as a memorial to his late majesty. Two years later the Hospital Guild, by a special donation of £151, completed the required sum of £1000. With the approval of the reigning monarch, a tablet was placed over the bed indicating its endowment by public subscription in memory of the royal patron who had laid the foundation stone of the building.

Moorfields has been fortunate in enjoying Royal Patronage

[12] Vol. 1, p. 160.

almost from the earliest days. This patronage has been represented by no mere formality, for its patrons have taken a real interest in the Hospital and consistently played a personal part in its activities. H.R.H. the Duke of York became its first patron in 1815, 10 years after its foundation. In the Annual Report for 1836 appears the announcement that Her Most Gracious Majesty had agreed to become patroness of the Hospital; that same year its title changed from the London Ophthalmic Infirmary to the Royal London Ophthalmic Hospital. In 1897 the Foundation Stone of the new Hospital was laid by H.R.H. the Prince of Wales, who was a patron at that time; another patron, H.R.H. the Duke of Cambridge, took the chair in the following year at the Festival Dinner at the Grand Hotel, an event which, it is recorded, was responsible for a marked increase in donations. By 1899 T.R.H. the Duke and Duchess of York had become Patrons, and it was they who opened the new building in the City Road on 27 June, 1899. The year 1930 saw the completion of the new fourth floor, which provided the private ward block and the new nurses' home; this addition was opened by H.R.H. Prince Arthur of Connaught. Five years later the King George extension was completed and was opened by T.R.H. the Duke and Duchess of York.

On 7 March, 1955 the Hospital was honoured by a visit from its patron, Her Majesty the Queen, on the occasion of the celebration of the 150th Anniversay. Her Majesty spent a long time at the hospital, visiting many wards, including the Children's, the theatres, the orthoptic department and the out-patient department, and taking tea in the Board Room where she talked to a large number of the members of the Hospital staff.

In 1961 the out-patients extension was complete and ready for occupation. It was named, "by gracious Command of Her Majesty the Queen, Patron of the Hospital", the Princess Margaret Wing—but unfortunately circumstances caused a last minute cancellation of the opening by the Princess. H.R.H. The Duchess of Gloucester most kindly deputised for her, and carried out the ceremony with her customary grace and charm.

Thus has the Hospital enjoyed and greatly valued the interest showed by its Royal Patrons. Amongst other things, this patronage constitutes just one further feature as a bastion against the depersonalisation which inevitably follows nationalisation.

Just as Moorfields may justifiably feel gratified by the Royal Patronage it has enjoyed since its earliest days, and especially in the practical interest shown by its Patrons, so it may rejoice in the enthusiasm shown and devoted service given by its lay-members, both the voluntary ones and the salaried officers of the Hospital. A glance at the appendices will show for what long periods many of these remained in office, as evidenced by the few names which cover a long span of years. This is well demonstrated in the list of Presidents, where seven names cover some 150 years. The record holder in the list is Sir John Lubbock, afterwards Lord Avebury, a colourful and distinguished character who was President for no fewer than 46 years. He came of an interesting family; the first member to receive an accolade was John Lubbock who was created Baronet in 1806. He was succeeded by his nephew, whose son became the President of the Royal Society and was a distinguished scientific author. His son John was created First Baron Avebury in 1900 when he had already been President of Moorfields for 33 years. Born in 1834, he became Vice-President of the Royal Society, a Privy Councillor, a Deputy Lieutenant, and a Justice of the Peace. He was M.P. for Maidstone for 10 years, an Honorary D.C.L. and Vice-Chancellor of London University for seven years. His scientific interests and achievements were considerable and extended further in the direction of social reform. Not everybody knows that he was the creator of Bank Holidays; this is recorded in an article in *The Times* of 28 August, 1971, which is quoted here in full.[13]

"Bank holidays are not what they were and this year's late summer holiday is no such cause for excitement as was August bank holiday in 1871. For that was the first holiday in Britain to be created by statute. Some months earlier the Bank Holidays Act had become law in time for Whit Monday to be a bank holiday, but the August holiday was an entirely new creation, greatly appreciated by the public who had already called bank holidays 'St Lubbock's Days'.

[13] Reproduced from *The Times* by permission.

28

The creator of the holidays was Sir John Lubbock, the first Lord Avebury, a banker, scientist, writer, social reformer and popular educator. He had been elected as a Liberal M.P. for Maidstone in 1870, and his Bank Holidays Bill was his first, and strikingly successful move in his long campaign to ease the lot of 'the most hardly worked classes of the community'.

Victorian employers were not known for their generosity in providing leisure for their employees. Sunday was a day of rest while Christmas Day and Good Friday were both legal holidays. But on no other day in the year was the worker entitled to be off work: Boxing Day, Easter Monday and Whit Monday were allowed only by generous masters. Lubbock's measure was intended to ensure, as he said, that 'nobody shall be compellable to do anything on a Bank Holiday which he cannot be compelled to do on Christmas Day or Good Friday'.

He later said that the easy passage of his Bill was because of its innocent-sounding title, which arose from the necessity to provide in it some provision for the payment of bills of exchange. He thought its fate might have been different had it been named the general holiday bill. But however restrictive the title appeared to be, the effect was to create almost immediately the general holidays he had had in mind.

After the Whit Monday, *The Times* had said that 'of the shops in the City four-fifths were closed by 5 pm. In other parts of the metropolis, although but few shops were closed, the aspect was that of a popular holyday, and had the tradesmen of London but arranged among themselves, the closing might, doubtless, with but little if any inconvenience, have been made general'.

Lubbock had a much longer struggle before his Shop Hours Regulation Act was passed in 1886. It restricted to 74 hours a week the working hours of shop assistants under 18. It was 1904 before he got his principal Early Closing Act through the Lords: 'after 30 years' work. Very thankful!' he noted.

Many of his 'most hardly worked' beneficiaries could appreciate some of his other activities. He was deeply interested in education, and was principal of the Working Men's College for 15 years.

But for much of his time he was working at quite a different level. As a boy and young man, a friendship with Darwin had led to a strong scientific interest.

In a later judgment Darwin bracketed Lubbock with Huxley; and indeed Lubbock was to achieve in his own right an international reputation as anthropologist, botanist, entomologist and geologist and his studies of ants, bees and wasps were of particular significance.

He was recognised for the exceptional qualities of kindness and courtesy he possessed and while his bank holidays may not have been the most important of his achievements, they are no bad memorial for a man with so much concern for humanity."

For Lord Avebury's successor as President the Hospital was honoured by Royalty—H.R.H. Prince Arthur of Connaught graciously consented to accept the Presidency, and served the Hospital with interest and enthusiasm for 25 years in that office.

Another faithful servant was Henry P. Sturgis, who was devoted to the Hospital and served as chairman for a period of 24 years from 1897 to 1921. He held this office during the important period of transition from Moorfields to City Road, and the records show with what enthusiasm and acumen he performed his task. He was most successfully careful to preserve cordial relations between the Committee of Management and the Medical and Surgical Staff. He appears as the central figure in the photograph of the Hospital dinner of about 1911 which hangs in the Residents' corridor in City Road.

Sturgis' record of devoted service was equalled by that of Theodore Luling who became a member of the Committee of Management in 1913, was elected Chairman in 1921, and held the office for 26 years. He was subsequently elected President in 1945, after a vacancy of six years following the death of Prince Arthur in 1938, though there is no doubt that he was in a position to exercise his good influence on Hospital affairs more effectively as Chairman than as President. Just as Sturgis had control at a difficult period—that of the move to City Road—so Luling had a similar opportunity, and grasped it avidly—for his term of office started with the years of reorganisation and reconstruction following the first war, and covered the important period which saw the planning and building of the King George V extension, and the difficult and dangerous second war period. It is further indicative of the value placed on his counsel that in October 1948 he was elected to a seat on the Board of Governors of the new constitution. Luling rendered wonderful service, and the Hospital could never thank him enough; on his retirement the gratitude to him was obvious and unstinted. From 1949 onwards the office was referred to as Honorary, doubtless in conformity with the altered climate induced by nationalisation. Perhaps the same circumstance was operative in preventing the office being filled at all after his death.

An important figure in a comparable capacity in the Westminster interest was the Earl of Arran who died in December 1958. He was Chairman of that hospital from 1901 to 1933, and again had his opportunity of guiding the affairs of the hospital at a critical time, in this instance that covering the move from Charing Cross to High Holborn. Largely due to his interest and influence the new hospital was opened free of debt; Lady Arran made herself responsible for raising the money to provide the eponymous Children's Ward. She was an almost daily visitor to the hospital. The successor to the title, the present Earl, has shown a similar interest in the hospital; he was Chairman of the High Holborn House Committee until very recently, and is at present Treasurer to the hospital. The Earl of Rothes has rendered invaluable services to the hospital and the institute; Christopher Malim as Chairman and his successor Francis Cumberlege leave us deeply in their debt.

And yet it is perhaps invidious to single out names for comment when one is considering the debt which the hospital owes to the non-medical men and women who have given so much care and time to its welfare. All are to be remembered with gratitude; some stand out by reason of specially memorable or specially long service. E. P. Carter was one such in recent times; he came on the Committee of Management of the old Moorfields in 1933; retired in 1960 but continued on the House Committees of both branches. He served on many committees in his time, and was most zealous in his devotion to Moorfields, especially in times of expansion and construction such as 1935 and 1960. Another was G. Parker-Jervis, who served on the Board from 1948—the date of the inception of the Health Service—until 1965, chaired the Staff Committee from 1948 to 1965, joined the House Committee in 1947, and continued after retirement as a co-opted member of both committees. And there were many more; they are not unwept when they leave us, as these two have done, but perhaps a little unhonoured and usually quite unsung while they are with us. The satisfaction of the duty is its own reward; nonetheless Moorfields appreciates their service and is the stronger for their devotion.

Some Secretaries to the Hospital have served for a remarkably long period—notably Robert Newstead (1872–97), Robert Bland (1897–1923) and Arthur Tarrant (1924–1957). Though he retired before the amalgamation, the record of J. H. Johnson is worthy of note—he was elected Clerk of the Westminster Ophthalmic in 1898, became Secretary in 1903 and held that office till 1946. There was some necessary adjustment of offices at the amalgamation. W. Merrill was secretary of the Central London Ophthalmic Hospital at the time, and became secretary to the combined Hospital in 1947, under the House Governor Tarrant; he died soon afterwards. J. P. Heming was Secretary of the Westminster Ophthalmic; he became Deputy House Governor of the combined Hospital, and Secretary at Merrill's death in 1949 until 1957 when he succeeded Tarrant as House Governor.

Tarrant's long spell of office included the periods of amalgamation and of nationalisation; one could sense that he did not altogether approve of the change. He recalls some interesting figures—for instance, expenditure of the Hospital for 1925, £29,172: for 1969, £1,435,355. The salaries of the nursing staff for 1924 amounted to £1746, and for 1968, £296,098; the corresponding figures for total salaries and wages were £10,924 and £1,104,032. He writes—"It is virtually impossible to realise the almost Dickensian atmosphere prevailing at the hospital in 1924. The general office had high desks at which clerks perched on high stools, and one would have been hardly surprised to see them using quill pens." He describes how, shortly after his arrival, an application for an increase in wages by the resident stokers was met by the proposal by the Committee of an increase of 1/- (5p) per week. Tarrant had come from the Manchester Royal Infirmary, whose administrators had few financial worries by reason of the staunch support forthcoming from the booming textile industry. The proposal rather shocked him; his representations to the Committee resulted in the increase being doubled.

Another faithful servant was S. Chivers, who was senior

records officer at the Central when the writer joined the staff there in 1931. When Chivers retired in 1960 he had given 41 years continuous loyal service to the Hospital, covering the period immediately following the first world war, and those of amalgamation, nationalisation, and metamorphosis.

Another body of people who serve the Hospital in a manner as quiet as it is invaluable are the Lady Almoners, re-titled Medical Social Workers under the new regime, unhappily as some think. No praise could be too high for the work they do, and one feels that no task could be at times more trying and more frustrating. Yet again the successes achieved and happiness created bring their own reward; many patients would be much the worse off without the Almoners to whom to appeal —perhaps a little less so lately than formerly, but nonetheless these ladies still perform an invaluable service, and the patients still need them. Further, the liaison they create and preserve between the medical officers and the patients is most important, and not by any means always appreciated; it would come as a shock to many surgeons if an appeal for help to the Social Service Department was not welcomed, and not dealt with efficiently and cheerfully.

The chaplains serve the hospital faithfully and well. Mention of this office first occurs in the lists in the annual report in 1835, and intermittently from then until 1850, after which the line is unbroken. At each branch there is a chaplain representing the Church of England, the Roman Catholic Church, and the Free Church, and a Rabbi to minister to Jewish patients.

At City Road there is a comely little chapel provided with a nicely toned Franklin electronic organ of 2 manuals and pedals. The chapel stands as a memorial to Lady Cooper[14] who gave the money for its endowment; it occupies the former site of the residents' dining room. In 1972 a pair of striking and beautiful stained glass windows was designed by Miss Rosemary Rutherford; these were finished and erected, and dedicated by the Suffragan Bishop of Stepney at a service held in the chapel in November of that year. Sadly, Miss Rutherford had died in

[14] See p. 101.

the meantime; the service of dedication was also a memorial service to her.

There is no chapel at High Holborn; in 1963 the House Committee commissioned Anthony Elson, who had been recommended by the Goldsmith's Company, to design a pyx for the administration of the Reserved Sacrament. The cost was defrayed by the Rose Hannah Wilson bequest; this handsome vessel provides for some 500 communions a year.

The present Church of England chaplain at City Road is the Rev. E. Rogers, who was appointed in December 1967 after serving for a considerable period as *locum* before this. He gives regular lectures in the School of Nursing, and co-operates with the Social Workers and the "Friends", who provide flowers for the chapel. It is worthy of note that, when the chapel came into existence in 1936, it was found that the legacy would not quite cover every required detail, and that the service books were provided by the nurses then at the hospital, who also embroidered the kneelers. The Friends later provided large print hymn books. Services are held in the chapel on Sundays and Wednesdays; these are relayed to the wards. After communion services in the chapel, bed patients are catered for on the wards. In the Rev. Rogers' time the acts of communion in the Chapel have twice exceeded a thousand in the year; in the last few years the numbers have fallen and last year were 690. This fact may well be connected with the modern tendency to reduce the numbers of in-patients over the weekend for administrative reasons. The Wednesday evening service is conducted alternately by the Anglican and the Free Church chaplain—at present the Rev. R. G. M. Tedcastle. The Roman Catholic priest is the Rev. E. Higgs, and the Rabbi is Mr Lev.

When the Royal Westminster Ophthalmic Hospital moved to Holborn in 1928 the rector of the parish of St Giles in the Fields accepted the post of chaplain. The present rector, the Rev. G. C. Taylor, R.N.V.R., has been chaplain since 1949 and it is his justifiably proud boast that on no occasion since then has the weekly administration of the sacrament failed to take place; deputies have officiated during holidays. His assistant curates have taken over the duties since 1961. Further, on one occasion only has the Sunday ward service been cancelled.

It is interesting to note that the successive rectors of St Giles are *ex-officio* trustees of the Bloomsbury dispensary, and have access to dispensary funds. By the rector's request in 1970 six play-back machines were purchased from this source for use in the wards, at a cost of £540; in 1972, £170 was similarly spent on six communicators, for use with deaf patients. This working together of the chaplaincy and technology is a pleasing feature and well in accordance with modern trends of thought in the Church. The present Roman Catholic priest at High Holborn is the Rev. Peter O'Reilly, and the Free Church chaplain the Rev. J. C. Askew, who has held the office for nearly twenty years; the Rabbi is Mr S. P. Cutler.

The appointment of Pathologist and Curator was a highly prized post in the old days, and indeed right up to the establishment of the Institute with its Pathological Department, which deleted the office. The principal reason for this was the unrivalled experience it provided in the study of the histology and pathology of the eye, for specimens were received from all over the country and from abroad. A secondary reason may be found in the fact that the post was regarded, and with good reason, as a propitious stage on the way to the Staff of the Hospital. Since well into the last century there have been but two Curators who did not in due course obtain appointment to the Honorary Staff—and these were both temporary substitutes not in the true line of succession. It is no wonder that for both these reasons the appointment excited keen competition, and the chosen surgeon considered himself very fortunate in his appointment. The post entailed attendance at the Hospital for half the day, six days a week; the main task consisted in examining and reporting upon the vast amount of material submitted from the Hospital and from outside. The Library was then at hand in the same building, adjacent to the laboratory, and the Curator was also librarian, sorting and collecting the many incoming journals, supervising their indexing and binding annually, and attending to the students' demands. As his title implies, the museum was also his care; new macroscopic specimens requiring documentation were always being added, and a specimen was kept of every section mounted for

35

microscopic examination; the reports were filed and indexed. In addition it was the Curator's duty to lecture regularly on the normal and morbid histology of the eye. When it is considered that the Curator probably held a post as surgeon to a Hospital, and was probably compelled to earn his living in private practice, it will be agreed that the holders of the post were a well occupied and devoted body of men. It is true, of course, that few of them had any special training in pathology and none in ophthalmic pathology, other than what a routine medical school curriculum would have provided of the former and the courses of instruction at Moorfields of the latter—if he had attended them; and there is no question of comparing the quantity and quality of output of the laboratory with that which we have seen emerge from the Pathological Laboratory of the Institute since 1948 under the brilliant leadership of Professor Ashton. The full-time appointment of a trained pathologist in adequate and well-equipped laboratories, with expert assistants, encouraged one to hope for advances in technique and discovery; and one's hopes have been fulfilled to an extent that no one foresaw or could possibly have foreseen.

Nonetheless a study of the work of some of the Curators of the past reveals interesting facts and remarkable achievements. J. H. Parsons wrote his four-volume "Pathology" early in this century, which marked an epoch in the subject and remained the standard reference book in this country for decades. The work of George Coats is too well known to need more than mention; Hudson produced some very good work, and many others gave what time was left in a busy routine to writing and research, and contributed in smaller ways to the progress of the subject. It is safe to say that none of them was attracted to the appointment by reason of the emoluments offered. The first appointee in 1857 received £25 per annum; his successor double that, while the next Curator, Edward Nettleship,[15] "in consideration of his very valuable and arduous services in the work of the Museum" finished with a salary of £75 per annum. Collins in Volume I remarks that the salary at that time seems to have been disproportionately small compared with the "liberal grants made for the upkeep of the Museum itself". It

[15] Vol. 1, p. 180 et alibi.

was a valid observation, and remained so; the next occupant of the post received £100 which was raised in 1877 to £120. It is of some interest to note that when, over half a century later, the present writer took office, the figure had not changed. It is also interesting to record the reaction of an outside body to the question of salaries. The Hospital received a visit from representatives of the King Edward's Hospital Fund on 6 June, 1904, which was followed by a letter strongly protesting against the expenditure on medical salaries. They considered that the post of Pathologist and Curator should be honorary (remember it entailed six half days per week) "unless the medical board chose to pay the salary out of money raised by Students' fees". There would, they said, be no difficulty in filling the post because it was a "stepping-stone" to the Staff. They went further than that. They expressed "great surprise" that the House Surgeons were paid. On being told, in response to an enquiry, that they were appointed for a year, they opined that the appointment should be for a shorter period and unpaid. House Surgeons came, they said, for experience, not for money!

After the rebuilding in 1935 the opportunity was taken by the Curator to improve the facilities offered by the pathological services, museum, and library. In addition to the main index of specimens examined, a cross index of main features in the pathological reports was started, some 300 headings being employed. The old jelly specimens in the museum were discarded except for a few kept for historical interest and those which had no modern duplicates. A new catalogue of the museum specimens was made, using a new system of classification, and a comparative anatomy section was started. The library was recatalogued under "Author" and "Subject" headings (this by a professional librarian) and for the first time the current periodicals were exposed on arrival for the use of students. In this year the Curator gave four courses of practical pathology, two courses of lectures and demonstrations in normal histology for Part I D.O.M.S. and four revision courses for Part II. One student took a course in extra pathology.

The idea of appointing a full-time Pathologist, with an adequate educational background and a knowledge of bio-chemistry and bacteriology which would enable him to undertake research at a level which the times then demanded, arose as early as 1939. A scheme for his duties and curriculum was drawn up in detail and the post was advertised; there were many applicants but none was considerable and no appointment was made. This provoked a rebuke from a well-known pathologist at a general teaching hospital, who complained of the waste of time and money incurred by the applicants when no appointment was apparently contemplated. This was not a correct interpretation of events and the situation was explained to him. It is understandable that the matter was not raised again in the next few years; in fact no full time pathologist was ever appointed to the Hospital and the post remained unchanged until the Institute was founded, though a Clinical Pathological Department was established in 1940 in connection with the Physicians department, Dr J. N. Cumings being appointed part-time clinical pathologist.

With the foundation of the Institute, integrated with the Hospital and containing its own pathological department, the joint office of Pathologist and Curator became redundant. When this change took place P. D. Trevor-Roper was appointed Curator to this new Department and supervised the transfer and reorganisation of the pathological specimens to their new site; there were over 1000 of these from the three Hospitals. The task was undertaken of remounting them in more modern fashion, in transparent plastic boxes; when this was completed they were re-catalogued. Specimens were added from home and overseas sources, and some added to the comparative section by gifts from the Zoological Society; anatomical dissections and pictorial wall demonstrations were exhibited. Antique spectacles and instruments were lent for exhibition in the show case at the Royal College of Surgeons which is rented jointly by the Ophthalmological Society of the United Kingdom and the Faculty of Ophthalmologists. In 1956 the museum was moved to better accommodation in the Department of Pathology; in this year also a series of Tutorial demonstrations were started, and demonstrations on normal ocular histology were added to the Curator's lectures. Trevor-Roper resigned in 1962, and his duties were taken over by the regular staff of the Department. The story of the work and achievements of the Pathological Department of the Institute since its initiation in

1948 could provide material for a volume in itself; an attempt to deal with this subject in a manner in some way commensurate with its importance will be made in the section dealing with the evolution and history of the Institute.

CHAPTER 4

Nurses and Nursing – Ophthalmia Neonatorum
Isolation quarters – Bacteriology – Lang Scholarship
Miss Lang's gifts – Gifford Edmonds Prize
Nurses' Home – Affiliation – Preliminary Training School
Refraction Department – School Children

EVEN towards the turn of the century the nursing side of the Hospital activities appears to have been of a somewhat primitive nature, and little attention had been directed towards its improvement. In 1884 the Surgeons became so disappointed with the situation that they conferred with the Committee of Management and decided, for a start, that the Matron must be a trained nurse. The lady then in office was retired on a pension and a trained sister appointed. The discovery of corruption of the nurses by the patients, and the summary dismissal of the head nurse for this offence, caused resentment among the nursing staff which unfavourably affected their reception of the new Matron. With the support of the authorities, however, she succeeded in establishing herself, and a complete reorganisation following, trained nurses being appointed to all the higher posts.

Interest in the specialist training of already qualified nurses increased; in 1896 courses of lectures to nurses by the surgical staff were initiated, and teaching in the wards became more organised. An important step was taken in 1907 when it was arranged that the district nurses employed by the Queen Victoria's Jubilee Institute should attend the Hospital for practical instruction. It was hoped that this might lead to more home treatment and diminish the need for repeated hospital attendances. At the same time the Hospital authorities became more concerned over the incidence of blindness from Ophthalmia Neonatorum which was said to account for 30 per cent of the inmates of blind asylums in England. They urged early treatment and reference to Hospital, and there was "a strong feeling" that the disease should be made notifiable; this in fact was enacted soon afterwards.

At Moorfields the 3rd House Surgeon was put in charge of in-patients suffering from this disease. It was also his duty to see and treat those attending as out-patients. He worked in the out-patient department in the mornings in a room which retained its title of "Babyroom" until the 1930's; his main occupation apart from this was to treat the cases of Trachoma—of which there might be a score in the morning—usually by the application of the "Copper-stick", and to refract and prescribe first glasses for patients recently rendered aphakic.

In 1918 the first special hospital for the treatment of ophthalmia neonatorum was opened—St Margaret's Hospital in Kentish Town—to provide accommodation for 30 infants and rather more than half that number of nursing mothers. The Committee of Management immediately responded by enquiring what facilities would be available for the teaching of students and nurses.

The question of Isolation Quarters in the Hospital, however, became more insistent, and the different authorities with their separate approach and varied interests spent a long time discussing the matter. The Committee of Management urged the appropriation of the area set aside for the chapel; the Medical Board rejected the suggestion on the grounds that the area was larger than the purpose demanded. Their counter-suggestion was for the use of the sick nurses' quarters on the top floor, which they contended would serve the purpose well, alternative nursing accommodation to be found elsewhere. This block was therefore set apart for the purpose; four cots and two beds were installed and the bed complement thus increased from 138 to 144. Sick nurses' quarters were provided by building small but conveniently arranged rooms within easy access of the nurses' rooms, the money for this being provided out of a legacy of £2500 bequeathed by a Mr Samuel Lewis. Part of this legacy was also used to implement the decision of the Committee, following a strong recommendation from the Medical Board, to install a Bacteriological Laboratory. This was built over the Pathology Department, and B. H. Wedd was appointed bacteriologist. His most colourful successor was S. H. Browning, appointed in 1910, who held the post for 33 years. Browning, a Guy's man, learnt his bacteriology at that Hospital under Professor John Eyre, a considerable figure at this time and a pioneer in ophthalmic bacteriology. Browning was a most entertaining character and a careful and successful teacher; many generations of students owe their solid grounding in bacteriology of the eye to his lectures and demonstrations. He was a great host and an entertaining guest, a qualified engineer and a maker of superb models; interested in so many aspects of life, and thus interesting himself. He was a founder member of the Oxford Congress, and attended until very near his end. The department dealt with all the routine bacteriology, and serological and other tests; Browning also conducted the V.D. Department for 24 years. Routine bacteriology and clinical pathology went to the Institute in 1946; the fate of the V.D. Department is described elsewhere.

A thoughtful and valuable action to benefit the clinical research side of hospital activities was taken by William Lang,[1] the surgeon who had done so much to advocate the importance of focal sepsis in inflammatory disease of the eyes. In the year of his retirement, 1912, he instituted the clinical research scholarship which bears his name. It provided £120 a year for the recipient, and £30 a year for expenses. Special permission was needed before any such research work could be undertaken outside the hospital. Lang's generous and far-sighted gift enabled many promising junior surgeons to gain valuable experience. Useful investigations have been made, and interesting results have emerged from their work. The Scholarship rather naturally lapsed during the years of the second world war; it was re-established, however, before the end of the war following the application of C. P. Schepens to pursue his researches into retinal detachment under its aegis. A research grant of £150 was made; the decision receives hearty endorsement from a consideration of the most important work Schepens has since done in this field. It was in fact while working at Moorfields that he evolved and perfected his binocular ophthalmoscope.

The goodwill of the Lang family towards the hospital was again demonstrated in 1961, when Miss M. Lang, William's daughter and Basil's brother, gave £10,000 to the hospital

[1] Vol. 1, p. 204 et alibi.

to provide grants for poor, especially elderly persons when they left hospital. Nor did it end there. In 1966 Miss Lang gave a similar sum to the Royal Society of Medicine for the benefit of ophthalmology. A triennial Lang Memorial Lecture was founded, the ophthalmologist who had the honour of giving it to receive £100; scholarships were provided for as well, it being stipulated that the recipients should be below consultant status. Provision is also made for financing ophthalmologists visiting this country from overseas.

A similar motive prompted the action which led to the foundation of the Gifford Edmonds Prize in 1921. This was presented by Mr William Edmonds and Miss Sophy Edmonds in the form of £2400 2½ per cent annuities, which provided a prize of £100 to be awarded every second year for the best essay on an advertised subject. The winner was at liberty to give a lecture on the subject at the hospital.

In 1911 a note of greater urgency was detectable in the references to the need for a Nurses' Home; it is interesting to notice the stimulus provided to this theme by the concern over Ophthalmia Neonatorum just referred to. An enquiry from the London County Council resulted in the setting-up of a joint Committee of the Committee of Management and the Medical Board to consider whether the Hospital would be prepared to admit both mother and child, and if so, how much accommodation could be provided. The Committee, while sympathising with the need for the better treatment of this serious disease, found it could not provide such accommodation. It took the opportunity of saying, however, that if funds were forthcoming to provide new accommodation for the Nurses, as well as for the necessary structural alterations and maintenance, then provisions could be made, in that part of the hospital now occupied by nurses, for a ward to accommodate twelve mothers with their infants. No response to this suggestion was apparently forthcoming.

In 1912 attention was again drawn by the hospital authorities to the necessity for a Nurses' Home; this was repeated in the two succeeding years, but no progress was made, doubtless because of the unsettled state of international affairs. The matter was raised again in 1921; in the following year the sick nurses' quarters were taken over for use by nurses on duty. The project received great encouragement in 1926 by the promise of a donation of £5000 by an anonymous donor, provided the remaining balance was raised. King Edward's fund gave a further £500 while approving the plans for this accommodation; £7000 remained to be collected. At the same time plans were developed for the provision of private wards at a cost of £15,000 and it was hoped that the two schemes could be implemented simultaneously, thus effecting a considerable saving on the estimated cost.

In an endeavour to achieve the ideal of securing one day off a week for every nurse, their number was increased in 1928 and some were housed in St Clements' Vicarage, which was easy of access from the Hospital. On the administrative and training side, this year saw an important step in the affiliation of the Nursing School with that of Guy's Hospital. The scheme, approved by the General Nursing Council, enabled a nurse to do two years training at Moorfields and then two years general training at Guy's, then to receive a Conjoint Certificate after passing the examinations. The scheme entailed the appointment of a Sister Tutor and the provisions of lecture room and classroom. Farre Ward was converted into the lecture room, and Critchett divided into two, renamed Farre and Critchett. In 1930 an arrangement was made whereby a limited number of nurses who had completed a three years General Training should be admitted to the Hospital for a six months period to receive special ophthalmic training and instruction. An examination was to follow, and the successful candidates were to receive a certificate and a badge. This marked the beginning of the scheme of the post-registration ophthalmic training of nurses, and of the "Moorfields Certificate". Three years later a scheme of affiliation, similar to that already operating with Guy's Hospital, was arranged with Charing Cross Hospital; this came into force in the following year. For her work in connection with the examination of Moorfields nurses, and her co-operation with arrangements for affiliation, the matron of Charing Cross was presented with the Moorfields medal by the Chairman at a meeting of the Committee of Management in January 1933. Again, in the following year, affiliation, with the same object, was arranged with St Mary's Hospital; and in due course the scheme extended to the Middlesex, the Royal Free, Addenbrooke's (Cambridge) and the Kent and Canterbury Hospitals.

In March 1935 a preliminary training school for nurses was established. The pupils were to receive three months training therein, before going to the wards for their two years training, and then passing on to one of the affiliated General Hospitals to complete their training for the final State examination.

Another question involving accommodation was that of the Refraction Department. Hitherto refractions had been done in quarters apart from the general out-patient department. Apparently the staff, which was voluntary, was inadequate, and some surgeons deplored the isolation suffered by them, and suggested an increased, paid staff, working in the out-patient department. The suggested change was considered at great length, and by May 1918 the Medical Board decided to recommend to the Committee of Management that the Refraction Department as such be abolished. The work was to be done in the large out-patient room under the supervision of the members of the Staff. Two assistants were to attend each morning, from 9 to 1 o'clock, not attached to any individual Surgeon; they were not expected to undertake more than 16 new cases each per morning. In case they had finished their quota before 1 o'clock (a hardly likely possibility) they were expected to assist in the clinics. At a date a few years before this an interesting minute appears in the minute books referring to the proposed opening of an optician's shop in the near vicinity of the Hospital. There was considerable concern over this proposal; it was immediately enacted that all prescriptions were to be written only on the out-patient notes!

Out-patient personnel and accommodation were also embarrassed by the attendance of large numbers of school children, especially on a Saturday morning, who were sent by the officers of the London County Council, the majority for refraction and glasses. The response of the L.C.C. Education Department to a request for their help in remedying the situation was initially unhelpful but they eventually decided to

45

convene a meeting with the Hospital representatives. Negotiations were prolonged, detailed and evidently delicate; the minutes of the Committee of Management for 1909 and 1910 are full of their records. The Hospital authorities had jealously to guard their undoubted right to be in sole charge of the work done, while ardently soliciting financial support from the L.C.C. for the setting up and running of the Department. It was agreed that not less than 3000 nor more than 6000 children should be sent to the Hospital during the next year; money was collected to provide and equip a separate refraction department for them and special prices were arranged for the glasses needed, *viz.* 1/9 (9p) to 3/- (15p) according to prescription. Attendance on each day of the week, at an agreed time, was arranged. In the following year, 1915, a new agreement allowed for 5000 children to attend; 5 surgeons, each attending twice a week, were to be responsible for these clinics.

The Department became a well established entity and continued for many years as a recognised department of the hospital. Then, at a time when change was a dominant feature of all hospital activity, change came to the "L.C.C. Department". On the formation of the Greater London Council, responsibility for the former L.C.C. School Eye Service passed to the Inner London Education Authority; this was in April 1965. The Medical Officers of Health of the new Boroughs became responsible for the organisation of the clinics. The closing of clinics was deferred until the end of the school year for reasons of administrative convenience; thereafter the children were referred by the school medical officers to the consultant ophthalmic clinics.

CHAPTER 5

The Ophthalmological Society of the United Kingdom
The outbreak of war – Sir Arnold Lawson
George Coats – Devereux Marshall – J. B. Lawford
Percy Flemming – The Physicians – Holmes Spicer
Claud Worth – Treacher Collins – Politics

THE Ophthalmological Society of the United Kingdom has, as one would expect, always been well served by the Surgeons of Moorfields. Of its 47 Presidents more than half have been on the Staff. It does not seem to be generally known that the Society did not hold annual meetings in its earlier days; in fact, the first of these was held in 1913, so that the meeting of 1972 was the sixtieth and not the ninety-second. Previously to that they had consisted of Ordinary, Clinical, Special and General meetings of a business nature. It is of interest to note that an application was made by the Society to hold a clinical session at Moorfields Hospital as part of its first annual meeting. Permission was granted and the session was duly held on 25 April, 1913. The change in procedure arose partly in connection with the decision of the Royal Society of Medicine to form a Section of Ophthalmology. It may seem strange at this distance in time, but there was a large corpus of opinion in the Society in favour of relinquishing its identity and amalgamating with the Royal Society of Medicine. A special meeting was called to discuss the question on 12 March, 1909; 95 members attended, showing the intense interest the subject aroused. Amalgamation was proposed by George Mackay and seconded by Edward Nettleship; an amendment was carried which postponed the question on the grounds that every member must be fully informed of what was going on, and a special committee was appointed to propound and circulate the arguments for and against. This having been done, another meeting was held at which Nettleship proposed and Parsons seconded the motion for amalgamation. Treacher Collins produced an amendment proposing an alteration of the rules of the Society to provide for "all the meetings in the year to be held during the course

47

of one week as is done by other national ophthalmological societies". Priestly Smith seconded the amendment, which was carried, and then carried as a substantive motion. At the same time the Society offered its help to the Royal Society of Medicine in the formation of an Ophthalmic Section. A special meeting of the whole Society on 11 July, 1912 finally decided against the proposal of amalgamation and at this meeting also the offer of the Royal Society of Medicine to house the Library of the Ophthalmological Society was accepted, and detailed arrangements agreed; the Royal Society of Medicine further offered the use of its premises for the Society's meetings. A tangible result of this facility was that it enabled the Honorary Treasurer to reduce the subscription from one guinea to 12/6d (62½p). Foreigners were admitted as members in 1910, and women in 1914.

The outbreak of war in 1914 naturally affected the Hospital in many ways. Many of the staff left to join the Forces and the out-patient staff became sadly depleted; soldiers added to the numbers of patients in this department. By the end of this year 13 of the staff had left to join the Forces—surgeons, physicians, clinical assistants and members of the nursing staff. In July 1916, in response to repeated approaches and demands from the Central Medical War Committee, the Committee of Management produced a statement showing that a medical staff of only 33 remained to serve the Hospital compared with a figure of 85 before the war; 21 medical officers had left for war service. A distressing report was received in November 1914 with regard to the fate of one of them—Angus Macnab, who had left his post of chief clinical assistant to become medical officer to the London Scottish. After a famous charge by that Regiment, the troops retired before the enemy, leaving Macnab tending the wounded. A counter attack repulsed the Germans, and Macnab and his patients were found where they had been left, all bayoneted to death.

The Committee of Management offered 30 beds for naval and military cases suffering from eye wounds and disease; the offer was accepted, and 20 beds set aside for this purpose in 1915. In the following year the number thus occupied was

Sir Arnold Lawson

increased to 30, and this number was maintained until the end of the war. In 1916, 197 soldiers were admitted. On 29 February, 1919 the Deputy Director of Medical Services, London District "closed the Hospital as far as military purposes were concerned".

The war years, and those immediately succeeding, brought many changes in the Consulting Staff of the Hospital. In 1914 Arnold Lawson[1] retired on the grounds of ill health and was succeeded by Foster Moore. This was many years before he reached the age limit—indeed, he was but 47 then. He was the fourth of seven sons of George Lawson,[2] who was surgeon to the Middlesex and Moorfields Hospitals and Surgeon Oculist to Queen Victoria. He was born at 12 Harley Street and spent his whole life there. He won important prizes at the Middlesex Hospital, and having gained his F.R.C.S. in 1893 he worked at Moorfields under Tweedy. With Fisher and Flemming he was appointed to the staff of Moorfields in 1900 when it was decided to increase the number of surgeons from 9 to 12. He

[1] Vol. 1, p. 200.   [2] Vol. 1, p. 124 et alibi.

was elected to the Staff of the Middlesex Hospital in 1910, and held several other honorary posts, including that of Ophthalmic Consultant to the Navy. In 1914 he became ophthalmic adviser to Sir Arthur Pearson—a most remarkable figure of the turn of the century. He became a newspaper tycoon of considerable influence by the time he was 40; at 42 his sight failed from glaucoma and he never read again; he became "the blind leader of the blind". He became Chairman of the Blinded Soldiers and Sailors Committee in 1914, and transferred his attentions to St Dunstan's in 1915. He became President of the National Institute for the Blind; helped Baden-Powell to found the Boy Scouts Movement; inaugurated the Fresh Air Fund which was instrumental in sending thousands of poor children for a holiday in the country; and applied his dynamic and sometimes difficult personality in many ways for the benefit of his fellow men. Sir Arnold was with him in the founding of St Dunstan's, for which work the former was appointed K.B.E. in 1920. Having been Vice President of the O.S.U.K., he was appointed Treasurer in 1918; his death in 1947 prevented the achievement of his ambition to hold office for 30 years. In dignity, charity, religious conviction and devotion to duty he ably upheld the example set by his distinguished father.

In 1915 George Coats[3] died, having been on the staff but 6 years, to be succeeded by R. Affleck Greeves. It is difficult to imagine what he might have accomplished had he been granted something nearer the normal span; what he achieved in a short life of 39 years, of which the last were impeded and handicapped by serious ill health, was impressive enough in all conscience. A Scot by birth, he showed promise from the very start; he trained at Glasgow University, Vienna and Moorfields. Clinical assistant to Collins and Flemming for two years, he became Curator and Pathologist in 1905, and clearly found his true métier there. While his interests in ophthalmic pathology were wide, perhaps the greatest was in vascular disease of the retina; the present generation will remember him best by the exudative retinal disease which bears his name. Congenital anomalies of the eye formed another aspect which claimed his particular attention, and a series of papers on this subject formed the basis of his Hunterian Lectures at the Royal College of Surgeons;

3 Vol. 1, p. 9.

George Coats

he was a member of the Zoological Society, and the comparative anatomy and pathology of the eye engaged his attention and formed the subject of more writings from his pen. An excursion into medical history produced, among other essays, a brilliant picture of the famous 18th-century eye quack the Chevalier Taylor, which appeared in the *Royal London Ophthalmic Hospital Reports*, Vol. XX, and was reprinted by R. R. James in his *History of Ophthalmology*.

His clinical appointments, many of which ran concurrently with that of his Curatorship, included the Great Northern Central Hospital, Moorfields, St Mary's and Great Ormond Street. His energy and application were quite remarkable; a naturally modest and retiring man, he was good company and cultivated many outside interests, notably literature and music.

He had an extensive musical library and was no mean performer on the flute. In all things he was his own severest critic; he was by no means disdainful of clinical work, but established a considerable reputation also in this field in the short time available. His health deteriorated in his last few years and seriously impeded his work in the last four or five; it was in an attempt to avoid this semi-invalidism that he submitted to operation, which was unsuccessful and which moreover revealed that, even had he survived, full recovery would have been very unlikely. In view of this his astonishing output and brilliant achievements are all the more remarkable; he achieved in a short ten years more than many do in a lifetime.

In 1918 the colleagues of Charles Devereux Marshall were shocked to hear of his death on active service. Marshall[4] was a remarkable character. He practised in Harley Street and was elected Surgeon to Moorfields in 1900 to succeed Tweedy, who resigned at the age of 51 and became President of the Royal College of Surgeons three years later. Marshall was also on the

C. Devereux Marshall

4 Vol. 1, p. 156 et alibi.

Staff of the Victoria Hospital for Children, Chelsea; his reputation for courtesy and kindness to his patients, clinical ability, and operational skill is very high. He was an enthusiastic yachtsman, and Surgeon to the Royal Naval Volunteer Reserve; on the outbreak of war he was called up for service, and had exciting and highly dangerous experiences in many theatres of war—Heligoland Bight, Suvla Bay, and throughout Gallipoli; the East Indies, and Mesopotamia. In 1918 at the early age of 50 years he died from cholera in Bombay. The tributes of his colleagues in the medical journals reveal the high regard in which he was held. Charles Goulden succeeded him on the Staff.

J. B. Lawford left the staff in 1918, this time by the normal process of reaching the age limit, to be succeeded by F. A. Juler.

John Bowring Lawford[5] was born in 1858, in Montreal, where his education began. Graduating M.D., C.M., in 1879 from McGill University, he came to London and held resident posts at St Thomas' Hospital. He became house surgeon, and

J. B. Lawford

5 Vol. 1, p. 162 et alibi.

later curator, at Moorfields, passed the F.R.C.S. in 1885, and was elected to the staff of St Thomas' in 1886 and Moorfields in 1890. An original member of the Ophthalmological Society of the United Kingdom, he was proud of having been a student of Bowman's. He held many important posts, the highest being that of President of the Ophthalmological Society of the United Kingdom; an interesting indication of the stage of clinical thought at the time is given by the title of his Presidential Address—"On inoculation treatment in diseases of the eye"— which covered vaccination, serum therapy, and anti-toxin treatment. His many valuable contributions to science are enshrined in the *R.L.O.H. Reports*, the *Transactions of the Ophthalmological Society* and the *British Journal of Ophthalmology*, of which Journal he was elected Chairman of the Editorial Committee in 1916, having previously edited its predecessor, the *Ophthalmic Review*. A quiet unassuming character, he was an outstanding clinician and operator, and rendered invaluable services to ophthalmology; with J. H. Fisher he was responsible for the certificate for blind registration which we now know as B.D.8. He greatly valued his honorary LL.D. of McGill, and his honorary membership of the Société Française d'Ophtalmologie, and was instrumental in establishing a close and lasting liaison between French and British Ophthalmology. He was a most loyal servant to Moorfields, and bequeathed the sum of £10,000 to the hospital at his death in 1951.

Another surgeon to retire in 1919 was Percy Flemming.[6] He was a man of a retiring and modest nature who wrote relatively little but was an outstanding ophthalmologist. He had a brilliant academic career at University College School and University College Hospital, and succeeded to the Ophthalmic vacancy on the Hospital Staff there on the resignation of Marcus Gunn, with Sir John Tweedy as his senior. He was elected to the staff of Moorfields in 1900, where with Gunn he was responsible for the founding of the School for Nurses. His second interest was archaeology. He was an authority on the history of London and naturally paid special attention to the Moorfields area, on which subject he lectured to the members of the Ophthalmological Society of the United Kingdom. Another special interest in this field was in the

[6] Vol. 1, p. 199.

Percy Flemming

monastic infirmaries, particularly that of Westminster Abbey; he was elected F.S.A. in 1931. Sir John Parsons, who was his colleague at both University College Hospital and Moorfields, spoke in the highest terms of his merits, and said he owed more to his help and encouragement in ophthalmology than to that of anyone else. Flemming was succeeded by Sir William Lister, reappointed to the Staff after having been first appointed in 1904 and serving for one year only; he had retired on grounds of ill health in 1905, when he had been followed by Claud Worth.

In 1919, James Taylor[7] retired from his position of Senior Physician to the Hospital. Ever since its foundation Moorfields has had a physician on its staff; throughout its existence it has been served, with energy and enthusiasm, by a succession of medical men of real loyalty and considerable eminence. This co-operation, which has been deeply appreciated by the surgical staff, has served to mitigate the disadvantage of isolation

[7] Vol. 1, p. 205.

which is the inevitable concomitant of work in a special hospital. The liaison between the physicians and surgeons at Moorfields has always been close, to the advantage of both, and more particularly of the patients. The isolation of specialism has in the majority of cases in the past been countered by the surgeon's also having a consultant post on the staff of a general hospital. The burden of work thus embraced was heavy, especially when the extent and variety of the teaching involved is considered. Some surgeons found the strain too much, and resigned from one of the posts; there is evidence in later years that even the younger men, with the rapid and wide development of the speciality which these years have seen, and the further development of specialisation within the specialty, are beginning to feel that one hospital provides adequate opportunity for their time and energies.

James Taylor was Physician to Moorfields for twenty years and his career covered a large and important span in the history of neurology and ophthalmology. He was elected to Queen Square and Moorfields in 1899; he numbered Hughlings Jackson, Gowers, Horsley, Nettleship and Jonathan Hutchinson among his friends, and died in 1946 at the great age of 87. A prolific writer, he assisted Gowers to edit the 3rd edition of the latter's Manual of Diseases of the Nervous System; he made a great contribution to the medical side of ophthalmology.

In 1914 it was found desirable to have an additional Physician on the Staff, and Gordon Holmes was appointed 5 years before Taylor retired. He served on the staff for 13 years, and like Taylor covered a long span and died at 89 in 1966. Between the wars he was one of the greatest clinicians and teachers in the English-speaking world, and did much to establish English neurology and enhance the knowledge of neuro-ophthalmology by research and clinical endeavour. A fellowship of the Royal Society and a knighthood testified to his merits.

W. J. Adie, who came from Australia, was a charming and lovable character whose career was cut short at the age of 48 years. Like Gordon Holmes, he became physician to Queen Square and to Moorfields; his name is particularly associated with narcolepsy, pyknolepsy and dystrophia myotonica and, of course, the tonic pupil—"Adie's pupil".

In 1930 it was found necessary to create the post of Assistant

Physician; Russell Brain, later Lord Brain, was appointed, and shared the medical responsibilities for a time with Adie. Famous for his work on thyroid dysfunction, he was for 7 years President of the Royal College of Physicians; many of the Moorfields physicians were on the Council of the College, and are listed in the appendix. So the distinguished list continues: Purdon Martin; Denis Brinton who, appointed in 1937, went abroad on active service soon after, and on his return resigned his post in 1945 on appointment as Dean of the Medical School of St Mary's Hospital; and S. P. Meadows—like many others, all on the staff of the National Hospital as well, and the last particularly distinguished as being the physician with the longest record on the staff of Moorfields in modern times, rivalling that of J. R. Farre (1805–1857) and F. J. Farre (1837–1880). At the amalgamation R. A. Hickling joined the staff from the Westminster, where he had served for 16 years, and Simon Behrman from the Central after 8 years there; in the same year C. J. Gavey and F. Elliott were appointed, the latter retiring in 1959, to leave the country and become Director of Neurological Research and Education, and Professor of Clinical Neurology at the Pennsylvania Hospital, Philadelphia. This list of eminent physicians constitutes a tribute to the interest and fertility of the common field of medicine and ophthalmology. One of the physicians named above once said that he found the clinical atmosphere of Moorfields so agreeable and stimulating that, had he been faced with the choice between Moorfields and his general hospital, he would have resigned the latter.

An important figure left the surgical staff when Spicer retired in 1920 under the age limit, to be succeeded by Basil Lang. William Thomas Holmes Spicer[8] joined the honorary Staff of Moorfields in 1898 on the sudden and unexpected resignation of Edward Nettleship. His medical education was obtained at Cambridge and St Bartholomew's Hospital, to the staff of which he was also appointed. Though Moorfields had taught Ophthalmology since 1811, the medical school did not crystallise into an individual entity till many years later; Spicer was its first Dean, elected in 1899, and the popularity and high standing of the School owes a great deal to his early

[8] Vol. 1, p. 180 et alibi.

W. T. Holmes Spicer

work. He was a first in another sphere, being the first Gifford
Edmonds prizewinner; his essay "Parenchymatous Keratitis:
Interstitial Keratitis; Uveitis Anterior" embodied the work of
a lifetime, and constituted the first monograph supplement of
the *British Journal of Ophthalmology*. He was a good linguist, a
keen motorist, and an exceptionally proficient water-colour
artist; like Lawford a pupil of Nettleship, to whose clinic at
Moorfields he succeeded, he was naturally an outstanding
clinician. He was large in stature and evidently disliked the
reflex in the patient's cornea of a large white coat—for he
always wore a butcher's short blue coat in the out-patients
department. He was widely read and of broad outlook, and
left a deep impression on ophthalmology, and an affectionate
and highly respected memory with his colleagues. Spicer's
retirement was soon followed by that of Claud Worth, who was
succeeded by Maurice Whiting.

Claud Worth

Worth began the Study of Ophthalmology under Henry
Power and Bowater Vernon at St Bartholomew's Hospital,
having qualified from there. He was elected to the honorary
staff at Moorfields in 1906, and had already made a speciality
of the study of squint. He was a pioneer in orthoptics and his
book on squint was the standard text book of the day, running
into many editions. In this subject he was immensely helped
by the possession of a charming gentle manner, which immediately inspired trust and confidence in his child patients.

His name would have been a household word in another
sphere if he had never embraced Ophthalmology, for he was
an outstanding authority on yachting, currents, charts, and all
that goes with seamanship. His knowledge of this subject was
encyclopaedic and his experience vast; one heard that every

responsible sailorman has, or at least had, his books on the cabin shelves. Further, he designed boats, and retired early in order to devote himself to his hobby but—sadly—an incurable disease prevented the full achievement of his ambition.

The year 1922 saw the departure from the hospital of that famous figure Treacher Collins,[9] of whom a biographical note appropriately opens this volume. He was succeeded by P. G. Doyne.

A noteworthy event for the hospital at this time was the recognition of the scientific achievements of John Herbert Parsons by his being elected a Fellow of the Royal Society. This distinction was closely followed by the honour of Knighthood.

E. Treacher Collins

[9] Vol. 1, p. 179 et alibi.

In 1917 a political issue presented in the form of a demand on the part of the trade unions concerning basic wages for hospital porters. An industrial Court was set up and recommended a specific award. After due debate and consultation Moorfields decided not to accept the recommendations of the Court. Apparently that was the end of the matter—an interesting result compared with the probable issue today. Again, in 1925 the Trades Union Congress enquired about conditions of employment of nurses. This caused some consternation, and the opinions and help of other hospitals were invoked; the nurses and the sisters of the hospital were asked their wishes regarding the completion of the questionnaire. Again, as far as one can judge from the records, the affair sank into a decent oblivion.

CHAPTER 6

Council of British Ophthalmologists
Association of British Ophthalmologists
Faculty of Ophthalmologists – Higher Diploma
The Royal College of Surgeons – Joint Secretariat
Out-Patients – The Slit Lamp – Wireless
"Your life in their hands" – Enquiry Officer

AFTER the first world war the feeling grew that there was a place for a body to promote the interests of ophthalmologists, and to deal with the administrative, political and public aspects of the specialty. Treacher Collins played a large part in the development of this idea, and in 1918 half a dozen senior ophthalmologists met, the Council of British Ophthalmologists was founded, and an executive Committee appointed.

The Council showed considerable activity right from the start. In July 1918 it set up a committee to determine a standard of illumination for distant test types, with Sir George Berry as Chairman, and the Director of the National Physical Laboratory, Sir Richard Glazebrook, and Mr Leon Gaster for the Society of Illuminating Engineers, as members. Its report was unanimous and makes interesting reading today, though there is a note of—to use a sadly overworked term in its usual incorrect fashion—nostalgia. Another Committee was set up in the same year to report on visual requirements for motor drivers, and a preliminary questionnaire was sent out to readers of the *British Journal of Ophthalmology*. The Council as a whole considered the question of undergraduate teaching and examination in Ophthalmology and made representations to the G.M.C. on the subject. They made extensive investigations and their report is long and important; it appears in the contemporary *Journal*, and is the subject of an annotation there. Yet another report of the Council appears on the desirability of a special qualification in ophthalmology; and finally in this year the Council is represented on a special joint Committee concerned with eye strain in cinemas. On all these bodies, offsprings of the parent Council which was largely the inspiration of Treacher Collins, the surgeons on the staff of Moorfields were strongly represented.

Of the many subcommittees later set up, one had the object of considering the advisability of enlarging the scope and the activities of the Council—a proposition which excited much interest at the annual meeting. The feeling was growing that there was a need for a more democratic advisory body—indeed in 1938 an Association of British Ophthalmologists had been formed, and the Council of British Ophthalmologists had responded to a request to appoint a representative on its Council. The Council of British Ophthalmologists was described as a self-elected body, of limited interests and commitments. It was in fact composed of the Presidents and Past Presidents of the Ophthalmological Society of the United Kingdom and the Section of Ophthalmology of the Royal Society of Medicine, together with nine members elected annually, four each by the Councils of these bodies and one by that of the Oxford Congress. Later the Master and Past Master of the Oxford Congress were added, and the number of elected members increased. The criticism was thus not wholly justified; nonetheless it was a somewhat Olympian hierarchy, or perhaps would seem so to the rank and file in Ophthalmology. It continued thus until the second World War broke out, when its activities were necessarily curtailed. No report of Council was issued between 1939 and 1943, when it met again and reorganised its constitution, electing Sir John Parsons as President, Greeves and McMullen as Vice-Presidents, Humphrey Neame as Treasurer and Frank Law as Secretary.

The Association was not sponsored to any important degree by the senior or the leading members of the specialty, but was more supported by those who came later to be known as ophthalmic medical practitioners. There was a definite and perhaps somewhat strange lack of interest amongst the "high-ups"; a total membership of 246 was achieved. The deliberations of its own Executive body were by no means always smooth.

The need for a more democratically elected body was recognised as clearly in the C.B.O. as anywhere; their aim was to establish a liaison with the Association of British Ophthalmologists and by their combined efforts to form a Faculty of

Ophthalmologists; a joint Committee was set up, but great difficulty was found in agreeing on terms of membership and policy. The C.B.O. decided that the situation was urgent enough to demand unilateral action; this was taken, the Faculty was formed, the secretary of the C.B.O. became its first secretary and Sir Stewart Duke-Elder its first President. A council was elected and met on 12 April, 1945, by which time 220 ophthalmologists had joined; the last minutes of the C.B.O. were read at this first meeting of the Faculty Council; and from that moment the former body ceased to exist. A similar fate befell the Association of British Ophthalmologists when, contacts being re-established, agreement on all details of amalgamation was happily reached. A detailed and exciting description of the origin and formation of the Faculty appears in the contemporary ophthalmic press.

Thus was the Faculty born—in a strongly controversial atmosphere, and not without complications in the process. It has prospered, and justified itself in becoming the Faculty we know today—a body interested in the scientific, political and sociological aspects of the specialty, negotiating for its members, organising study tours and return visits of leading ophthalmologists, and generally serving the interests of its members the electorate and—equally important—their public.

One of the last activities of the C.B.O. and one of its most important, was the negotiation with the Royal College of Surgeons in regard to the institution of a higher Diploma in Ophthalmology. Hitherto those seeking the higher posts in our specialty had to hold the Fellowship of the Royal College of Surgeons in, of course, general surgery. Admittedly an F.R.C.S. diploma "with Ophthalmology", was in existence, but the requirements were too exacting; candidates had first to pass the usual Final Examinations for the Fellowship, and few then thought the further academic ordeal worth it—if one's memory serves, indeed, there was but one holder of the second diploma! The Charters of the Royal College of Surgeons were accordingly modified to permit the inauguration of the special diploma, which has become the first class qualification we know today. A further enlightened and forthcoming action on the part of the College was to invite a representative of Ophthalmology to sit on its Council; the C.B.O. submitted six names and one was chosen—the forerunner of the regular representatives nominated by the Faculty today, all of whom, with two exceptions, have been Moorfields surgeons. A list appears in the Appendix.

The modern generation, aware that the close connection of Ophthalmology with the Royal College is a relatively modern phenomenon, would be surprised to learn of the number of Surgeons of Moorfields who have served on the Council of this College. There have been no fewer than twelve; perhaps even more surprising, the Hospital Staff have provided five Presidents of the College. It is true that for the better part of the last century ophthalmic surgery was combined with general surgery; indeed, in those days all the surgical staff of the Hospital had to be either general surgeons or demonstrators of anatomy at a general hospital. The last member of the staff to combine the two disciplines was Silcock (1886–1904). Nonetheless it is a formidable and gratifying list which appears in the Appendix. Sir John Tweedy was the first surgeon practising purely as an ophthalmologist to become President. Though he does not strictly comply with the terms of the subject matter of this book, it would be inappropriate to exclude here the name of G. J. Guthrie, who was a member of the Council of the College from 1824 to 1836 and President in 1833 and 1841. The justification for his inclusion lies in the fact that in 1816 he founded the Westminster Ophthalmic Hospital.

Another feature connected with and arising from the College which closely involved the Surgeons of Moorfields was the Joint Secretariat. This was yet another brain-child of the then President Webb-Johnson who designed and initiated it for the combined purpose of providing an amenity for the surgical specialties and at the same time strengthening their interest in and connections with the College. It has certainly succeeded in both these objects. The Faculty joined the Secretariat in 1945, and the Ophthalmological Society of the United Kingdom in 1947; every representative of each body on the House Committee, which controls and coordinates the Secretariat, has, with one exception, been a Moorfields Surgeon. Again, the list appears in the Appendix.

6

Just as financial worries and difficulties appear to have intruded throughout the history of the Hospital, so have the difficulties of maintaining an efficient outpatient service which affords a minimum of delay and discomfort to the patient. In the minutes of 1917 we read of a complaint from a Governor concerning a patient who "waited from 9.30 a.m. till 2.0 p.m.", another from "8.30 a.m. till 3.45 p.m.". In 1923 it was reported to the Committee of Moorfields that 163 patients were turned away in the month of April; a reproving letter was sent to the Medical Board, who replied with less acerbity than good sense that the situation would be remedied by the provision of more paid assistants.

Whatever the provisions, however, the situation will never be completely and satisfactorily resolved in an ophthalmic clinic; the nature of the work involved precludes this, and it is this and not the Hospital authorities or Surgical Staff which is to blame. An appointment system which will be more or less strictly adhered to may be practicable for the Physician or the Neurologist or the General Surgeon; but since the ophthalmic patient may need anything from a glance and a prescription to an hour's investigation, the allocation of a set period for each patient is a scheme doomed to failure. The only solution is to recognise—exploit, if you will—human nature; it is the patient who is allowed to sit for an inordinate period before being given any attention at all who becomes the complainant. If he is greeted by the Surgeon or his assistant soon after arrival, and some little interest shown, and perhaps the beginning of his history taken, he will wait, in the vast majority of cases, almost indefinitely and quite uncomplainingly for his turn for further attention. And this is indeed no fabricated routine, for so frequently the use of drops and the time required for their action demands it.

In fact, an effort which seems in retrospect hardly likely to relieve the situation effectively was made in 1926 by the election of twelve paid assistants, to be called Out-patient Officers, one to each surgeon; these, however, were to replace the existing 9 Refraction assistants. They were to receive the same pay as those they replaced (£100 per annum) and to be inferior in rank to the Chief Clinical Assistants; they were not to be absent when their Surgeon was on holiday. The situation has been eased in part by the introduction of special clinics in recent times.

Another irritation, admittedly minor but nonetheless disturbing, now beset the authorities, this time a nuisance in the form of Cohen's Fried Fish Shop! Mr Cohen decided to set up his establishment on the corner of City Road and Peerless Street, to the consternation of the authorities, who decided to object and to solicit support in their complaint. This was forthcoming—following a change of wind—from Dawson's, the large store which stood on the island site on the opposite side of the road. The nuisance was abated, but not before the invocation of the hospital solicitors.

The year 1923 marked the introduction into the Hospital of an apparatus destined to revolutionise the examination of the eye—the recently developed Slit-Lamp of Professor Gullstrand of Sweden. The generosity of the Ladies' Guild and of Sir William Lister provided 4 instruments, and a new department was set up; members of the Staff travelled to the continent to acquire the technique, and courses of instruction were commenced. To one old enough to do so, it has been fascinating to follow the development of this pioneer instrument into the sophisticated apparatus which it is today, together with the concomitant evolution of technique.

This year saw also the purchase by the Hospital of an electric ophthalmoscope—an innovation which revolutionised ophthalmoscopy. It cost £12, and the authorities ruled that it should be carried by the senior House Surgeon when he accompanied the Surgeons on their rounds of the wards.

The amenity represented today by the media of radio and television is so familiar that the relatively recent origin is apt to be forgotten. In 1923 a Marconi Wireless Installation was presented to the Hospital by Mr Godfrey Isaacs; it took the form of one set of instruments and a loud speaker which "could be moved from one room to another". Two years later the *Daily News* sponsored the provision of a comprehensive installation with ear-phones for every bed, and loud speakers in the recreation and day rooms. Moorfields was the first London Hospital to be thus equipped; and the Wireless for Hospitals Fund was inaugurated. Sir Arthur Stanley as President of this Fund handed over the apparatus on 23 September; the Lord Mayor and Lady Mayoress accepted the gifts on behalf of the Hospital. The response of the patients was such that they spontaneously requested that a message of grateful thanks should be sent to the donors. In the following year the newly established British Broadcasting Corporation permitted the first wireless appeal in aid of the funds of the Hospital. Wireless engineering techniques advanced at a rapid pace and the installation became obsolete; in 1934 the *News Chronicle* through its "Wireless for Hospitals Fund" provided the Hospital with a new and up-to-date installation. Again, in 1949 the equipment was replaced by an installation purchased from Phillips Electrical Ltd; by 1953 there were repeated complaints from patients and staff of poor reception and electrical interference, and the Board were asked to provide a new installation from Central Rediffusion Ltd, at an annual rental of £275. In view of the relatively short period since the last installation the Board at first demurred; Phillips were called in and advised that the apparatus was functioning normally and the Post Office Engineers did everything possible to eliminate interference. The advice of an expert Radio Engineer was sought before any decision was made. He recommended a thorough overhaul of the existing apparatus, and it was decided to carry this out at an approximate cost of £15, before making a final decision on replacement. The figure seemed very modest; nonetheless the set continued to function satisfactorily for some years. Developments and improvements have continued to demand subsequent modification and replacement; television has been installed, and is now to be found even in the ward common rooms.

The BBC Television Series "Your Life in Their Hands" contained one programme devoted to ophthalmology, which the hospital was asked to provide. Many aspects of the hospital activity were "featured"; one of the surgeons performed a cataract operation which was included (though no detailed surgery was shown). To judge by the correspondence subsequently received at the hospital, the programme was received with the greatest interest and enthusiasm; it is understood that the Surgeon's "fan-mail" was extensive! A copy of the film and its sound track was presented to the hospital. Apart from the invasion of the main theatre the project caused little disruption of hospital routine, though the apparatus and staff involved were as extensive and cumbrous as usual; preparation for the 28 minute film occupied many more than that number of hours.

In 1893 an enquiry officer was appointed whose duty it was to ascertain the financial situation of an applicant for treatment, and to ensure that no such person was admitted into the Hospital if he could afford to pay a private consultation fee. It is recorded that, in 1897, 602 people were refused on the grounds that they admitted that they could afford to pay a fee, and further that they did not know that the Hospital was open to the poor only. His activities are referred to in every subsequent annual report to the year 1920 when we hear no more of him; it is stated after that year that the Secretary's assistant interviewed each new patient, doubtless for the same purpose. It is surely no coincidence that this was the year of the appointment of the first Lady Almoner; her duties are described as entailing the after-care of both in- and out-patients and their social welfare, and to the interviewing of in-patients in order to ascertain what payment they could make towards their maintenance while in Hospital—a slightly different function from that of the Enquiry Officer. An Assistant Almoner was appointed in the following year; it is implied that she was partly engaged in similar enquiries.

There was also a paid officer whose duty it was to interview patients before sending away those who were in excess of the permitted daily number. The authorities in 1919 began to question the value of this office and the justification for the expense involved. "Do other hospitals", they ask rather pathetically in the minute books of that year, "have to deal with larger numbers of patients than their medical officers can treat, and do they take such careful precautions to avoid suffering and hardship?" They emphasised that the interview ensured the admission of those in pain or in need of immediate attention, those who had travelled far and those who had attended previously and been sent away, and even those whose home circumstances would make another attendance a hardship. In 1929 it was thought that the Social Service Department was not covering the needs of all patients. All in-patients and some out-patients had been interviewed in the past; a relevant sub-committee decided that all out-patients should be referred to the department in future. Accordingly another assistant Almoner was appointed, making three in all.

CHAPTER 7

Physiotherapy – Children's Convalescent Home
The Medical School – Coloured Students
M. L. Hepburn – J. H. Fisher – B. T. Lang
A. C. Hudson – Building – Amalgamation
Sir William Lister

THE acknowledged beneficial effect of sunlight on patients suffering from debilitating diseases, or local diseases having a constitutional basis, encouraged the ingenious to devise methods of applying this remedy by artificial means. The Carbon arc and, later, the Mercury Vapour lamp were used for this purpose, and proved of value not only in this field but also in the treatment generally of undernourished and sun-starved children, of which there were numbers even as late as the period after the first world war. An experimental start in this field of therapy had been made in 1925 when a Mercury Vapour lamp was given to the Hospital by the Medical Research Council. A clinic was established on three days a week and general irradiation was given. A year later the first report stated that the results had "exceeded expectations", and the authorities were thus encouraged to establish a definitive department, first entitled, aptly enough, the Ultra-Violet Ray Department, later renamed the Physical Therapy Department. Its first medical officer in charge was W. S. Duke-Elder. The value of the treatment was greatly increased when the potentially beneficial effects of ultra-violet rays, as well as other forms of therapy, applied locally to the eye were discovered. The instrument used was a Gullstrand Slit Lamp, supplied throughout with a quartz lens system, and modified and adapted for the purpose by Duke-Elder—a highly efficient if expensive piece of apparatus. Frank Law succeeded Duke-Elder as director of the Department in 1936, and designed a simpler apparatus which cost around £20, and served the purpose quite reasonably well. The Department was open every day and the staff were kept busily employed; besides local and general ultra-violet light applications, treatment included ionisation by Zinc and other medicaments, and Diathermy, which proved of great value in many cases. The general feeling was that the department served a useful purpose and was indeed in a manner indispensable; yet it closed down finally at City Road in 1959 and at High Holborn in 1966. Various factors combined to bring this about; amongst others, and perhaps the two most powerfully operative, were the improved health of the populace, especially the younger element, and the introduction of antibiotics. It is difficult to see why one department outlived the other for so long, though it is true that the High Holborn branch always seemed to have a relatively bigger turnover; moreover both the medical officer in charge, and his assistant, were specialists in physical medicine. Perhaps the little extra and justifiable *amour propre* thus engendered helped to prolong the life of the department. The only remaining need in this field would seem to be for the services of a physiotherapist to look after the welfare of elderly patients temporarily bedridden, by providing massage, active and passive movements and such measures, which are so valuable in those circumstances, especially in the prevention of thrombosis. A constant worry here has been, and still is, the shortage of physiotherapists, especially those available part time—a state of affairs which cannot but be worsened by the increased interest in, and care for, the geriatric patients, where the services of the exponents of such therapy are in greater demand than anywhere else.

A Children's Ophthalmic Convalescent Home was opened at Mayfield in Sussex in 1925 under the Supervision of Miss E. Nora Myers, a former Assistant Almoner at Moorfields. It was intended for children suffering from non-infectious eye trouble, especially those requiring prolonged convalescent treatment; in those days phlyctenular ophthalmia provided an ample clientèle. Sister Kitchen, lately retired from the post of out-patient sister of the Hospital, was appointed Matron, and Moorfields patients were received at a reduced fee. Mayfield was a most useful and important part of the Hospital's resources and its facilities were eagerly used and much appreciated. In 1934 Miss Myers decided that she must give up the administration of the Home; the Hospital authorities were naturally most anxious not to lose the facilities provided, at least until the proposed new Convalescent Home was a going concern. Negotiations for the provision of this latter had only just begun, and it was therefore agreed that the Hospital should assume the administrative control of Mayfield for a preliminary period of one year, with the consent of the official trustees of charitable funds. The committee of the home was reconstructed; warm thanks were expressed to Mrs Myers and Miss E. N. Myers for establishing the Home, and especially to the latter for making herself responsible for its administration from its inception.

Only two years later, owing to the continued diminution in the number of children requiring the facilities of the home (in itself a gratifying reason) it was decided to close it down. The name "Violet Foster Ward" in the Hospital commemorates the fact that it was in memory of Violet Foster that Miss Myers originally founded Mayfield.

It took a very short time for the Hospital authorities to realise that teaching should play an important part in its activities. Only five years after its foundation—the year of the lamented death of its founder—we read that the authorities had "been occupied with the means of extending the benefits of the Infirmary beyond the immediate circle of its operation. With this view (*sic*), they have adopted the usage of other Infirmaries —that of permitting the practice of its medical directors to be attended by students: by which act they provide that a knowledge of the diseases of the eye shall be more generally diffused among the members of the medical profession".

In the following year, Travers, the successor to Saunders, brought his pupils from St Thomas' Hospital for instruction and was thus the first to implement the decision of the Founders of the School of Ophthalmology, the first in the English speaking world. Emerson said that Michelangelo, as architect of St Peter's, "builded better than he knew"; the same comment applies to the founders of the school who did not know into what a magnificent tree the sapling they had planted would grow. And at a great pace; we read in the Report of 1828 that "more than a 1000 pupils instructed in its Science have diffused its benefits over various remote parts of the world so that its

73

services are perhaps as well known on the banks of the Ganges as on the banks of the Thames". No mean achievement in eighteen years.

The year 1899 saw the opening of the Hospital on its new site in the City Road and also the foundation of the Medical School in its own right, replacing the original School of Ophthalmology, with Holmes Spicer as its first dean. Under his wise guidance the school developed and prospered to become one of the most important institutions of its kind in the world; his devoted successors have added lustre to its pattern. It would be difficult to choose an area on the globe where ophthalmology is practised without finding there one who owes at least part of his training to Moorfields.

In 1919, at the request of the Medical Board, some efforts were made to provide facilities for students, though not on a very large scale. By a re-arrangement of rooms, not involving structural alterations, the students were provided with a sitting room, dining room and cloakroom. By 1924 the numbers receiving instruction annually reached the figure of 185; in addition to those from this country, students came from 9 different countries as far apart as New Zealand and China; 46 came from India.

Active consideration was given, in 1932, to the formation of a new School and Finance Committee, composed of representatives of the Committee of Management and the Medical Board. A detailed and informative memorandum on the origin and management of undergraduate medical schools in various London hospitals was drawn up by J. H. Fisher and Charles Goulden; the relevant portions of this were applied to the proposed new Committee, and a scheme of management and finance drawn up. The Committee was to consist of five members appointed by the Medical Board and three appointed by the Committee of Management; the Dean to be Chairman.

It was revealed in 1926 that 30.05 per cent (*sic*) of the students attending the Hospital were coloured. The Committee of Management wrote to the Medical Board as follows: "That in view of sundry complaints that have reached the Committee of Management in regard to the number of coloured students, they are of the opinion that it is desirable that there should be a Conference of the Medical Board and the

Committee of Management to consider the question of placing a limit on the number of such students attending the practice of the hospital." To say that this reads strangely today is to state the obvious; what is far more relevant is to consider its impact in the light of the boast made nearly a hundred years before, quoted on page 73. The Medical Board replied that they did not consider that the Medical School suffered any detriment from the presence of coloured students, and no action was considered necessary. They had heard that the presence of coloured students had an adverse effect on the entry of American students, but observed that the number of American students attending had begun to decline before that of the coloured students had reached its present level. They also pointed out that the hospital provided a unique training for Part I of the D.O.M.S. which was appreciated by all students, coloured or white.

The matter raised its head again in 1930 when the Chairman pointed out that the percentage of coloured students was steadily increasing and was now approximately 50 per cent. He added that he had assisted in drafting the plans for the reconstruction of the out-patient department, but had little inclination to devote the time and thought and energy which would be necessary to enable the scheme to be brought to fruition, if he were to find that the Hospital was ultimately rewarded by an influx of coloured students in even greater numbers than at present; he stated emphatically that he "would not be a party to it". Such expressions read strangely today; to some it may well have seemed that they read strangely at that time. The Chairman went so far as to suggest the numbers to be admitted to the school each year, not in percentages but in actual figures—30 in 1931, 20 in 1932, and a future limit to be fixed below this latter figure. The enthusiasm of the Medical Board for these suggestions was naturally lukewarm. J. H. Fisher produced a long memorandum which was submitted to the Committee of Management; its main suggestion was that instruction in Part I of the D.O.M.S. should be given at a central institute apart from any of the eye hospitals and that by concentrating on the subjects it might be possible to shorten the course to three months or even less, which would enable the examination to be held three times a year instead of two.

75

Passing of the examination was to be a necessary preliminary to the admission of a coloured student to the clinical practice of the Hospital. This lengthy reply would appear to constitute a tactful disagreement with the objections of the Chairman; careful perusal of it does not immediately reveal any obvious reason why the number of coloured students at Moorfields should be reduced; it does, however, say that "Moorfields by its prestige and the dilution of coloured students by white would attract the great majority of white students from the pool of men who had passed Part 1".

The Medical Board decided to call a special meeting to discuss the matter further. As a result of its deliberations they replied to the Committee of Management in firm dissenting fashion. They could find no convincing evidence in favour of the suggestion; they could find no objection to the *status quo* either from among their number or from other sources; they could find no evidence that the present arrangement had any deleterious effect. They found the suggestion that Indian students should attend classes at Moorfields and pursue their clinical studies elsewhere impracticable because of timing; a similar objection was raised to Fisher's proposals. They recalled that Indian students were British subjects and had equal right to instruction with students from the Dominions and Colonies. They made great play of the potential financial loss which the Committee's suggestion would entail; indeed one can read that this argument was used as a means of tempering blunt disagreement. One cannot but admire the dignified attitude of the Medical Board in this controversy; one cannot but feel that their reply was justified and indeed, correct.

Spicer had been succeeded as Dean by Malcolm Hepburn who had previously been Sub-dean. Hepburn retired from the Hospital under the age limit in 1926, and at the same time from the office of Dean which he had held with great distinction for 6 years. He was succeeded on the staff by Humphrey Neame, and as Dean by C. B. Goulden.

Malcolm Langton Hepburn was a most attractive personality and embodied all those qualities which make up the character enshrined in the now somewhat forgotten term "gentleman".

Malcolm L. Hepburn

A Londoner, educated at Uppingham and St Bartholomew's Hospital, he entered general practice in Lowestoft, where he became Surgeon to the Hospital. He returned to London in 1904 and became a student at Moorfields, his natural ability in the specialty soon became evident, and led him via the Central London Ophthalmic Hospital and the Hampstead General, to Moorfields and the Royal Free. He succeeded Holmes Spicer as Dean at Moorfields in 1920 and held this office until he retired in 1926. He was for two years President of the Ophthalmological Section of the Royal Society of Medicine, and his Presidential Address revealed his special interest in inflammatory lesions of the Choroid and the fundus changes associated therewith. The subject of his Doyne Lecture in 1935 was closely akin. He was for many years Secretary of the Council of British Ophthalmologists, the precursor of the Faculty. He was a good player of ball games and dearly loved his weekend

77

tennis parties, held on a lawn in the grounds of the church in which he read the Lessons every Sunday. His main outside interest was in climbing. A member of the Alpine Club, he was a distinguished and experienced climber, and his contributions to the *Journal of the Alpine Club* on the subject of mountain sickness were recognised by his election to the Fellowship of the Royal Geographical Society. But above all he was a man of great personal charm and impeccable integrity; genial and generous minded. He inspired real affection in all who knew him.

The Senior Surgeon, J. H. Fisher[1], reached the age limit in 1927, and retired, to be succeeded by Miss I. C. Mann, the

J. Herbert Fisher

[1] Vol. 1, p. 200.

first and so far the only woman to achieve such a position in the Hospital. Gordon Holmes (see page 56) also retired in this year, having served the Hospital as Physician for 14 years; W. J. Adie succeeded him.

John Herbert Fisher was born in 1867 and went to Exeter School. He had a brilliant career in the Medical School of St Thomas' Hospital which he entered at the age of 19, and was Dean of the Medical School and Chairman of the Committee of Medical and Surgical Officers of the Hospital in due course. He played rugger for his hospital and county, and took the highest qualifying honours. In a most impressive series of house appointments he became House Surgeon to Nettleship, and this decided the choice of his life's work. He succeeded Nettleship on to the staff of St Thomas' in 1895, and retired in 1924. Having been clinical assistant at Moorfields, he was elected to the Staff in 1900, remaining until he reached the age limit in 1927. He joined the Ophthalmological Society of the United Kingdom in 1895, was Secretary from 1907 to 1910, Vice President from 1918 to 1920 and became President in 1920; his Presidential Address entitled "The Personal Equation" was original, carefully phrased, broad in outlook and, you may be sure, beautifully delivered—for his rich sonorous voice enunciating his well-constructed rounded periods will ever remain in the memories of those who were privileged to hear him. Add to this a highly dignified and handsome, almost ambassadorial, appearance and a charm of manner second to none, and you have a true picture of J.H. He served for eight years on the Council of the Royal College of Surgeons, which even in those days was an unusual distinction for a specialist; his long period in office was said to be due, in part, to his reputation for financial acumen. He delivered a Hunterian Lecture and the Bradshaw Lecture in 1930. He did more than his share of administrative and committee work, and had an immense reputation as a Chairman. He served Ophthalmology well and left a pleasing, lasting memory to his many friends.

Two other vacancies occurred in the Honorary Staff soon after this—one caused by the death of B. T. Lang and the other by the resignation, long before reaching the age limit, of A. C. Hudson. They were succeeded by W. S. Duke-Elder and Rupert Scott respectively.

Basil Thorn Lang made his mark in Ophthalmology even though the time allowed for him to do so was lamentably short. He had been married but eleven months and was only 48 years old at his death in 1928. The son of William Lang[2] he came to Moorfields after a distinguished career at Cambridge and St Bartholomew's Hospital. Having already specialised in ophthalmology, and gained useful operative experience in India under "Jullundur" Smith and Colonel Elliot in Madras, he joined the R.A.M.C. at the outbreak of the first world war and applied his inventive gifts and technical knowledge to the production of the first mobile X-ray unit in the forces; when King George V met with his accident in France Lang was immediately sent for as Radiologist. On his return from the front he was first

Basil T. Lang

[2] Vol. 1, p. 204.

appointed to the Staff of the Western Ophthalmic Hospital, and, having been Lang Research Scholar, attained the Staff of Moorfields in 1920.

He had an original, inventive mind and applied his gifts to his specialty. Well versed in physics and mechanics, he devised and patented many inventions, including a long distance range finder and—it is said—the first steam motor car, apart from his various ophthalmic instruments. He was a generous, helpful soul and a great asset to the teaching staff; a man of unusual vivacity. The writer, then senior house surgeon, well remembers being called to the telephone on a busy morning to agree with a senior member of the honorary staff the appropriate adjective to include in his obituary; "ebullient" was suggested; the epithet was endorsed, and work resumed!

Arthur Cyril Hudson was a remarkable and memorable character who, though he lived till 1962 after retiring in 1928, never seemed to fit in to the hurried, brash atmosphere of his later days but rather to belong to a more spacious Edwardian or even Victorian era. He was an authority on Persian rugs and was consulted by those who dealt in such things professionally; his house held a collection of beautiful antiques, and one dined

A. C. Hudson

81

there well and graciously, off Spode. He played lawn tennis for Cambridge when up at Trinity and rugby football for his College, and never lost his interest in this and other games, which he patronised generously at St Thomas' Hospital. His hobby was salmon fishing; the residents regularly received a salmon from Scotland when he was up fishing. On one occasion after his departure north an anxious 'phone call was received at the Hospital by Cresswell—Cresswell was the head porter, a retired sergeant R.A. in the Corps of Commissionaires, and a splendid character—to the effect that he had left all his rods and gear behind. "Oh dear, Cresswell, I shall lose a day's fishing. Do send them on at once." From the next stop farther north came another call—"It's all right Cresswell, they're on the rack." His nature was gentle and gracious. Add to the personality which the above qualities must have engendered the fact that he was extremely well educated, and well informed in his speciality, and so conscientious that time had no meaning for him, and it will be seen that one has a very human doctor, whose colleagues respected him even if his eccentric ways sometimes caused the need for some revision of routine and time tables. It was not unusual to see him enter the luncheon room well after the majority had finished lunch, cut a piece of bread and put it in his pocket and quietly glide from the room— doubtless back to his beloved out-patients. He was an excellent clinician, and a first-class undergraduate teacher at St Thomas' Hospital. One was, however, sometimes compelled to wonder what the patient thought. During operations there were frequent calls of distress or request for more or different instruments (by name) to "George"—George Maynard, in charge of the instruments in the theatre, as conscientious and devoted to his job as Hudson. Perhaps after a difficult manoeuvre or a deviation from intention, one heard "Oh dear, Oh dear, *look* what I've done!" To a fully conscious patient hoping for the best (but doubtless prepared for the worst) this must have been a little disconcerting. But everyone forgave him and his patients loved him. Incidentally, he was a superb operator, an artist with the Graefe knife. He retired from Moorfields at the age of 53 but continued at his undergraduate hospital until retiring age. An unforgettable character.

By 1927 the Committee of Management felt that they could postpone no longer the overdue additions and alterations in the fabric of the Hospital which they had been contemplating for years. Draft plans were drawn up, revised, and revised again; they provided for the provision of 21 nurses' rooms (which would entail the extension of the main staircase, lift and walls), for 15 private rooms, with separate theatre, and for an increase in the general ward accommodation by 10 beds. The approximate cost was to be £28,000: £15,000 was in hand, so the problem for the year was that of collecting a balance of £13,000, and a further £30,000 for routine maintenance.

Though a minor matter, the financial side of the purchase of a piece of equipment at this time caused considerable interest. It was a new Giant Magnet. It is recorded that James Dixon first used a magnet in an attempt to remove a metallic foreign body from the eye in 1858, but that its power was insufficient for the purpose. The original Haab Magnet had been installed in 1899, and a Mellinger Ring Magnet in 1917. One of the Staff consulted with Professor Haab over the new purchase, and the replacement was carried out at a cost of £45. The Medical Committee apologised, rather piquantly, for the expenditure of such a large sum on one instrument, but pleaded in extenuation that more than twice that amount was frequently awarded in a Court of Law as compensation for the loss of an eye!

Many would be surprised to learn at how early a date the idea of Hospital amalgamation and the formation of an Institute were being discussed. In the mid-twenties of this century the Hospital Secretary approached the Secretary of the Central London Ophthalmic Hospital to arrange a meeting between the Committee of Management and Medical Board of each Hospital with a view to discussing such a plan. Three members of the Committee were appointed, and the Medical Board were invited to appoint three representatives.

The reason for the matter being raised at this time was that both Hospitals were considering large extension schemes which, if carried out, would surely postpone any amalgamation scheme "for at least a generation". The aim was to build a completely new hospital, and a medical school expanded into an Institute, on a site in Bloomsbury near to a General hospital, and to amalgamate the two governing bodies and the medical and surgical staffs of the two hospitals. The project was considered in very great detail, including the financial aspect; the Rockefeller Foundation was to be approached for a grant to cover the building costs. It is probable that the importance of the issue was a factor in causing an alteration in the rule governing retirement age, which was then 60; the Committee decided to present to the Annual General Meeting of Governors an amendment of Rule VII of the regulations of the Election Committee, enabling a discretionary extension to the age of 65. This was immediately followed by a request from the Junior Surgeons that the two Senior—Sir William Lister and Sir John Parsons—be invited to prolong their tenure of service to the age of 65, both being due to retire in 1928.

Negotiations proceeded for over six months. The Rockefeller Foundation declined to offer aid for the plan; the negotiations with the Central London Ophthalmic Hospital over amalgamation were suspended, and the joint Committee was dissolved. This was doubtless a disappointment to all, and to none greater than to Sir William Lister, who had been actively concerned in the negotiations. He retired in 1929, when the possible reason for prolonging his tenure of office referred to above had become invalid. He was succeeded by Robert Davenport.

William Tindall Lister[3] was a worthy representative of the old school of courtesy, sympathy, and sincerity. He was the nephew of Lord Lister, a connection of which he was justly proud; J. J. Lister, F.R.S. was his grandfather. He qualified from University College Hospital, and then joined Tweedy's clinic at Moorfields, becoming curator and then surgeon to the Hospital, but ill health soon compelled him to resign the appointment; the heavy out-patient duties at Moorfields and the London proved too much. After the war, in 1919, he resigned from the London and returned to work at Moorfields as successor to Percy Flemming; he was elected to the Committee of Management, and served the hospital in this capacity, and as surgeon, until 1929, having gone a year or so past the normal retiring age at the request of the Committee of Manage-

3 Vol. 1, p. 206.

84

Sir William Lister

ment in view of impending developments in the ophthalmo-logical world in London.

At the outbreak of the 1914 war he was put in charge of the ophthalmic services of the B.E.F., and carried out the task in a brilliantly efficient manner, of which his colleagues in France spoke with unstinted praise. His work at Moorfields on his return was enthusiastic, and tireless. He became particularly interested in the emerging surgical treatment of retinal detach-ment, a condition hitherto either left alone or hopefully if feebly treated by rest in bed, hot air cradles and mercury inunctions. He visited Vogt, Gonin and Koby in 1929, and on 27 December of that year he performed at Moorfields, assisted by C. D. Shapland, the first operation for retinal detachment by Gonin's method of cautery puncture to be carried out in this country. The subsequent progress of this line of treatment, and its development through multiple trephining with or without caustic, diathermy, light coagulation and the Laser beam, is common knowledge; but what a fundamental and historic milestone was passed in that first decade when, through an appreciation of the pathology of the condition and of the importance of the hole in the retina, the success rate of treatment rose from zero, eventually to reach the astonishing height which it occupies today. He was a superb operator in every branch of intraocular work, a ready and patient teacher, and generous in praise of his pupils' and colleagues' achievements; one of the greatest clinicians of his time—accurate and thorough in observation and investigation. It is probably without precedent that he declined to become President of the Ophthalmological Society of the United Kingdom, although actually elected to that office. A modest and retiring man, with a Quaker background, his approach and attitude were gentler than those of most of his colleagues and all of his juniors, to the extent that some wrongly considered him old-fashioned. The writer remembers an incident in the theatre which caused a slight raising of the eyebrows—no more—when a well-meaning if brash American, having watched him remove a cataract with characteristic skill, put his expressions into words which one may surmise were quite new to the surgeon he was praising: "Say, Doctor, you remove a pretty crystalline!" One recalls with most respectful amusement the graphic histrionic illustrations which so often accompanied his description of an accident involving the eye. The "dashing cavalry officer"—here followed some very accurate and impressive cavalry sword play; how the schoolboy cricketer suffered a hyphaema when hit in the eye by a bail—the crouching expectant wicket-keeper attitude, the staggering step backward with hand over eye. It was all so human, and added much to the charm—and interest—of working with and for him. He was devoted to the welfare of Moorfields, and was a generous benefactor over a long period. The writer is in a position to know that many an anonymous donation to the funds or amenities of the Hospital are properly traceable to him. Again, after his death Lady Lister instituted an Award in Ophthalmology with a donation of £3000.

Like Malcom Hepburn, Lister was a keen mountaineer and a member of the Alpine Club; an enthusiastic photographer, his work in the field of micro-photography, mountain and architectural photography was outstanding. His consulting room was decorated with superb Alpine photographs, some of which had demanded hours of patient waiting to achieve just the effect he wanted.

At his passing in 1944 one of his old friends and colleagues wrote, "At no time has the leaven of such characters been more needed than today."

CHAPTER 8

Building and Extension – Academic Activity

WHEN the King Edward's Fund approved the plans for the additional nurses' accommodation on the fourth floor in 1924, the Distribution Committee enquired if the Special Committee dealing with the matter had considered opening some of the 18 beds as pay-beds. This stimulated further interest in the pay-beds question, and efforts were made to provide as many pay-beds as possible in order favourably to influence the subscriptions of the Fund. It was suggested that the two-bedded wards adjoining the cataract wards be set aside for patients who could subscribe four guineas a week towards their maintenance, but who could not pay for medical attention. The present sister's day rooms "might be utilised for unruly patients" in the place of the two-bedded wards, and movable partitions be erected in the two cataract wards to provide four cubicles in each ward. The scheme was implemented and it was at once seen that it fulfilled a useful purpose; regulations were drawn up concerning fees, payments, and administration, and the accommodation, which was kept filled, was officially labelled the "Cubicle Wards". The success of this tentative venture encouraged the authorities to include such accommodation in the great rebuilding scheme of 1935; a five-bed cubicle ward was provided on each of the first and second floors.

As soon as it became evident that the plan for amalgamation and the formation of an Institute was not going to materialise, at any rate in the near future, the plans for the scheme of an extension were pursued even more actively than before, and the efforts of the Appeal Department increased; a start was actually made on 17 July, 1929. The three stage scheme comprised the following:

1. a. Provision of private ward block
   b. Additional accommodation for the resident medical staff
   c. Additional accommodation for nursing and domestic staff

2. a. A reconstruction and enlargement of the out-patient department
   b. Increased accommodation for the medical school
   c. Extension of bacteriological and pathological laboratories
   d. New and larger library and museum
   e. Additional in-patient operating theatre
3.   Provision of a convalescent home

During the first stage practically the whole of the third floor had to be closed; nursing staff were accommodated outside, and the bed complement was reduced from 122 to 100. When the out-patient department was under consideration the Committee was enabled to acquire some property leased by Messrs Lipton's in Cayton Street, and the Ecclesiastical Commissioners, as Ground Landlords, very kindly extended the lease from a few years to such a length as to allow it to correspond with that of the main hospital, which expires in 2893. This acquisition provided room also for a new Physiotherapy Department, as well as Library and Museum and medical school. At this stage a broadcast appeal for this object by A. J. Allen raised the considerable sum of £4600.

The provision of private accommodation had had to wait some years; by 1930, however, a private ward unit had been built. This unit (comprising 17 rooms and an operating theatre) together with two new blocks to accommodate 32 nurses and 8 domestic staff was completed in December 1930 and opened by the President, H.R.H. Prince Arthur of Connaught, on Monday the 8th of that month, in the presence of a distinguished gathering including the Lord Mayor of London, the Lord Bishop of London, representatives of the lay and medical governing bodies, and a company of 300 supporters of the Hospital. The cost was £41,365. There were 209 patients admitted in the first complete year of use, which proved the value of this additional service. The success of the private unit caused the authorities to decide, after the major rebuilding scheme was completed, to increase the unit by 14 beds by the conversion of nurses' bedrooms into private rooms. Thus were created the "upper and lower corridors" of the private wing. The necessary nursing accommodation was provided in the new Nurses' Home on the fourth floor.

The Building Committee immediately thereafter turned its attention to the extension of the out-patients' department and the rest of the building scheme, though some measure of postponement was inevitable in view of the serious economic crisis which the country was experiencing. Indeed, at one stage, in view of this crisis the second part of the reconstruction scheme was postponed indefinitely, and it was also decided that it was inadvisable to expend the sum of £700 for the provision of temporary accommodation. A change of attitude was, however, induced by an offer from the King Edward's Hospital Fund at this time to contribute a sum equal to the amount raised during a period from a date to be fixed by the Fund to the 31 July next following. In the new circumstances it was decided to commence building operations by 1932, which would allow time for the collection of more money to take advantage of the offer of the Fund, for the preparation of plans, specifications, and estimates, and for the provision of adequate temporary arrangements for carrying on the work of the out-patient department during the period of reconstruction. It was encouraging that the Annual Report of 1932 was able to announce that the Income and Expenditure account for the year had been balanced and that over £28,000 had been raised on behalf of the reconstruction and extension fund, with promises amounting to £7500 more. Accordingly, in view of this gratifying financial recovery, the second, larger part of the rebuilding scheme was put in hand.

This was the programme:

(a) The out-patient department, with its ancillary services: refraction department, spectacle room, dispensary, social services department, registration and enquiry offices, etc.
(b) Minor operation theatre and casualty department
(c) Pathological department
(d) Bacteriological department
(e) Physiotherapy department
(f) Orthoptic department
(g) Medical school, with lecture theatres, museum and library
(h) Fourteen additional rooms for private patients
(i) Ten cubicle ward beds
(j) Additional nursing and domestic staff accommodation

(k) Dining room for medical and nursing staff

(l) Chapel

A formidable list. There were also subsidiary plans for modernising the engineering services of the Hospital, providing new boilers with mechanical stokers and calorifiers, air conditioning plant, water softeners, etc. In this connection an important modification in domestic routine occurred in mid-1933 with the proposal to establish a Works Department. Minor emergency plumbing had in the past been carried out by the Engineer's Department; all other work had gone out to contract. A full time carpenter had been appointed in 1925 and it was estimated that this step had resulted in an annual saving of £50. Details of personnel, time sheets, material, books and stock lists were all fully considered; it was hoped that the annual saving would be not less than £250 a year. It was rightly remarked that such a department would be even more justified and more economical after the completion of the Extension scheme. H. Harman was appointed foreman, and held the post until his retirement in 1954, taking no small part in the development of the department into a most important part of the hospital. He, and indeed his son "Willy" with and after him, served the hospital loyally, cheerfully, and well. He was succeeded in this important department by A. Wright as Works Supervisor.

Demolition began on 18 March, 1933, and included the contiguous disused warehouse which had been acquired from Lipton's. A temporary structure was built over the Peerless Street forecourt, to provide accommodation for the Registrar and enquiry offices, and refreshment room; a staircase between the Hospital and the adjoining Peerless Buildings gave access from the ground to the first floor, where Sedgwick and Alexandra wards, with the adjoining day room, had been adapted for use as the out-patient department. The second floor day room was converted into a ward which enabled a bed complement of 136 (from 152). The front elevation of the new buildings was completed by the end of 1933; the porch was embellished by a most attractive low relief sculpture, executed and presented by Eric Gill, of the restoration of sight to blind Bartimeus.

As is usual in such ventures, the hoped-for date of completion receded gradually. The autumn of 1934 had been envisaged;

The last day in the old Out-Patients, City Road; 10 March, 1933. On the left are seen Arthur Cowell (Appeal Secretary) and H. T. Payne (Accountant) leaning against the pillar, with Arthur Tarrant (Secretary). At the back are the four surgeons of the day (left to right) Scott, Goulden, Davenport, Doyne, and behind is Creswell, the Hall Porter, in the uniform of the Corps of Commissionaires.

A Surgeon's Clinic before the Rebuilding

this changed to the Spring of 1935. Similarly the estimated figure for the total cost began to rise. Starting at £89,000, it reached £112,000 in 1934; £7000 remained to be raised. The offer from an anonymous donor of £4500, provided the buildings were opened by 31 December, 1934, was generously extended to 31 June, 1935.

The opening sentence of the Annual Report of the Hospital for 1935, runs as follows: "The year 1935 will rank with those of 1805 and 1899 in the annals of Moorfields." It was well said. 1805 saw creation; 1899 translation, and 1935 amplification. The last was certainly a great year for all concerned, and a triumph of endeavour and faith—for the governing body for its organisation, for the lay staff for its loyalty and determination, for the appeal side for its most successful activities, and for the surgical and nursing staff for its devotion and application in circumstances which were at times difficult, to say the least.

The new building was named, by gracious command of His Majesty, the King George V extension; the opening ceremony took place on 16 May, 1935. The Hospital was again honoured by the presence of royalty, for the ceremony was performed by T.R.H. the Duke and Duchess of York. An impressive reception committee received them at the entrance to the Hospital; the Chairman read an ample and dignified address in which he described details of the building and its construction. His Royal Highness replied in a gracious and congratulatory speech which concluded by his declaring the extension open. The Lord Mayor of London thanked Their Royal Highnesses for the honour they had done the Hospital, and the Bishop of London offered a prayer and pronounced the Benediction. The Royal visitors made an extensive tour of the building, and various presentations were made. A dignified and memorable occasion which was a source of great gratification to all concerned in the venture.

At the time of the occupation of the new out-patient department a scheme of "sifting" was introduced into the out-patient routine. All patients, old and new, were cursorily examined by a medical officer before being passed on to the Refraction Department, Casualty Department (minor operations, etc.) or to the Surgeon's Clinic. It was hoped that this would reduce the waiting period for all out-patients, and facilitate the clinical

93

Their Royal Highnesses The Duke and Duchess of York after opening
The King George V Extension, 16 May, 1935

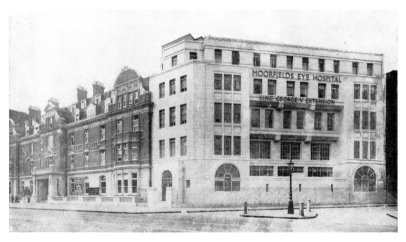

The New Extension 1935

teaching activities of the Surgeons. The scheme was rather a disappointment and caused unforeseen drawbacks; it was abandoned a few years later.

Encouraged by the success of the rebuilding scheme, and stimulated by seeing their labours being brought to fruition, the authorities began to cast a critical eye on the 36-year-old original part of the hospital, and to note that it compared unfavourably in appearance with the new wing. A decision was made to embark upon a scheme of modernisation and decoration, notably of the wards and main sanitary block, in spite of the estimated cost of £9500 and in spite of the knowledge that the recent addition would increase maintenance costs by some £5000 a year. The scheme was submitted to King Edward's Fund and was begun in July; one effect was to be an increase in bed complement from 175 to 200. The additional beds were available in March 1936, and the Lady Cooper Memorial Chapel was available in November.

Apart from the modernisation of the older parts of the Hospital, various other improvements were carried out. Modern shock proof equipment was installed in the X-ray department; hot cupboards and additional cooking apparatus were installed in the kitchens; the main chimney stack was repaired and raised in an endeavour to achieve natural draught for the boilers; and store rooms were provided on the first and second floors.

The list of improvements to the Hospital which were carried out following the modernisation scheme in 1937 (which in turn had followed the big rebuilding of the year before) is again an impressive one, ranging from various domestic additions and modifications to the transfer of the L.C.C. school children's clinic to the out-patients department, and the conversion of the former into a students' dining room. Most of the main works and all the accessory work like painting and carpentry were carried out by the Works department and engineering staff which effected a material saving in costs.

This is a record of effort, initiative, and achievement on the part of the hospital authorities; important alteration and expansion had been achieved. What, it may be asked, was the comparable output in the medical field? How did the clinical and academic activity proceed and progress? It has been said that very little original work emerged from the Hospital at this time—indeed, the whole inter-war period has been described, as far as this country is concerned, as "Ophthalmology in the Doldrums". This is a little ungenerous, while carrying enough truth to demand an answer. There were many reasons why the academic activity of the Hospital proceeded at a slow pace at this time, but it must be said at once that it is not true that nothing new or useful appeared. Not every age, however, can be one of new discovery and advance; not every epoch produces the combination of original mind and academic inclination. Discoveries in ophthalmology in the first part of this century that proceeded from this country were largely of a clinical nature; pathological research turned on the revelations of the light microscope, and the histological and cytological potential of this instrument was running out. The voluntary system was demanding more and more of a surgeon's time; what was left had in large part to be utilised in earning a living. There was no central body to co-ordinate and stimulate ophthalmic research; individual workers of ability, particularly the more junior, did not have available to them the comprehensive scientific facilities to which we are today so accustomed; financial resources, both for the research worker and for the expenses of the investigation, were by no means generally available. The whole environment tended to encourage clinical ophthalmology, and the research was mainly clinical as well. The scientific education, and the opportunity for research, afforded to the young ophthalmologist of today is unrecognisably better than that offered to the immediately preceding generations.

Further, the routine clinical work, the daily duty of seeing and treating large numbers of out-patients, and caring for and operating upon in-patients, was carried out under much less propitious conditions and with far less help, personal and instrumental, than obtains today. And, after all, this work had to be done; someone had to answer the increasingly clamorous demands of increasing numbers of patients. The surgeons of the period we are considering were more prepared to submit themselves to this daily absorbing routine than are their successors of today—and patiently, devotedly, and conscientiously did they perform this task. And who shall say that this background of labour, with its accumulation of knowledge and frequent expression of ideas, results and suggestions which it produced, played no part in a build-up which led in due course to the advances, clinical and scientific, which followed later? It is by no means suggested that the discoverers of recent times climbed upon the shoulders of their predecessors in order to achieve their ends; rather that the ground was inevitably being prepared by the succession of dedicated workers at a time when scientific progress was dormant, who thus played their part, if obscure and unseen, in the more dramatic advances which the next period produced. This is not put forward as an excuse or an apology; it is a highly tenable thesis, expressed not for the first time. Virginia Woolf has proffered a similar view in a different context. " . . . Without those forerunners, Jane Austen and the Brontës and George Eliot could no more have written than Shakespeare could have written without Marlowe, or Marlowe without Chaucer, or Chaucer without those forgotten poets who paved the ways and tamed the natural savagery of the tongue. For masterpieces are not single and solitary births; they are the outcome of many years of thinking in common, of thinking by the body of the people, so that the experience of the mass is behind the single voice."

This would appear to present a very relevant parallel.

8

CHAPTER 9

Orthoptics – Registrar – Sir George Saltmarsh
Lady Cooper – Treacher Collins – Sir John Parsons
Sir Stewart Duke-Elder – R. Foster Moore
Mydricaine – Inheritance and Disease – Catering
The Truck Act

IN 1931 it was considered desirable to make a practical enquiry into the possible value of orthoptic investigation and treatment. With this end in view a department was established for a preliminary period of one year, with a medical officer in charge receiving a salary of £150 a year. Details were left to two members of the medical staff and the Secretary, who was authorised to purchase equipment for a sum not exceeding £45. The medical officer was to be supervised by a sub-committee of the Medical Board; Mrs Duke-Elder was appointed, and within a few months the authorities decided that the department had already justified itself, that it was past the experimental stage, and that a limited number of treatment cases be accepted. Sessions were increased to five a week, and the appointment of an assistant was recommended at a starting salary of £150 per annum, changing to £1.1s. per session after 3 months. In view of the fact that the work of the medical officer in charge was considered to be research work under her grant from the Medical Research Council, she generously offered to forego her salary both for research work and for training the assistant. The Department went from strength to strength, and in 1933 there were over 4000 attendances. Its success was acknowledged and rewarded by its inclusion in the great rebuilding scheme of the thirties; in the completed building the Orthoptic Department shared the whole of the first floor with the Physiotherapy Department. In 1947 the two part-time orthoptists were replaced by a full-time orthoptist at a salary of £210 per annum, which enabled another six sessions of Orthoptic work per week to be undertaken.

After that further change became necessary consequent upon the amalgamation of the Hospitals. Miss Pugh and her staff at

City Road were all transferred to the Central Branch, together with all records, apparatus and such patients as were at present under treatment; the functions of the department were to be research, teaching and demonstration, the last mainly to D.O.M.S. candidates. Miss Mayou, the orthoptist in charge at the Central, was similarly to be translated, with staff, students and apparatus, to the City Road, where the routine work of the branch would be carried out, and the School of Orthoptics would continue. There was a medical officer in overall charge at each branch of the Hospital where routine clinical work continued—J. H. Doggart at Moorfields and T. K. Lyle at Westminster.

Expansion was necessary at this latter branch, and in June 1947 an attempt was made to acquire part of 177 High Holborn for the purpose. Attention was called to the fact that the premises had previously been a hospital; nonetheless the Ministry of Works refused, saying that they were earmarked for Government purposes. The Ministry of Health were then approached, but could be no more helpful; the Minister, however, made vague promises in the field of a Civil Building Licence; it was decided to proceed with the original scheme of alterations to the basement. In January 1949 the Ministry of Health reported that the Ministry of Works no longer required the property. The former Ministry instructed the Hospital to "proceed on the lines of the conditions detailed in B.G. (48) 49"—the technique and jargon of bureaucracy were creeping in—and with renewed interest the matter was taken up again. In November the hospital was informed that they could proceed with their plan for the adaptation of the building and it was decided, in view of the additional space thus provided, that the department should take over the space previously used as lecture hall and laboratories.

It became evident at this time that the services of a Registrar to the Hospital were necessary, to concern himself with the preservation and classification of case records, the compilation of a list of cases available for demonstration at the various students' classes and courses, and similar duties. In January

99

1932, C. Dee Shapland was appointed at a salary of £50 per annum, to attend three half days a week. He was succeeded four years later by H. Ridley, and in 1938 Hugh Skeoch took over, to hold the post for over twenty years. At the time of the amalgamation H. E. Hobbs was registrar to the High Holborn Branch; he indicated his desire to relinquish the post from 1 May, 1957. The assessment of hours relinquished by him was divided between two Consultants, P. McG. Moffat and J. R. Hudson, each of $4\frac{1}{2}$ hours a week; the former in respect of his duties in a visual aid clinic which he had inaugurated 18 months before, and the latter for the supervision of the Registrar's department, Operating theatre, Casualty department, and instruments and equipment. In view of the fact that Mr Hobbs was carrying out research on orbital tumours at the Institute he was offered an honorary contract as Consultant while so engaged. He was succeeded by G. C. Swain; S. J. Crews took over in the following year, and D. P. Honey in 1959. He resigned in 1959, as did Skeoch from the City Road Branch. Hudson was appointed "Consultant in Charge" at High Holborn, while Charles Cook was appointed at City Road with the same title. From then onwards the new set-up has obtained, and the post of registrar as such has disappeared. Many of the routine duties previously undertaken by him were taken over by the secretary to the department, Miss Bush, whose efficiency and enthusiasm over a long period have been a source of strength to the department. She has a great flair for collecting patients as clinical material for the *viva-voce* examinations for the F.R.C.S. and D.O., which are held at the hospital. It is not by any means an easy task, nor particularly to one's liking; but she was infallible, and the patients turned up not only in adequate numbers, but willingly and cheerfully, and in many cases repeatedly! In 1963 Charles Cook alone was listed as Consultant in Charge of Registrar's department, J. R. Hudson resigning from the post at High Holborn; and in 1973 Cook resigned from City Road.

With the appointment of a Medical Records Officer, of a medical secretary to each clinic, and so on, many of the duties previously undertaken by the Registrar have been dispersed. A full-time secretary works in the department at High Holborn, supervised by some part-time clinical assistants serving four sessions a week between them; Redmond Smith keeps an unofficial eye on the department at City Road.

The best remembered registrar is undoubtably H. H. Skeoch, who held the post a great deal longer than anyone else. After his departure we no longer find a registrar's report in the annual report of the hospital. Skeoch initiated these, and their omission may well be considered a loss; in them was to be found an analysis of the surgical work for the year, and this exposition of clinical and surgical trends year by year provided very interesting and valuable material.

The year 1931 saw the untimely death of Sir George Saltmarsh. Although elected to the Committee of Management only 5 years before, he had shown the greatest interest in the work and progress of the hospital, and identified himself with it in an unmistakable fashion. He died in the "Royal Scot" Express disaster on 22 March.

Lady Cooper and Treacher Collins died in 1932. Lady Cooper, the widow of a former Lord Mayor of London, joined the Committee of Management in 1923, and she was an indefatigable worker for the Hospital and a generous benefactress. She was Chairman of the Ladies' Guild, and the recipient of many honours and distinctions. One of her last gifts was a donation of £1000 for the provisions of a Chapel; this was included in the reconstruction scheme, and is today a focal point in the Hospital, decorated and furnished in admirable fashion. Of Treacher Collins, who died on 13 December, we know so much that there is no need to say more—and a biographical note of this great man constitutes the first item in this volume. He held appointments in the Hospital from 1884 to 1922, and remained Consulting Surgeon till his death. The Annual Report contains a eulogium in the warmest terms and gives a page to a biography and another to his photograph. The hospital had suffered the "irreparable loss" of "one of its most loyal friends". Less than a week after his death, members of the surgical staff had begun to talk of a permanent memorial; one of the members wrote to the Chairman suggesting this, and enclosed a cheque to start the Fund. J. H. Parsons, Foster Moore, and C. B. Goulden were appointed representatives of the Medical Board on the projected Joint Sub-Committee, and the preliminary suggestion was made that the Fund be used to endow the Pathological Laboratory, which would be named after Collins. By September 1938 the Fund had reached £600. Collins left a legacy of £500 to the Hospital with the wish that the income therefrom be applied to the general purposes of the Hospital.

Sir John Parsons retired from the Staff on 20 June, 1933. This was a few months before he would have been due to retire anyway, under the extended age limit which had been introduced in 1928. H. B. Stallard was appointed to fill the vacancy thus caused. It is no exaggeration to say that Sir John Herbert Parsons,[1] C.B.E., D.Sc., LL.D., F.R.C.S., F.R.S. was a unique figure in the history of ophthalmology and no disrespect to say

Sir John Herbert Parsons

[1] Vol. 1, p. 206.

that he was not a devoted clinician, not even an outstanding clinician; and yet in spite of this he did more to advance the science of ophthalmology than anyone of his time. He served Moorfields as Surgeon for 28 years, but in an almost perfunctory way; he did practically no teaching, and did not spend too long in his out-patient clinic; yet in that time, and throughout his life, he served ophthalmology and thus Moorfields in a way that continues to be a source of wonder and admiration to those who follow his career. He was physiologist, psychologist, pathologist and philosopher, and his interests and activities in these fields were all directed to the impact which they had on his chosen specialty, ophthalmology. He was a prolific writer, both of contributions to the journals and of books on subjects as separate as optics, pathology, and perception; perhaps rather strangely, he wrote in 1907 a straightforward clinical text book, *Diseases of the Eye*, which nonetheless was quite first class and continues to re-appear in new editions to the present day— a quite remarkable achievement. His four volume *Pathology of the Eye* (1904–8) was a monumental work.

He served on the Medical Research Council for 4 years, and took full advantage of the opportunity this afforded to advance research in visual problems, and to provide scope and funds for work in this field for his more junior colleagues. He was a member of numerous committees dealing with all aspects of the Science; he was consultant to the Home Forces in the 1914 war, and his lectureships and academic honours were too numerous to mention here. All are recorded in detail elsewhere; it is necessary here to restrict oneself to his record in the context of Moorfields. As a man he was, indeed, rather shy, though some might not have suspected it; a rugged uncompromising attitude cloaked a nature which was friendly, tolerant and generous, and above all, scrupulously honest. In a word, a great man; we shall not look upon his like again.

Sir Stewart Duke-Elder, G.C.V.O., M.D., F.R.C.P., F.R.C.S., F.R.S. resigned in July of 1936, to be succeeded by the author of this book. He was on the staff a surprisingly short time, some might say—as indeed he was. There were many reasons; around this time Sir Stewart was dogged by persistent ill-health, and had the additional burden of the worry of the serious illness, involving operation, of his devoted and loyal

Sir Stewart Duke-Elder

partner and colleague, Lady Duke-Elder. In addition, he was engaged in research, had an immense and fashionable private practice, and had already begun to write upon his subject—a beginning which developed into the many-volume works of later years. The duties of two hospitals were clearly too much; indeed, one cannot really picture him as tied down to the humdrum routine of out-patients, as some of it undoubtedly is. He found he could not devote the necessary time to Hospital duties; his decision to resign was a loss to the Hospital and to himself.

A short biography of William Stewart Duke-Elder presents one with a more difficult task than that presented by any of his colleagues before or since. One hardly knows where to start and certainly has difficulty in finishing; in almost every direction there is an *embarras de richesse*. His career as a student was brilliant and precocious; he has collected nearly every relevant academic honour there is. In 1952 he was appointed Surgeon-Oculist to Her Majesty, having previously served Their Majesties King Edward VIII and King George VI in a similar capacity; he became Extra Surgeon-Oculist to the Queen in 1965. His labours on behalf of ophthalmology have been stupendous. He was largely responsible for the creation of the Institute of Ophthalmology, of the Faculty of Ophthalmologists, and of the Ophthalmic Fellowship Diploma of the Royal College of Surgeons. One hazards that his writings surpass, in quality and quantity, those of any previous author in any branch of medicine; apart from numerous articles in journals, and smaller text books, his *Textbook of Ophthalmology* in 7 volumes, an individual effort produced between 1932 and 1954, became at once the standard work on the subject in the English language, while the 15 volumes of the *System of Ophthalmology*, begun in 1957 and now nearing completion, and written with the assistance of colleagues at the Institute, is taking its place as an even more comprehensive, authoritative, and up-to-date reference book. His occupation with the political and sociological aspects of Ophthalmology has been tireless; his influence on the position and development of the specialty is indeed difficult to compute.

One's chagrin in attempting the well-nigh impossible is relieved by the self-imposed limitation of these biographical notes on retired surgeons to a consideration of their careers for the most part in the context of Moorfields. Sir Stewart was appointed to the Staff in 1928 but he retired in 1936, later to be appointed Consulting Surgeon; he remained longer on the staff of St George's. Thus his participation in the clinical activities of Moorfields was short; but in 1946 he was appointed to the Committee of Management and served on that and its successor the Board of Governors until 1970, and on various committees, so that his connection with the hospital was merely altered and not severed by his retirement. Add to that his Directorship and, on retirement, his Presidency of the closely integrated Institute, and one sees that his influence on the Hospital has been continuous. One will never be able to estimate the value of that influence to the Hospital nor, indeed, to Ophthalmology as a whole and to ophthalmologists at large; one stands amazed at the untiring energy, devoted application, and supreme ability involved. His accomplishments cannot be summarised; the only adequate comment which occurs to the writer is contained in the slogan which the latter saw, long years ago in the first world war, displayed in letters six feet high across the front of the Hôtel de Ville in Peronne: "*Nicht Fragen, Nur Wundern.*" Its application then was a mystery to him; it has come in useful half a century later.

In August 1937 Foster Moore retired from the Staff and was succeeded by E. F. King. Robert Foster Moore was a scholar of Christ's College, Cambridge, and came down to St Bartholomew's. After qualifying, he was demonstrator of anatomy for 6 years, and had an authoritative knowledge of

R. Foster Moore

his subject; this period of his career developed his ability for teaching, which he increased throughout his hospital life, though he could not be persuaded to lecture in the medical school. His main interest within his specialty was in medical ophthalmology and he spent long periods in the wards of his physician colleagues at St Bartholomew's; his *Medical Ophthalmology* was a classic. He had his full share of academic honours, and presided over the Ophthalmological Society of the United Kingdom in 1936. His characteristics were integrity and a staunch dislike of the non-authentic; he was a man of very determined opinions. A whimsical and slightly cynical humour was sometimes employed in demonstrating these features. One remembers one gem in particular: "I am prepared to admit that vaccines, given in sufficient quantity and sufficiently often, may have some slight nutrient value." He enjoyed the effect such *obiter dicta* created. An amateur of Gilbert and Sullivan, his main outdoor interest was in fly fishing; on retirement he lived by the Nadder near Bemerton, where he fished and gardened. Calligraphy fascinated him, as did symmetry; he was more than adept as a water-colour painter. Ambidexterity was another ploy which he cultivated, and utilised it outside as well as inside the operating theatre. He could write his two last initials, one with each hand and simultaneously, so that while perfectly decipherable they looked strangely symmetrical. An interesting, determinate, staunch character whom one does not forget.

Mydricaine came into use at this time. It was a preparation elaborated by the Pharmacist B. S. Clarke as a powerful mydriatic. While repeated instillation was necessary for Glaucosan, it was claimed that one sub-conjunctival injection of Mydricaine was equally effective; further, it was put up in ampoule form and had an indefinite shelf life. It consisted of atropine, cocaine, suprarenin, chlorbutol, sodium chloride and sulphurous acid; glaucosan was a synthetic suprarenal alkaloid plus optically inactive methylaminoacetopyrocatechol. The pharmacist sought permission to patent this preparation and commercialise it from the Hospital. Permission was granted, with the proviso that the patent should embody the Pharmacist's name and address and not that of the Hospital, which should receive its supplies of the drug at cost price. This arrangement produced a complication which was evidently not expected; the pharmacists at two other London hospitals requested to be supplied with the formula, and their request was supported by the Medical Board, but the Committee of Management demurred because they had agreed that the preparation be patented—and patented, be it remembered, at the request of the Medical Board, in the name of the pharmacist and not of the hospital. The Committee did not consider it reasonable to rescind the resolution—if indeed this were possible, or would effectively negative the patent—and the Medical Board had to agree.

The Medical Research Council in 1933 requested the co-operation of the Hospital in an investigation into inheritance and disease. The suggested scheme seemed to the Medical Board rather complicated and impracticable, and a simpler scheme, confining the investigation to in-patients, was devised. The Board agreed to participate, and the house surgeons were instructed to complete the necessary forms as part of their routine duties. This was the start of the various measures subsequently taken to make more use of the invaluable records which the Hospital routinely produced; a complete and complicated clinical index evolved, and in due course such cognate subjects as genetics as applied to ophthalmology were taken care of by special departments, and medical officers appointed thereto, as will appear in subsequent pages.

Soon after the rebuilding and the general reorganisation which succeeded it, the desirability of separating the catering arrangements from the nursing administration was discussed. A catering sub-committee was appointed and recommended this divorce. It emerged that this would not be in accordance with the wishes of the Matron. From this situation arose—as so often happens on similar occasions—the knowledge that there were many points of difference between the Matron, the Governing Body, and the surgical staff. The matter aroused much discussion and the writing of memoranda; the Matron resigned after representations from the Committee. A "Food Supervisor" was appointed at once and a Steward's department established; immediate improvement in the catering services was noted.

It was at about this time that the interesting incident of the resident stoker occurred, as a result of the provisions of the Truck Act, a statute of 1831, extended in 1887, which deals with problems which may arise in the case of an employee who receives part or all of his earnings in kind—and indeed requires that they shall be paid in money. The strange-sounding title derives from the verb to truck, or barter, or the noun truck, meaning exchange of goods, and survives in the colloquialism "to have no truck with" a person. A precedent had been set by an employee of a city firm, thus remunerated, who on leaving his employment successfully sued his previous employers for a considerable sum. A stoker at the Hospital had been employed on a residential basis and thus could be considered as having received part of his wages in kind. On leaving the Hospital at about the time of the case quoted above he brought a similar action against the Hospital. The case was of interest not only to the Hospital but generally, for doubtless a success on the part of this employee would have encouraged many others similarly situated to follow suit. It emerged in the course of the action that the provisions of the Act did not apply to domestic servants, and the case in fact turned on the definition of this class of employees. It seemed a tenuous point on which to decide such an important issue; at one stage in the action learned Counsel spent some time trying to prove that a Hunt employee was a domestic servant. Counsel briefed by the Hospital was for long doubtful of its chances of success, but his efforts and those of his colleagues prevailed in the end and the Hospital secured judgment, though heavy costs had to be met.

CHAPTER 10

X-ray Department – Prince Arthur of Connaught
R. A. Greeves – R. S. Scott – C. B. Goulden
Second World War – The routine in war time
The Royal College of Surgeons Chair – Institutes
National Health Service – The Hospital is bombed
Recovery

THE X-ray Department of the Hospital came into existence only 3 years after the discovery of X-rays by Professor Röntgen in 1895, mainly on account of the enthusiasm and ingenuity of Mackenzie Davidson[1] who, with many other ophthalmic surgeons, at once saw the possibilities of the new discovery in the field of intraocular foreign bodies. His application to the problem was so helpful that an X-ray Department was established, with himself as honorary medical officer in charge; £80 was voted for the cost of apparatus and an annual £25 for running costs. Davidson held the post for 11 years, was knighted for his work in this field, and retired in 1910. One of his first achievements was to devise a method of taking stereoscopic X-ray photographs; he then evolved a most successful—and the first—method of localising intraocular foreign bodies. His services to the hospital were commemorated in 1924 by the reconstruction of the Department and the provision of new apparatus; Lady Davidson and other friends contributed the required sum of £725. They were also recalled by a tablet on the wall of the Department. Advances in the therapeutic application of X-rays caused the department to be renamed the "X-ray and Electrotherapy Department" in 1911; the title reverted to "X-ray Department" in 1939 though the significance of the change is not clear from the records. The treatment side received much more emphasis on the appointment of Dr Lederman in 1941. He relinquished his charge of the Department in 1946; in 1948 he was officially appointed Consulting Radiotherapist to the hospital, and radiography put into other hands by the appointment of Dr Murray. In 1951 the title of

[1] Vol. 1, 186.

Dr Lederman's post received the prefix honorary without any apparent change in the routine. He did much to develop the application of radium and other radioactive materials to ophthalmic conditions; for convenience of working, the actual treatment was transferred in 1948 to the Royal Marsden Hospital, then named the Royal Cancer Hospital. A registrar from Moorfields was appointed in 1949 to ensure close liaison, and a Consultant Ophthalmic Surgeon from the Staff in 1950. Around that time it became a more common habit to bring radioactive material to Moorfields for its application, usually in the theatre; the obvious potential dangers involved in this practice resulted in the setting up of a Radioactive Protection Committee to the Hospital, with a physicist in charge.

The arrangements for X-ray investigation at High Holborn came under review in 1953. These had hitherto been scanty; intraocular foreign body localisation was not practicable and many cases had been sent for X-ray to other Hospitals— notably to City Road. A new department was therefore constructed providing facilities comparable with those at City Road. A radiographer took up training at City Road with a view to part-time employment at High Holborn. The department opened in September 1954 and at once provided a welcome relief from the pressure of work at City Road; the second radiographer also simplified the problem of weekend emergency calls. In April 1956 Dr Douglas Gordon was appointed Consultant Radiologist to the High Holborn branch.

Soon after this a special clinic was established at the Hospital by H. B. Stallard, whose work on the treatment of intraocular neoplasms is well known. A further clinic for treatment, follow-up and teaching was established at the Hospital in 1964 under the supervision of Dr Lederman, Professor Barrie Jones, and M. A. Bedford; close liaison with the Royal Marsden department was preserved. Stallard retired in 1965, and his work was taken over by this Radiotherapy Unit, which is one of growing activity and increasing importance. In 1972 M. A. Bedford, one of the team in this unit, was appointed Consultant Ophthalmic Surgeon in charge of the Radiotherapy Clinic, of which the title was subsequently altered to Oncology Clinic. The centre of gravity for this work thus shifted to City Road.

A radiological Safety Committee was called for in 1965 at all Hospitals using radium and other radioactive materials. At Moorfields the Medical Committee recommended the following constitution—the consultant radiologist of each branch, a physician (Dr Gavey), any surgeon using radioactive material on the hospital premises, Dr Lederman, a radiological protection adviser and a radiological safety officer, for which post they recommended the hospital radiographer. They asked the Board to appoint a Physicist as radiological protection adviser in accordance with official requirements. Dr Lederman retired from the Committee at the end of 1968; he was not replaced, and a survey of the protection arrangements at that time pronounced them very adequate.

Concurrently with these advances, equally great and equally important ones were taking place in the field of Radiography. The art has been revolutionised since the second world war, and an enormous increase in application and value has taken place. The injection of air and radio-opaque material into tissues, cavities, and vessels has opened up a new world in this field of investigation; its application in ophthalmology has been keenly adopted and exploited by the present director of the department, Glyn A. S. Lloyd, whose co-operation is invaluable and whose publications continue to instruct and please. He is also working in the field of ultrasonics; the easier reflection of ultrasound at the interface between two soft tissues enable its presence to be detected and localised, which X-rays would fail to do. These latter rays lose considerable energy on passing through dense structures such as bone (hence the normal radiograph) whereas ultrasound passes through practically without loss. Holography, which is in effect a record of wave front interference, was demonstrated optically in 1949; the application of first the laser beam and then sound waves has facilitated and improved this important method of investigation.

His Royal Highness Prince Arthur of Connaught died on 12 September, 1938. He had been President for 23 years and had thoroughly justified his position by his interest in and work for the Hospital. He presided at the Festival Dinner at the

Mansion House in 1925, and officially opened the first portion of the scheme of extension in 1930. The Hospital this year also lost by retirement the services of Affleck Greeves, and by resignation those of Scott and Stallard, though the last was reappointed to the staff in 1947. They were succeeded by C. D. Shapland, J. H. Doggart and N. H. L. Ridley.

Reginald Affleck Greeves came to Moorfields after a spell of general practice in the Transvaal and a period of office as Surgical Tutor and Registrar at Guy's Hospital, whence he had qualified in 1903. He joined the staff of the Middlesex Hospital in 1914 and that of Moorfields a year later, having held the post of Pathologist and Curator for the previous two years, thus repeating a sequence, already established, which was to persist until the advent of the National Health Service. He told an amusing story of his visit to Moorfields for the purpose of

R. Affleck Greeves

113

calling formally on the Staff as a preliminary to applying for the appointment. He was met at the door by a gentleman leaving the Hospital in shirt sleeves and entering a car; another left in a short white coat and walked up the City Road; yet a third in a long white coat emerged. Greeves wondered what sort of an odd place he was visiting and even whether he wanted to associate himself with it; he was relieved to hear that the explanation of these queer happenings was that a thief had entered the cloakroom and stolen all the surgeons' coats!

Greeves' professional strength lay in his powers of observation and clinical acumen, based as it was on sound pathology. As a clinician he towered over most of his contemporaries; for years he conducted the class on ophthalmoscopy and instruction on fundus appearances—one of the most popular in the curriculum, and one which led to his being appealed to as an expert in this field to the end of his professional career. His personality was not immediately endearing; one had to know him—but how well worth the effort, for he was really a most valuable character, always ready to help, always interesting, and frequently exhibiting engaging characteristics which gave a hint of his Irish origin. He was a competent, but not a brilliant nor even a natural operator; nonetheless the writer—who assisted him in private for many years—can testify to the very satisfactory results of his surgery, possibly attributable to his desire to do what was necessary with all reasonable speed, finish, and bandage the eye. *O si sic omnes.*

Rupert Strathmore Scott, having started his medical education at Cambridge and qualified from St Bartholomew's Hospital, returned after service in the first world war to become ophthalmic house surgeon at Barts. In due course he was appointed to the staff in 1924, and to that of Moorfields in 1928, having previously held, like so many others who achieved Consultant status there, the post of Pathologist and Curator. Rupert Scott really was the beloved physician; his kindly human interest and immense care was obvious in all his work. He approached surgery a little nervously; probably for that very reason it was of the highest standard, as one who was his house surgeon can fully testify. He also had a keen sense of humour unsuspected by those who knew him little, sometimes exercised against himself. Once asked, after leaving Moorfields,

Rupert S. Scott

whether he still operated at Barts, he replied with his most engaging stammer "Oh, yes, I do the extractions on Tuesdays and the e-e-eviscerations on Fridays!" Extremely handsome, immaculately dressed, supremely dignified, he would have looked just at home on the steps of the Embassy; had he chosen thus, medicine would have been robbed of one of its most staunch, valuable and charming exponents.

In 1939 C. B. Goulden retired from the Staff under the age limit, and also from his post as Dean of the Medical School; he was succeeded by Arthur Lister in the former and by Robert Davenport in the latter. Charles Bernard Goulden rendered service to Moorfields as valuable as any of his colleagues before

C. B. Goulden

or since. He was a resident from 1904 to 1907, then went to Bristol for a time and coached in anatomy. From there he went to Oldham where he was appointed to the Infirmary—but he found the North Country antipathetic and was not happy there. (His landlady showed some surprise when she found on his arrival that his luggage included two pianos!) As was the custom in those days he did many operations in patients' homes—he described one cataract operation with the kitchen table as operating table. At the outbreak of war he organised the local Red Cross with great skill and efficiency; he went to France in 1916, and served at Boulogne and Rouen. While at Boulogne he and Whiting, who was there too, found the anaesthetists lacking in availability, and, indeed, for their purpose, in efficiency; consequently they dispensed with their services, and gave anaesthetics for each other for the rest of their time there. Goulden's musical bent found outlet even there; he started and conducted a male voice choir; and produced "Box and Cox", playing a lead himself.

His chief at Boulogne, Sir William Lister, persuaded him to come south, and he soon gained appointment to the Staff of Moorfields and the London Hospitals. In the mid-twenties the slit-lamp was developing, and Goulden went to study the technique of its use at Zurich with Vogt, returning to undertake instruction on this subject. He succeeded Hepburn as Dean and held the office with great efficiency for 13 years. He was a superb clinician and a good teacher, his operating a model of calm efficiency. An interesting little habit of his was to change his glasses for a binocular loupe in the middle of an operation; no harm ensued, for he was fully conscious of what he had done and nothing but the business end of a sterile instrument touched the eye. In due course he became President of the Ophthalmological Society of the United Kingdom, and filled the office with distinction, exploiting his interest in and knowledge of history by choosing Purkinje as the subject of his Presidential address; he was also President of the Section of Ophthalmology of the Royal Society of Medicine. He was Surgeon Oculist to the Household of Her Majesty Queen Mary from 1937 to 1948; during the second war he was ophthalmic consultant to the Ministry of Health. He translated Koby's text book of the slit-lamp and wrote a valuable book on Refraction, besides contributing steadily to the ophthalmological journals. He was a thoughtful and invaluable colleague, a keen amateur of music and history, and a good companion, interested and interesting. He once said to Whiting, presumably with colloquially excusable hyperbole: "My real interest in life is music; I do eyes for a living." But he "did" them very well.

Already in 1937 meetings had been arranged by the Hospital Association at which advice on air raid precautions were given by Home Office authorities. At the time of the Munich crisis in the following year the Hospital was ordered to make provision for the treatment of general surgical cases and for the dismissal of patients to their homes to make room for any air raid casualties; essential internal arrangements were made which involved the Hospital in considerable expense.

The events of 1939 were of course dominated and clouded by the outbreak of war. In September, all patients who could leave without detriment to their eye conditions were immediately sent home; services for the civilian sick were in no way disturbed. The Ministry of Health required that 82 beds be placed at its disposal for the reception of air raid and service casualties. It was reasonably assumed that London would be the centre of attack in the event of air-raids; the Committee

Unusual Duties

of Management therefore acquired St Mary at the Cross Hospital, Edgware, and by 2 October were ready to accommodate 53 patients. 88 beds were retained in the City Road; all children went to Edgware. The Finsbury Borough Council took over part of the Hospital as a First Aid Post, and the dining room on the ground floor was converted for use as a decontamination centre, with arrangements for the use of a portion of the room by the Hospital until required; rent and compensation rates were calculated. Part of the basement was excavated and provided with auxiliary lighting and air-conditioning for use as an air raid shelter as need arose. Most of the Physicians and Surgeons were allocated to posts under the Emergency Medical Service; when it was seen to be unlikely that any casualties would occur in the immediate future—that the "phoney war" had begun—they were released for part time duty and returned to the Hospital.

The Senior Surgeon F. A. Juler, who was appointed Consulting Ophthalmic Surgeon to the British Expeditionary Force, returned from overseas in June 1940 and resumed his duties as Honorary Surgeon to the Hospital. J. H. Doggart and Arthur Lister were released from their duties to take up service appointments. Ill health caused the resignation of A. J. B. Goldsmith from the post of Curator in 1939, and his duties were taken over by C. D. Shapland who had been appointed Medical Officer in charge of the Hospital by the Ministry of Health, and also Medical Officer in charge of St Mary at the Cross Hospital, Edgware. In January 1940 A. G. Cross was appointed Curator. With regard to personnel in the out-patient department, the reduction in attendances necessitated the replacement of 24 out-patient officers by 12 Refraction assistants; further, the office of First Assistant Medical Officer was abolished, resulting in the resignation of five more medical officers; the London County Council school department was closed, and the appointments of the five medical officers to the department suspended.

Like many other surgeons, all of whom are indicated in the list in the Appendix, Charles Goulden remained at work in the Hospital after his retirement until circumstances became more normal and the younger members of the Staff had returned from their service duties. Goulden had been appointed Ophthalmic Consultant to the Emergency Medical Service, and at a meeting of the Committee on 8 September, 1939, convened to consider urgent matters arising out of the emergency, he reported that while the Committee of Management would still be responsible for the administration of the Hospital, they would be under the instructions of the Ministry of Health. At this meeting final notice to terminate their appointments as from 30 September was given to six first assistant medical officers, 23 out-patient officers, 3 medical officers to special departments, Pathologist, and Registrar. This decision was, however, soon rescinded in the case of the Registrars' and Physiotherapy departments, which latter was continued on a part time basis.

It is seen that although ample preparations were made for the evacuation of civilian patients and for the reception of civilian air raid casualties and service cases, the prolonged lull enabled the Hospital to carry on and to provide most of its normal services during this "phoney war". An indication of the increasing confidence arising while the peaceful conditions at home still obtained is given by the decision made at the end of the year to open 6 private beds on the 4th floor. This enabled the Cubicle wards, the side ward on the 1st floor, and Nettleship ward to revert to their normal use. Two years later 4 more private beds and 10 cubicle beds were opened. In September 1940 all this was changed. Heavy air raids began on the 7th, and the destruction of the neighbouring City of London Maternity Hospital, the Royal Chest Hospital, and (later) St Matthew's Hospital gave the authorities furiously to think. Admissions were limited to acute conditions, and numbers to those who could be accommodated at night in the basement air raid shelter.

In the difficult and claustrophobic surroundings, once again goodwill and devotion to duty worked wonders. The trek below began at dusk; at six o'clock supper was served; dressings followed, and the patients were bedded down for the night. The atmosphere of cheerfulness and trust was wonderful. All patients, doctors, nurses, cooks, maids and porters slept in shelter in the basement—all save some brave and devoted lay staff. They undertook night duty under a rota and patrolled the hospital on the look-out for immediate danger, notably from incendiary bombs. And the next morning they carried on with their day's work. The new conditions necessitated the immediate transfer of the majority of patients to Base hospitals adminstered by the Ministry of Health. The activities of the out-patient department had remained at a remarkably high level; over 43,000 new patients attended in 1940, with total attendances of 130,500 compared with 53,000 and 177,000 in the previous year. This was naturally followed by a definite

Carrying on

fall in attendances after the start of the air raids in September; the figures for November were half those for that month of the previous year. The L.C.C. school children's department was reopened in March of this year; a certain relief followed the transfer of the First Aid Post to other premises in August. An indication of the part which the hospital was playing at this time is given by the fact that on 30 December, following the heavy raid on the night of the 29th/30th which destroyed a vast

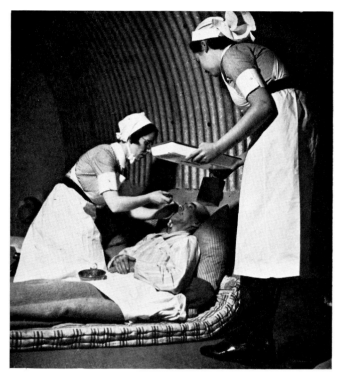

Routine in the shelter

area of central London and caused the "Second fire of London", 231 casualties were treated.

An interesting account of the Hospital routine at this time, necessitated by war conditions, was written by the Secretary, Arthur Tarrant, for *The Medical Press and Circular*; it was reprinted in the *British Journal of Ophthalmology* (1943), **27**, p. 312 *et seq.*

After the collapse of France in June 1940 air raids on London and the surrounding districts became more frequent and more intense; it was decided to close down the Edgware hospital, and this was done on 13 July. It had provided a valuable 55 beds from October 1939 to July 1940, in which period 670 patients were treated and 644 operations performed.

The bombing of London became less heavy towards the end of the year 1941 and, in November, 74 beds were made available at City Road. In January and May the Hospital suffered further from the bombing, though mercifully not by a direct hit, but no interruption to routine was caused. £5000 was spent in first aid repairs; it was estimated that full repairs would cost a further £4000. E. F. King and A. G. Cross, Pathologist and Registrar, left to take up service duties; A. J. B. Goldsmith was appointed Pathologist. King returned to civilian tasks in November 1944.

A considerable increase in the volume of important work was enabled in March 1942 by the opening of a unit of 62 beds at Mount Vernon Hospital, Northwood. 55 beds remained open in City Road making a total of 117 available. 2289 in-patients were treated during the year, 1009 of them at Northwood; the out-patient figures remained steady, while 772 patients were transferred to Base Hospitals under the Ministry of Health. A wing ward at City Road was set aside for the use of junior army officers (15 beds); the other wing ward was divided by

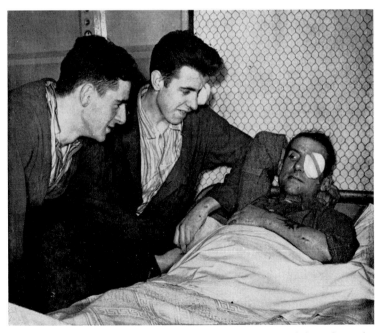

Reputedly the first Casualty of World War II; an eye injury from the Maginot Line, under the care of Frank Law at City Road.

partitions into seven cubicles, which were to be used for private patients until they were required for senior officers.

In spite of conditions the work of the Hospital was not confined to routine; progress was made in various fields. The science and art of the manufacture and fitting of contact lenses proceeded to advances and improvements; chemotherapy in the form of Sulphonamides was proving its value, and knowledge of the action and value of vitamins progressed to the advantage of ophthalmic treatment.

In May 1942 C. D. Shapland left for service in the Army and V. B. Purvis was appointed resident Registrar.

In 1942 the Royal Eye Hospital persuaded the Royal College of Surgeons to approve the establishment of a Chair of Ophthalmology, in that hospital and under the aegis of the College. This action met with considerable criticism from the surgeons of Moorfields, and indeed, those of the other eye hospitals of London. At the outset it was thought that the time was hardly suitable for such a venture, with the war still in progress, surgeons fully occupied with emergency duties, and many away on active service. Further, the idea of co-operation with the Postgraduate Medical School with a view to the creation of an Institute and association with London University was in the air; there was further some doubt as to whether the Royal College were fully informed about the identity of the eye hospitals of London. Representations to this effect were actually made to the College; the point was also made that the usual milieu of a professorial chair was a University. Nonetheless the scheme materialised a year or so later; Arnold Sorsby became the first professor and personally certainly justified the venture and his appointment. As will be seen, the professorship eventually became incorporated in the Moorfields group after amalgamation.

By August 1944 the Royal Eye Hospital announced the setting up of an Institute of Ophthalmology. There was an impressive list of Patrons, and another of Scientific Advisers; a panel of Medical and Surgical advisers, and a list of 20 Ophthalmic Advisers, gathered from all over the country. It was stated that the amenities of the Institute would be open to all ophthalmologists. It was a private foundation and was therefore an entity quite distinct from the Hospital and Medical School.

A definite approach to Moorfields inviting discussion of the subjects of postgraduate education and research was made by the British Postgraduate Medical School in March 1944; Moorfields responded warmly. A comprehensive memorandum was drawn up by a member of the Committee of Management; the Dean replied to the Dean of the School pointing out the desire of Moorfields to inform the other ophthalmic hospitals of the impending negotiations (a broadminded and thoughtful gesture); and a meeting at Moorfields followed, on 27 April, of 4 representatives each of the Hospital and Medical School. The discussion was prolonged and fruitful; one of the emerging recommendations was to approach the Central London Ophthalmic Hospital to discuss the founding of an Institute there. The matter of widening the teaching scope of the School was also mooted and the hope expressed that the final F.R.C.S. examination might be so modified for the specialty as to be restricted to ophthalmology. The representatives of the Moorfields Medical School issued a subsequent confirmatory memorandum, but added that the time was not right for final decisions when so many interested were away on Government service; "any attempt to plan in detail is premature and inexpedient".

The Government at this time was actively preparing for the initiation of a National Health Service. The British Hospitals Association prepared a memorandum on the subject, as did the B.M.A.; the senior surgeon prepared comments on both papers which were circulated to the staff, and following a special meeting of the Committee of Management, two lay representatives were appointed to attend a meeting of the London Voluntary Hospitals Committee called to discuss the memoranda and the Hospital Association's questionnaire.

The year 1943 was comparatively quiet as regards enemy activity at home—the previous onslaught of heavy bombing had subsided and the new terror of flying bombs had not begun. Hospital activity increased as a result; 63 beds were in full use at Northwood, and 2930 patients were treated; 609 were transferred to Base Hospitals for in-patient treatment. Work also increased in the out-patient department; over 66,000 new patients attended and total attendances were 165,000. On the nursing side a step was made in the direction of improving pay and conditions by the adoption of the Rushcliffe report, the provisions of which, it was hoped, would aid recruitment to the profession. Harold Ridley left the Staff temporarily to assume uniform. S. H. Browning resigned from the post of Bacteriologist after holding it for 33 years, but continued as Medical Officer to the Venereal Diseases Department for a further year when he was succeeded by Dr V. E. Lloyd. In the following year the Hospital's record of merciful freedom from serious damage was rudely broken. At 7.30 a.m. on 29 July a flying bomb—Hitler's secret weapon No. 1— struck Block K of the building, which included the male and female cubicle wards. Jordan, night porter since 1927 and well remembered by the more senior of us, rushed to telephone the Secretary, in a state of considerable and understandable commotion of mind. "Mr. Tarrant", he cried, "we're hit, we're hit!" Three men and four women lay there in the cubicle beds, and all perished in the cataclysm. It was a heartrending experience for all the 161 persons who were in the Hospital at the time—81 patients and 80 staff. The damage was so extensive and severe that all had to be moved; six patients were sent to their homes, three to St Bartholomew's and 65 to the Three Counties Hospital, Arlesey, Beds. 12 of the staff were admitted to various hospitals; of the nine nurses who went to Arlesey, two were subsequently warded.

Damage was not confined to these wards. The nurses' home, medical school, including lecture rooms, museum, and library, all suffered; the Casualty department, two out-patient theatres and the sanitary block were virtually demolished. First aid repair was immediately initiated, but drastic rearrangement was necessary to enable out-patient activity to resume. The Central London Ophthalmic Hospital generously placed their out-patient department at the disposal of the Hospital, and for some weeks the work was done there, by which time it was

Bomb damage

War damage 1944

possible to use part of the repaired department at City Road. Earlier in the year 168 beds had been in use—106 in City Road (50 of which were reserved for Emergency Medical Service use) and 62 at Northwood. 40 beds in City Road were ready for use by November and 54 by the end of the year, making a total of 116.

A touching response from colleagues abroad followed that catastrophe. The American Academy of Ophthalmology and Otolaryngology sent a gift of $1000 towards the rebuilding of the Museum and other departments of the School, a gesture that was very much appreciated.

Recovery from the shock of war damage was creditably speedy. It will be recalled that damage from blast occurred on 3 occasions in 1941, but the main damage occurred from the direct hit in July 1944. Temporary repairs and re-occupation of departments soon followed; the rebuilt Casualty Department was put into commission in May 1945, thus freeing the maintenance block on the second floor which had been taken over for Casualty work in the meantime. Most of the private ward block was re-opened in November of that year, and 78 beds in the main Hospital were in use by the end of that year, which with Northwood's 62 made a total of 140 compared with the normal 200.

The year 1945 saw the appointment of Miss Mann as Professor of Ophthalmology at Oxford following her period as Margaret Ogilvie reader; the return to duty of J. H. Doggart on his release from the Royal Air Force and of H. H. Skeoch as Registrar on release from the Army; and the retirement under the age limit of M. H. Whiting who, in common with others before him, remained temporarily carrying out the full duties of Surgeon to the Hospital. Early in 1946 A. G. Cross was released from the forces and resumed his appointment as Curator and Pathologist.

The Hospital was anxious to close down Northwood and re-open the equivalent number of beds at City Road as soon as possible. The Medical Board recommended the postponement of the move until scaffolding had been erected and the flank wall on the east side of the Peerless Street block had been examined in order to ascertain how long it would take to put the wards in order for the reception of patients. In spite of some risk entailed in the immediate use of the wards, the decision was nonetheless made to effect the transfer without delay, and this was done in February 1946; by the end of the year 179 beds were in use. Later and closer examination of the wall revealed that it would have to be pulled down to second floor level. This reduced the accommodation in Alexandra ward on the first floor and Saunders on the second, and eliminated the use of Prince of Wales ward, third floor, and five private rooms on the fourth floor until the wall was rebuilt. This was achieved by the end of the year.

CHAPTER 11

Federation – Regionalisation – Amalgamation
Highgate – Nursing Training and Accommodation
Ophthalmic Nursing Board – Convalescent Home
Matron – Anaesthetists – Institute
XVI International Congress – Accommodation – Change

AN interesting and relevant development occurred in 1943 with the setting up of a Joint Committee of the Ophthalmic Hospitals of London charged with the duty of formulating a scheme for Federation of these Hospitals. A very detailed outline was produced, and considered by the Medical Board, who decided that, though they were generally in favour, they considered that it would impinge upon the provisions of the Hospital's Royal Charter of Incorporation and recommended postponement of further detailed consideration of the Scheme. At this distance in time the decision reads rather ambiguously. Only two hospitals, the Central and the Western, reported fully in favour of the Scheme. The Joint Committee continued in being as an advisory and initiating body.

A concomitant and related scheme of regionalisation of the Ophthalmic Hospitals of London was also being considered at this time. This was associated with the consideration of the establishment of research facilities on an organised basis in the Hospital. A research sub-committee had already been set up, which had considered the conditions of the appointment of a research fellow and the terms upon which he would work. The five hospitals failed to reach a unanimous conclusion on regionalisation. Moorfields was at a disadvantage regarding research in its distance from any general hospital, but in view of its otherwise convenient situation and of its recent costly extension and modernisation there was no question of removal. The Royal Westminster appeared favourably situated; the other three demanded consideration in that some said that a London Hospital should have a minimum of 50 beds, which they had not. Ophthalmic services south of the Thames appeared poorly developed; the removal of the Royal Eye to a central area there, and its expansion, appeared to be indicated. Association of the Central with a nearby General Hospital was advised; the same applied to the Western. Further comment was withheld until after publication of the Goodenough Committee Report.

In 1944 an official approach to the Central London Ophthalmic Hospital was made with an ultimate view to amalgamation and the utilisation of all or part of the Central as an Institute. Good progress was made in discussion, and the King Edward Hospital Fund was approached. Here the Medical Board intervened with an objection to lay negotiations of such a nature, and a request that their view should always be ascertained in such a situation. The Committee of Management asked the Medical Board to reconsider its resolution after the matter had been discussed with the Medical representatives on the Committee. This they did, and it was rescinded; but the request to be kept informed of any such negotiations was repeated. In the meantime the Dean had convened a meeting of the 5 Deans of the London Ophthalmic Hospitals, who had suggested the formation of a Planning Committee of 3 representatives from Moorfields and 2 from each of the other Ophthalmic Hospitals. The 5 Deans had further been invited to attend the next meeting of the School Council of the British Postgraduate School.

Though still negotiating for amalgamation with the Central London Ophthalmic Hospital, the Medical Board submitted a memorandum in January 1945 which suggested the sale of the present site and buildings and rebuilding either on a Bloomsbury site near University College Hospital, or near the Middlesex Hospital or the Royal Free Hospital, in the interests of teaching and research. This view was doubtless stimulated by the recent extensive damage to the Hospital and the knowledge that a large rebuilding problem would present as soon as circumstances allowed. An approach was actually made to University College Hospital in February 1946 with a view to the building of a new Eye Hospital of 300–400 beds in the vicinity of the general hospital. In October it was learned that the Colonial Office was desirous of building a hospital for Tropical Diseases near University College Hospital and had an eye on the site in which we were interested. The preliminary negotiations were therefore speeded up and steps taken to obtain an option on the site.

At this stage it was decided to elect Sir Stewart Duke-Elder to a seat on the Committee of Management. It was realised that his academic and personal connections with University College and University College Hospital would be valuable when considering the scheme for the establishment of an ophthalmic hospital in the Bloomsbury area and of an Institute associated with those bodies. He had in fact largely conducted the preliminary negotiations in that field.

The plans and ambitions for amalgamation with the Central received a check when the Charity Commission expressed the view that the constitutions of the Hospital forbad the development of these plans. Their jurisdiction to vary charitable trusts, they said, only arose when those trusts had failed, wholly or partially; and they could not see that the Central London had in any way failed. With this the negotiating committee fully agreed; but they tried to emphasise that the idea was not to "put an end to" the Hospital (the Commission's phrase) but to alter the purpose of all or part of the buildings in a manner which would entail no sacrifice of beds. In view of this difficulty the question of simple amalgamation *per se* was kept constantly in the foreground; the idea of change of site to the Bloomsbury area was alive; and the question of amalgamation with the Royal Westminster Ophthalmic Hospital had also arisen, and meetings to discuss this had already begun between the authorities of the two Hospitals. This idea developed rapidly. Meetings were held at frequent intervals, and it soon emerged that the Westminster looked favourably on the proposal. Of course difficulties were met with, and conflicting interests had to be resolved; a chief stumbling block was the "loss of identity" to be suffered by the combining Hospitals, together with the feeling that amalgamation between two bodies of unequal size implies the absorption of the smaller into the larger. Many and long were the discussions; an obvious and understandable *amour propre* actuated many concerned. The Chairman of the Westminster drew up seven "points" which he considered had to be satisfied before agreement could be reached; this produced a slight stiffening reaction amongst the representatives of the other Hospitals, especially Moorfields. Though a cautious approach was understandable, it was clear that the Westminster would not be allowed to stand alone as soon as nationalisation was accomplished, and if left to the tender mercies of the politicians might well find itself amalgamated elsewhere, or even absorbed, in a much less desirable milieu—which accounts for and excuses the attitude of the other hospitals. To one at least who was taking part, as regards the Westminster's seven points it occurred that there was a parallel here with the situation at Versailles which arose during the peace negotiations of 1919 when President Wilson produced his fourteen "points" for satisfaction, which provoked from Clemenceau—"The Tiger"—the brilliant and scathing comment "Le bon Dieu lui-même n'avait que dix!"

On the whole, however, discussion was forthcoming and productive. By April 1946 the question of amalgamation with the Westminster was agreed upon. It will be readily seen what a vista of arrangement, rearrangement, negotiation, and organisation the project opened up: a glance at the official documents and minute books of the period amply confirms this. One is quite amazed at the vast amount of work which was accomplished in so relatively short a time. The Bill to enable amalgamation with the Central was already in hand; this had to be withdrawn and amended to suit the new conditions and include the Westminster. Much discussion occurred over the title of the new combined hospital; negotiators were all unwilling to agree to the elimination of the name of their own Hospital. In an effort to treat all alike the title "The London Eye Hospital" was proposed, but was rejected; in the end the unfortunately clumsy title "Moorfields, Westminster, and Central Eye Hospital" was agreed upon, which mercifully survived but a short time. The governing bodies were decided upon; special departments provided for; financial arrangements outlined; re-arrangement of clinics agreed; nursing administration and arrangements revised; everything from the seniority of surgeons and the remuneration of clinical assistants to the allocation of works department personnel. The facility and speed with which this was all accomplished and the amicable reconciliation of disparate and divergent views is a tribute to the statesmanship and diligence of those concerned. At first it was arranged that some clinical work should continue at the Central; by September it was agreed, not without some misgivings in the Central camp, that it should all be transferred to the other two hospitals and the whole of the premises at Judd Street should become the Institute.

No time was lost in the steering of the Amalgamation Bill through its various stages. It became an Act and received the Royal Assent on 26 July, 1946 and came into operation on 1 January, 1947 at which date the three hospitals became one entity with the title of "Moorfields, Westminster and Central Eye Hospital".

The decision to amalgamate was a momentous one for all concerned. It followed an appreciation of the changing times and the need for more organised teaching and research. It was accelerated by the approach to Moorfields by the British Postgraduate Medical School (University of London) who had decided to initiate in the first instance the establishment of four Federated Specialist Institutes of the British Postgraduate Medical Federation, of which one was to be in Ophthalmology. It became apparent that the combined facilities of the three hospitals would provide the most appropriate milieu for the project, and the eventual result was their amalgamation and the official recognition of the Institute on 1 March, 1946. The newly constituted hospital provided a total of 341 beds, which included 65 pay beds, and facilities for treating 7400 in-patients and 90,000 out-patients a year. By comparison, the figures at City Road for 1946 were 3465 and 66144 respectively. The transfer of the out-patient department of the Central London Ophthalmic Hospital to the Westminster Branch was completed by May 1947; new patients there rose from 25 to 60 a day, and old patients from 92 to 206. It was decided to close the 34 general ward beds there on 6 October, and open a Ward of 20 beds at the Westminster Branch on that day; 11 private rooms were retained at the Central. The Museum and Library were also transferred to Judd Street at this time.

In January 1947 an approach was made from the administrative officers of the 5 postgraduate teaching hospitals with specialist Institutes suggesting the formation of a Committee to represent the interests of these hospitals. Representatives were appointed, and meetings began. Lord Rothes, the deputy Chairman of the Hospital, was nominated as a delegate to serve on the Central Health Services Council which was to be set up under the National Health Service Act. The Association approached the University Grants Committee for financial assistance in setting up the Teaching Institutes. Apart from this the Hospital on its own account approached the Ministry of Health for financial help in view of its estimated deficit of £80,000 in the current year; the response was affirmative and full details were asked for. Some misgiving arose at a later meeting of the Association whether there might be a conflict of interests and powers between the Institutes and Hospitals in view of the terms of the Memoranda of Association of the Institutes; reassurance on this problem was sought and gained from the Hospital's solicitors.

While the negotiations for amalgamation were proceeding attention was given to the necessity of providing more accommodation for the nurses in all the three hospitals. Two houses in Highgate, 17 and 19 View Road, were deemed suitable and an offer made for them was accepted. The hostel was opened in July 1946 and 15 nurses accommodated there, repairs and installations in the rest of the building proceeding with a view to accommodating further staff, when it would be possible to open the remainder of the private ward block on the fourth floor at City Road for private patients.

In September of that year the Matron, Miss Buck, retired after 4½ years excellent service to the Hospital. The Assistant Matron, Miss MacKellar, was at once appointed Acting Matron, to occupy this position until the nursing arrangements of the new hospital had been clarified, when the appointment of Matron would be considered.

In 1947 the shortage of nurses, which was seriously impeding the intended developments following amalgamation and the formation of an Institute, was causing increasing efforts to be made to find additional nursing accommodation. At the same time the general question of the recruitment and training of nurses was exercising both the Faculty of Ophthalmologists and the nursing authorities; the former had produced resolutions supporting the Matrons of the Ophthalmic Hospitals who had been called to a meeting at Moorfields to discuss the matter, following a Report on the subject just issued by a working party set up by the Ministry of Health. The Medical Committee asked that representations be made to the Ministry of Health that the Ophthalmic Hospitals should be enabled to recruit nursing applicants at the age of 17 and provide a year's training before they commenced their general training. Severe disquiet was caused in nursing circles when it was learnt that the working party had made no mention of ophthalmic nursing as a nursing speciality. The necessity for the official recognition of ophthalmic nursing was emphasised; the meeting urged that it should be taught in the eye wards of hospitals under the control of a trained Sister, and that when nurses desired to continue in this branch of nursing, the training should be supplemented by a period of at least one year as Staff Nurse under supervision.

In the meantime efforts to acquire further accommodation for the nursing staff had been unremitting: many sites had been inspected, and offers made, but nothing materialised until the Royal Stuart Hotel, in the Cromwell Road, came onto the market. This was considered a suitable building; it would accommodate 140 people, and if acquired would enable the disposal of the accommodation at Highgate. It was decided that the acquisition of the property would be dependent upon financial assistance from the Ministry of Health. The response was at first a little disappointing, and preliminary arrangements were made with the Bank for the provision for an overdraft of two thirds of the amount required, with an equitable charge on the deeds of the property as security. Then the Ministry indicated a change of attitude, and authorised the purchase; arrangements for the deal were at once set in train, and it was completed on 1 March, 1949, the building, renamed Stuart House, thus becoming the property of the Hospital under the Ministry of Health; 80 nurses and staff were at once accommodated.

The acquisition of Stuart House freed View Road, Highgate, for other purposes and, in spite of the previous condition imposed by the Ministry that the purchase of Stuart House should entail the sale of View Road, in September 1949 permission was given to retain it and convert it for use as a Hospital Annexe. This at once eased the question of a Convalescent Home which, it may be recalled, had been exercising the minds of the authorities for many years. Highgate was at the outset used for the reception of children, for which there was an inordinate waiting list at both branches.

In 1952 No. 15 View Road, Highgate—a house adjoining the Hospital Annexe at Nos 17 and 19—came onto the market and it was at once realised that the acquisition of this property and its incorporation into the Annexe would serve a most useful purpose. It could provide nursing accommodation, and also, by the provision of more beds and an operating theatre suite, increase the effective bed complement of the hospital, and thus favourably affect the waiting list which at this time stood at well over 2000. The lease was purchased and the structural alterations completed for the building to be ready for the admission of patients on 18 January, 1954. In the first 3 months 146 patients were admitted.

A special meeting of the Nursing Committee held in April 1949 discussed a letter from the General Nursing Council which criticised the Affiliation Scheme with four years training, and recommended that the full General Training period should be three years in which, apart from "the four main branches" of nursing, experience should be gained in some of the special branches. Four were mentioned, Ophthalmology not included. The recommendations of the meeting of Matrons, to which reference has already been made, were revised. The main points were: recruitment between the ages of $16\frac{1}{2}$ and $18\frac{1}{2}$ years; a two-year course to be recognised as a pre-nursing course; and the taking of the Preliminary State Examination and probably the Ophthalmic Certificate Examination as well. This pre-nursing course, it was suggested, should allow a remission of six months from the Nurse's three year general training period.

At a moment when 28 beds had been closed at High Holborn because of the shortage of nurses, the Nursing Committee of the hospital was naturally very concerned over the situation; their concern was not lessened by the fact that the Faculty of Ophthalmologists were divided in their opinion over the necessity for stipulating that this longer period of training for Ophthalmic nurses was essential. There was some relief on learning that the Council would recognise the arrangement whereby one year of the three years general training should be spent in a Special hospital, though for a limited and experimental period only. Nine general hospitals had intimated their willingness to continue to accept Moorfields' nurses at the end of a year's training.

In view of all the above it was considered advisable to set up a body to control and regulate conditions in the ophthalmic nursing field. A meeting of the Nursing Committee of the Hospital was held in October 1950 which concerned itself with the report of the meeting of Matrons referred to above, confirmed the conclusions in the report and made but minor amendments. An Ophthalmic Nursing Board was to be set up which would standardise training, conduct examinations, grant an ophthalmic nursing certificate, and generally control the whole field of ophthalmic nursing. The Board was constituted early in the following year; there was a medical and nursing member for each of eight areas in the United Kingdom; co-opted members included a representative from the International Council of Nurses, one from the Royal College of Nursing and the Matron of the Royal National Orthopaedic Hospital, representing an allied speciality with similar problems. Frank Law was elected the first chairman and Miss MacKellar, the Matron of Moorfields, was appointed Secretary and Registrar—positions which they both held for over 20 years.

At the end of 1951 the disturbing news was received that the General Nursing Council was introducing a ruling whereby student nurses would not be accepted for training under the age of 18 years. The possible adverse effect of this ruling on recruitment and staffing at Moorfields, where they were accepted at the age of 17, was obvious. Representations were made to the General Nursing Council that the existing practice be continued.

Reference was made above to the question of a convalescent home. About a year before the completion of the great reconstruction of the early thirties Mr Smithers, a partner in the firm responsible for the building work, made an offer of a portion of land 15 acres in extent, near Bishop's Stortford, as a site for the erection of a convalescent home. This offer was most gratefully accepted, and arrangements made for a member of the Committee to inspect the site. Other ophthalmic hospitals in London, and some general hospitals with ophthalmic departments, signified their willingness to take advantage of the facilities afforded by the proposed home.

At the same time the Secretary of the hospital was in communication with the Zachary Merton Trust who indicated that they were prepared to consider providing such a home for the hospital. In the circumstances it was decided to decline the offer of Mr Smithers. A year or two later, however, (rather strangely it may seem, after all the previous negotiations and the collection of over £8000 to this end) doubts began to arise over the necessity for a convalescent home. In five years the numbers referred for convalescent treatment by Moorfields fell from 226 to 126. Enquiries about collaboration were made of other ophthalmic hospitals and six general hospitals; whilst most said they would make use of the facilities offered by the proposed scheme, there were many qualifying expressions and it became clear that the sense of urgency previously detectable had waned considerably. The Hospital solicitors were approached in 1943 over the proposal to rename the Convalescent Home Fund the Lister Fund, and to appropriate the income for research purposes.

Miss Long resigned in 1952. She had been matron of the Central, then matron of the Westminster, and then matron of the Westminster Branch after amalgamation—an association extending over 21 years. Miss MacKellar had been matron of the Moorfields Branch since 1947; she was now appointed matron of the combined hospital, and Miss H. G. Wylie was appointed assistant. Her duties were to lie largely in the Westminster Branch, where she was to reside. On the resignation of Miss Wylie in 1957 the opportunity was taken to remedy the situation caused by the arrangement made in 1952 which had not proved satisfactory. It was found that, residing at Holborn, she had been out of touch with the nursing routine as practised at City Road, and found it difficult to act as a substitute for the matron of the combined hospital in the latter's absence. It was felt at High Holborn that the assistant matron at that branch should have a greater degree of autonomy, and that the assistant matron at City Road should take over the nursing administrative duties there in the matron's absence. The establishment decided upon was: a Matron of the hospital, and an assistant matron at each branch, of equal status.

The question of providing the services of specialist anaesthetists instead of relying upon the House Surgeons had arisen before the war, but in the confusion of that time the project lapsed. In June 1946, however, at the request of the Medical Board, a panel of anaesthetists was enrolled, to be available for operating sessions as required and on request. With the great increase in the use of general anaesthesia in the ensuing period —local anaesthesia became a rarity except for the relatively trivial manoeuvre—the situation was regularised by the appointment of anaesthetists to the staff of the Hospital. There are now eight holding part-time appointments at one or the other branch.

At the end of February 1948 the remaining portion of the Central still in use for clinical purposes—the private ward block—was closed down, rendering the whole building available for the necessary structural alterations which would convert it into the Institute. The conversion was completed in the autumn, and the Institute was formally opened on 4 November by the Earl of Rothes, its Chairman, and Deputy Chairman of the Board of Governors of the Hospital, in the presence of a distinguished company from interested Government Departments, the University of London and the Postgraduate Medical Federation, from provincial and Scottish Universities, with of course many of the past and present staff of the three hospitals. Three guest speakers attended by invitation—Sir John Parsons representing British Ophthalmology, Professor Alan Woods American, and Professor Weve European. All four orations are recorded in full in the First Annual Report of the Institute. Sir Stewart Duke-Elder was Director of Research and there were four established departments: Pathology under Norman Ashton, Medical Illustration under Peter Hansell, Allergy under David Harley, and Orthoptics under Mary Pugh. In addition, there were a dozen Research Units, some under the aegis of the Medical Research Council.

The building was of six floors. The basement was given over to kitchens, cafeteria, technicians' rooms, workshops and store rooms. Administrative offices, and teaching and research clinics occupied the ground floor, with a small research orthoptic clinic. The first floor housed the department of medical illustration, and research rooms; library, museum, and lecture rooms occupied the next floor. The third floor was given over to the departments of pathology and bacteriology, with seven research laboratories and an X-ray room. The remainder of the building was occupied by twenty-three research laboratories. At the time of the official opening the academic session was dealing with 126 postgraduate students, and 15 full-time research workers were on the staff.

It was expected that the transfer of all the laboratory facilities from the Hospital to the Institute would enable 41 additional ward beds to be opened by the conversion of this laboratory space into wards—24 at City Road and 17 at Holborn—and it was hoped to start conversion operations in 1949. At the same time consideration was given to the rebuilding of Block K, destroyed by the flying bomb in 1944, which would further increase the bed complement.

The Institute, once constituted, was soon full of activity and indeed, though those who did the work would know the answer, to the observer it seemed that it was a very short time before it was a going concern—and going at a remarkable pace. The teaching side it took over, as it were, ready made from the medical school; but the other activities lost no time in gaining momentum. In its second annual report we read the reports of four active departments—and a score or more of different lines of research in progress are described. Exchange relations with over eighty publications had been established by the Library, and the results for students in the examinations for the D.O. and the F.R.C.S. were impressive and encouraging.

An important step relating to the financial arrangements between Hospital and Institute, which had necessarily provoked much discussion at the outset and still called for periodic supervision, was taken in 1951. Following a suggestion from the Institute it was decided to allocate a sum of £25,000 from the Endowment Fund of the Hospital for the purposes of Research, to be made available for the Institute at the rate of £5000 a year for five years. The Institute was to furnish a report each year on the way the money had been allocated, and they were to be allowed to carry forward any unexpended monies to the following financial year.

It was not long before the Institute was, like Oliver Twist, asking for more. At a meeting of the Board in November 1955 a report from the Director of Research was received, describing the work of the past year and the uses to which the Endowment Fund money had been put, accompanied by an eloquent *cri-de-coeur* describing the inevitability of retraction and the postponement of intended research projects unless increased funds were made available. The general response of the Board was, of course, sympathetic, even from those most concerned with the conservation of financial resources; but even they appreciated the identity of the aims of the Hospital and Institute, and the value to the hospital of research at the Institute. The discussion was long and serious; prospects such as the imminent cessation of income from legacies and contributions were countered by observations on the size of the Endowment Fund at this time compared with that at the time of the amalgamation (it had increased threefold). In the end the open-handed triumphed over the cautious; it was agreed that a grant of £8500 be made for the year 1956, and one of £10,000 per annum for the succeeding five years. The Director left the meeting in a glow of vindication and modest pride.

In 1954, Dr C. H. Greer, the assistant pathologist, left to take up the appointment of Director of the newly-created Pathology Department in Melbourne, which is associated with the new Institute for Ophthalmic Research in Australia. In this year two important new departments were established—a uveitis clinic concerned with the aetiology of intra-ocular inflammation, which soon began to indicate the importance of Toxoplasmosis in this context, and a Virus Research Department, concentrating at first on the problem of Trachoma. Organisation of a research team for field work in the Middle East was begun, and connection established with the Ophthalmic Hospital of the Order of St John in Jerusalem.

Honours and awards continued to fall to members of the Institute Staff at this time. The Gonin medal went to Duke-Elder; the Nettleship Prize and the Middlemore Prize to Ashton; the research medal of the B.O.A. to Fincham; L. C. Thomson gave the Ettles Lecture of the B.O.A. and was appointed Edridge Green Lecturer at the Royal College of Surgeons. Once again the Department of Medical Illustration gained a prize in the award of a silver cup by the *Presse Médicale de France* for a film on corneal grafting as performed by A. G. Leigh, submitted to international competition. In addition several distinguished postgraduate degrees were awarded to other members of the Institute and Hospital. In the following year Duke-Elder was awarded the Lister medal and, having delivered the Bowman Lecture of the O.S.U.K. in 1957, received the Bowman medal. Ashton again received high recognition by being awarded the Proctor medal—the first non-American to be thus honoured—and the following year the University of London conferred upon him the title of Professor. "For unto everyone that hath shall be given, and he shall have abundance." And most deservedly so.

The Hospital, between 1926 and 1936, received substantial funds from the estate of William Shepherd through the kind agency of his son Sir Percy Shepherd, who took a great interest in the Orthoptic Department. In November 1957, at the Public Trustees' discretion, the sum of £20,000 was allocated to the Hospital from this source, and a further £4000 in April 1958. It was the testator's wish that the legacies should be used for research; the former sum was passed to the Institute, the latter was taken into the Endowment Fund for a similar purpose. The name of the Testator is commemorated by the endowment and naming of two beds, by a tablet in the Orthoptic Department, and by eponymous fellowships and scholarships at the Institute.

In 1950 the XVI International Ophthalmological Congress was held in London. This posed some problems for the organisers since the previous Congress had been in 1937, which practically precluded precedent and provided few with experience from which to work. Sir Stewart Duke-Elder was President and Frank Law Secretary-General; the Staff of Moorfields were well represented on the organising bodies, and their ladies on the social side. The Institute played its part in offering a series of scientific demonstrations, 14 in number; the hospital provided operating sessions at both branches, some of which were televised—a new departure in operative demonstration. The Congress was an unquestioned success; 2000 members attended from 64 nations; royalty graced the occasion, H.R.H. The Duke of Gloucester giving the opening oration.

The problem of accommodation was constantly before the authorities at this time; more nurses were required, and an increase in bed complement was needed—the waiting list was over 2000. One great difficulty bedevilled the whole problem—the uncertainty whether the move to a site in the Bloomsbury area would really come about and, if so, when, and whether any development on the City Road or Holborn sites, however urgent and necessary, would prejudice the chances of a move westwards, which was considered the ideal plan, in the long run. It must be acknowledged that the Ministry had been very mindful of the Hospital's needs in the relatively short period since the inception of the National Health Service. The Royal Stuart Hotel had been purchased to provide a nurses' home; the two houses at Highgate had been retained for use as a Hospital annexe instead of being sold as originally agreed; 177 High Holborn had eventually been acquired to accommodate a Contact Lens Clinic; and authority had been given to the Hospital to proceed with the development of plans for the utilisation of the site of 12,400 sq. ft adjoining City Road (the Mora Estate, 7–15 Cayton Street and 3–4 Cayton Place). To this was added the remaining portion of the site, another 8200 sq. ft when it transpired that the Improved Industrial Dwellings Company did not in the end intend to build flats here to replace those that had been demolished by enemy action. In spite of the recent acquisition of Stuart House, it was hoped to provide accommodation for all nurses at the hospital sites as soon as possible, if only on account of the expense involved in the present arrangement; transport alone cost £2550 a year. When this aim was being considered it was necessary to remember that it was the policy of the Ministry to provide accommodation for nurses away from the hospital at which they worked.

It is probably true that Moorfields has experienced more changes, alterations, and metamorphoses than any other hospital of similar age; but none more fundamental than those which occurred in the fifth decade of this century. The Moorfields, Westminster and Central Eye Hospital Act of 1946 came into force on 1 January, 1947, to be followed by the National Health Service Act, 1946, which became operative on 4 July, 1948. By the first Moorfields lost its identity, and became part of a complex with two other hospitals and an Institute, with a reorganised administration and an enlarged horizon; by the second it lost its voluntary status in a system which the British people may properly remember with pride, acquired the official status under the new regime of a Teaching Hospital, and became part (though, in common with a few other hospitals, in a privileged manner) of a vast organisation which even to this day cannot be said to be firmly established, or even, some would say, to have justified its existence. The Royal London Ophthalmic Hospital became the Moorfields, Westminster and Central Eye Hospital for a few years, then to be granted the title of Moorfields Eye Hospital, its familiar if unofficial name for a hundred years or more, with the gracious and indeed enthusiastic collusion of those whose loyalties had previously lain elsewhere. The Committee of Management, which at the first change had become the Board of Management, at the second became the Board of Governors; and the Secretary became the House Governor. And yet—*plus ça change* . . . something fundamental has persisted; the hospital continues its work of prevention and healing in amplified form and continues to excite and exercise the loyalty, enthusiasm and devotion of each succeeding generation of doctors who see in its milieu the most appealing way of self-fulfilment. Organisation and administrative acumen alone cannot do this; the hospital, in its original form and even more in its amplified

145

form, is a body from which the personalities of its servants have succeeded in creating a living entity, a thing with an individuality and an appeal which is quite peculiar to it. A senior administrative officer of the hospital once said to the writer that, though he had worked in many and various hospitals, none other had the spirit and character of Moorfields. Long may it continue.

CHAPTER 12

National Health Service – Payment of Staff
The Board – Education – Opticians
Royal Marsden Hospital – F. A. Juler
M. H. Whiting – P. G. Doyne – Humphrey Neame
Resident Staff – Swanley – St Anne's, Tottenham
Contact Lenses – Ida Mann – Dermatologist

THE first shiver of apprehension over the status of the Voluntary Hospitals was felt in 1929, when the passing of the Local Government Act transferred the control of Poor Law Infirmaries from Local Boards of Guardians to the County authorities, who were made responsible for the co-ordination of all hospital services in their area, including the Voluntary Hospitals. The Teaching Hospitals hoped that they would be exempt from any extension or amplification of this policy; fears for the future of the voluntary system became widespread. It was evident that a vast body of opinion was in favour of its retention; even *The Times* expressed its views strongly, as the following quotation from an issue at this time demonstrates: "The Voluntary Hospitals of this country knew their business and consequently stand much higher in public esteem than any of their State-aided or rate-aided competitors. Such a hospital service as this country possesses could not be reproduced by any conceivable effort of public authorities or expenditure of public money. Nor is it likely that the service would remain undamaged if its basis were to be changed. The Voluntary System, it may well be contended, must be preserved intact if its virtue is to continue undiminished."

Nonetheless the opinion grew, in official circles, that the voluntary system had had its day, and by the time the war started the majority of those in power were convinced, to the regret of many working at voluntary hospitals, whether as clinicians or administrators. There was no doubt that the climate had changed and the attitude to voluntary service had become modified; it was becoming less popular, and certainly less easy, to give of one's services as to half one's time in voluntary fashion to Hospital work and to earn one's living at home in the other half. It would probably be fair to say, however, that the change of attitude derived primarily more from those in central authority than from those at the hospitals.

The valuable features of the voluntary system appeared to be known and generally accepted, even to the Labour Minister of Health at the time: It is interesting and indicative, however, to note the probably unconscious emphasis which he lays on the administrators, while omitting (at least in this utterance) any reference to those who do the clinical work of the hospitals. To quote his words: "There is a richness and experience in the field of Voluntary Hospital administration which, necessarily, we must call upon. There are some parts of the country where the hospital service is almost entirely voluntary. We could not man the Committees and Regional Hospital Boards unless we had particular regard to those who have been serving the hospitals for many years. We know what a great part the voluntary hospital system has played, and we must decant the best experience of the voluntary hospital administration into future hospital service, and we must have regard to these considerations."

It came to be accepted that the change would take place and a National Health Service would be established; what was unfortunate was that the matter became more and more a party political issue, and its conception and development were unduly hurried, with the result that by the time it came into force it had not received the consideration and collaboration of the leaders of the medical profession sufficiently to make it popular with the majority of those professional men who were to be responsible for implementing it. Be that as it may, the National Health Service Act was passed in 1946, and came into force in July 1948. The trials and tribulations of its implementation, and its subsequent modifications, effected and projected, will be known to all who read these words.

Though not at all apropos, it is also interesting to note that before the inception of the National Health Service—actually in January 1948—a move had been made by the governing body of the Hospital towards payment for the honorary staff. Indeed, it was stated that the profession itself had been considering, even before the outbreak of war, the desirability of appropriating a certain proportion of the payments now being made to the hospitals by patients, and that this fact combined with the change in the economic situation, justified the Board in their attitude. A request was made by the Board of Management that the Medical Committee should debate the offer of a payment of £750 for surgeons per annum and £400 each to the physicians and the ear, nose and throat surgeon, and should submit written majority and minority reports. This the Medical Committee were unwilling to do; but the medical members of the Board of Management reported that 14 members of the staff approved the principle, 8 disapproved, and 3 abstained. After discussion, a resolution was put to the committee and carried *nem. con.*, the medical members abstaining. It was added that nothing in the arrangements was to prejudice any subsequent agreement on rates of pay under the National Health Service, nor was it obligatory for any member of the staff to accept payment. It was resolved to change their title from "honorary" to "visiting".

A communication from the Ministry of Health now informed us that the Hospital had been officially designated a "Teaching Hospital"—a title granted by them to indicate that the Hospital "appeared to provide facilities for undergraduate or post-graduate clinical teaching". The designation conferred on the Hospital a special status, and a separate governing body—the Board of Governors.

The change in the constitution of the hospital consequent upon the inauguration of the National Health Service entailed the resignation of seventeen members of the Board of Management when this body was replaced by the Board of Governors, which was appointed by the Ministry of Health and included representatives of the Ministry, Regional Boards, and other bodies. Some of the seventeen remained in touch by serving on various sub-committees. One of the most devoted and valuable of these was Sir Harold Morris, K.C., who joined the Board in 1932, was Vice-Chairman in 1945 and 1946, and served on the House Committee and the Medical School Committee. At the time of the drafting of the Act of Amalgamation his legal knowledge was particularly valuable.

Before nationalisation the Medical School was already recognised by the University of London and the Conjoint

Examination Board. As nationalisation approached attention turned to the provision of even more adequate facilities for ophthalmological education and research. As discussed elsewhere, consultations began with the British Postgraduate School (University of London) over the establishment of an Institute for teaching and research; in the following year negotiations were complete and the "(University of London) Ophthalmic Institute of the British Postgraduate Medical Federation" received official recognition. Corresponding in time as it did with the amalgamation of Moorfields with the Royal Westminster and the Central London Ophthalmic Hospitals, the supply of clinical material and teaching staff was assured. From now on the story of the School becomes that of an integral part of the Institute. Thither the Dean's office and Secretariat were transferred. During the previous 25 years systematic lectures and practical classes had been added to the teaching routine which for the preceding 100 years had consisted of instruction in outpatient clinics, wards and operating theatres. The lectures and classes, as well as supplementing the practical clinical teaching, also included instruction in the subjects basic to ophthalmology, and this prepared students for the diplomas and degrees in that subject. The fuller opportunities offered by the foundation of the Institute resulted in a considerable expansion of the teaching patterns, and in its first year the total number of students was well over 100, of which 30 were aiming at the Fellowship in Ophthalmology of the Royal College of Surgeons. This diploma had come into being soon after the war by virtue of the efforts of some ophthalmologists and of the forthcoming and farseeing co-operation of the authorities of the College, notably the President, Lord Webb-Johnson; while the primary examination was a necessary preliminary, the final examination was in opthalmology, the value of the test being greatly enhanced by the inclusion of general surgeons and neurological and general physicians in its examining body. The greater space and new apparatus, the enlarged library and museum, which followed the opening of the Institute provided many advantages to both teachers and taught; the serious disadvantage entailed was the separation of the Teaching School, with the laboratories, library and museum, from the Hospital. It must be added that the division of the Hospital itself, consequent upon the amalgamation with two separate geographical entities, constituted another great disadvantage, not the least from the administrative aspect.

With the increase in numbers and in the field of teaching covered it became evident that the burden could not continue to be carried by the senior staff alone. Junior lecturers were consequently appointed, who undertook a considerable part of the basic and routine lecturing and teaching. Further, members of the staff of the Royal College of Surgeons undertook the teaching of Anatomy and Physiology and a tutorial system of tuition was introduced for the more advanced students, and for those entering for the Fellowship Diploma, with beneficial results. The number of students taking the courses continued to increase year by year; they came from all quarters of the globe. In 1954 a Reader in Ophthalmology was appointed in the person of E. S. Perkins; he at once took over the teaching of those with little or no previous experience in the specialty, and in consequence the staff of Junior Lecturers was reduced in number to one. In 1956 there were 196 students from 31 different countries. Also in this year the facilities for resident appointments, with all it means in the way of instruction and experience, were greatly augmented, as described later.

The advent of nationalisation caused a change in the optical services to the Hospital which had been unchanged for a very long time; Messrs Hawes and Son had been dispensing opticians there since 1842. There could be few instances of a comparable firm serving such an institution for so long, and with such diligence, and loyalty; it was a matter of great disappointment to many when it was learnt that conditions would prevent the continuance of their contract after the inauguration of the National Health Service. In the early days the financial arrangements were interesting and enlightening. The original contract made no provision for any payment to the Hospital by the opticians; nonetheless since 1903 they had made an annual donation of £5 which they increased in 1920 to £200. By 1928 the Committee considered that some modification of the conditions was justifiable, and a spectacle sub-committee sat and reported. As a result the yearly donation from the opticians was increased to £700. Soon after, however, a reconsideration by the Committee suggested that the contribution be on a percentage basis; this was fixed at $17\frac{1}{2}\%$ on the gross receipts, and became operative on 1 January, 1929, to be reviewed in 6 months. At that review the opticians offered to increase the percentage to 40% from 1 July, 1929, for seven years. In the three years 1930–32 the amounts received were each well over £4000; in 1950 16,976 prescriptions for spectacles were written at City Road and 9410 at Holborn, where Messrs Bowing had done the dispensing since 1907. On the inauguration of the N.H.S., a directive from the Ministry of Health required the work to be done by manufacturers and prescription houses under contracts negotiated by the Ministry. This year therefore saw the end of the long and loyal service to the Hospital rendered by these two firms.

F. A. Juler would in ordinary circumstances have retired in 1940, but on his return from overseas in that year he continued to act as surgeon to the Hospital, and remained so doing after his official retirement in 1942; he finally left in 1947, in which year also M. H. Whiting, P. G. Doyne, and Humphrey Neame all retired; the first had reached the age limit two years before this and the second one year, but both continued in office until their successors were appointed. These were H. B. Stallard, A. G. Cross, and A. G. Leigh; the first was made full surgeon in the next month in recognition of his previous services as honorary surgeon from 1933 to 1938.

Frank Anderson Juler, another son who followed his father in ophthalmology, was a well-beloved, kindly, gentle man whose genius lay in being kind to his patients and helping his junior colleagues. As a student his academic career was very distinguished, and he soon reached the heights of his specialty, being appointed to the staffs of Moorfields and St Mary's, and gaining high academic honours. Further, he was Surgeon Oculist to two royal households, and served in the two world wars, being ophthalmic specialist to the B.E.F. in France in the second. A first-class golfer, he reached the final in the Jubilee Vase at St Andrews; his house was permeated by the love of music, his wife and four daughters being most accomplished

Frank A. Juler

musicians who often entertained their fortunate friends at
musical evenings, to Frank Juler's great delight.

Maurice Henry Whiting came down from Cambridge and
established himself in Ophthalmology just before the first
world war, going through the house at Moorfields. He served in
France throughout the war, and came under the influence of
Sir William Lister in the course of his duties. Perhaps to this
influence of a first class operator may be attributed some of
Whiting's outstanding flair in this branch of the specialty. He was
a superb performer; the noticeable feature dominating all his
delicate movements was rhythm. There was rhythm in the very
way he turned from the table to the instrument trolley, and
back again—no hurry, no delay, just smooth faultless rhythm.
His results compared with anybody's and bettered most. He
held the office of Pathologist at the Central London Ophthalmic

Maurice H. Whiting

Hospital after his return from the war, and at the same time acted as surgeon, though not elected to the Staff. He served on the Staff of Moorfields for 24 years and was one of those who, due to retire in the war years, carried on till the end of the war to replace younger surgeons who had donned uniform. He was also on the Staff of the Middlesex Hospital, and of St Saviours; he was one of a succession of Middlesex Surgeons who seemed to have made a "corner" in the staff of Paddington Green Children's Hospital, now absorbed with the Western Ophthalmic into the St Mary's Group. He was a very devoted and meticulous clinician, sparing nothing for his patients, and an excellent teacher; he was elected President of the Ophthalmological Society of the United Kingdom in 1950. He is one of the few who, having seen the fundamental changes which medicine in general and ophthalmology in particular underwent after the war, is still witnessing the continuance and development of those changes. One wonders whether he finds the prospect unvaryingly alluring.

Philip Geoffrey Doyne was the elder son of the famous Robert Doyne, the founder of the Oxford Ophthalmological Congress, and it was a matter of immense gratification to him to become master in 1943. From Winchester, Trinity, Oxford and St Thomas' Hospital he served in the 1914–18 war and afterwards joined the Staff of St Thomas' and Moorfields, as well as Great Ormond Street. Here was a very charming, quiet, conscientious surgeon who was everybody's friend. He was on the Council of the Oxford Congress for years, and his interest never failed, nor his capacity for considered counsel and helpful advice. He

P. G. Doyne

155

was interested in games and rowed for his College; he never lost his interest in rowing, especially when latterly living near Henley. But his great athletic distinction lay in fencing; he was in the Olympic team, and was twice British Amateur Foils champion; he fenced regularly until he was sixty. This is of particular interest to Ophthalmologists if the story be true that he was operated upon by his father for squint in his youth, which would make the possession of binocular vision doubtful. His severe and progressive ill-health in later years was a source of great distress to his colleagues and friends.

Humphrey Neame was a member of a famous family and he served ophthalmology well. From the London Hospital, he saw service as a Surgeon in Serbia during the Balkan war, and also in the first world war with great distinction, being awarded

Humphrey Neame

156

the Croix de Guerre. He specialised in ophthalmology after his war service, and, having been Curator and Pathologist at Moorfields, was appointed to the Staff of University College Hospital in 1923 and to Moorfields in 1926, having already been on the staff of the Central. He was an astute clinician and a keen observer; his interest in later years centred on the cornea and he produced many papers of importance dealing with superficial corneal conditions.

In January 1930 a joint Committee of the Medical Board and the Committee of Management was appointed "to consider the administration of the Resident Nursing and Surgical Staff, and any rearrangements of these duties if considered necessary". One of the reasons for this was doubtless the reorganisation necessary as a result of the impending opening of the private wards. As a result of the findings of this Committee the number of residents was increased from three to four, designated Senior Resident Officer, and first, second, and third House Surgeon respectively; their duties and responsibilities were defined in detail. A similar report covered the activities of the Nursing Staff; it would not appear to contain recommendations for any drastic changes.

The increase in work, both in volume and complexity, demanded further increases in the numbers of resident medical staff. At City Road in 1947 this number was increased from four to six; at High Holborn in 1958 where at the amalgamation there had been three, another was appointed making a total of four. We shall see later how these numbers were further increased in 1959 and again in 1963.

In the past it had been the custom to provide sanatorium treatment for those patients suffering from ocular tuberculosis who it was thought would not respond to treatment at home. This was made possible by the collection of special monies for the purpose, a task most diligently pursued by the Almoner's department. When the decision was made by the Committee of Management to pay the previously honorary staff, some surgeons thought it anomalous that they should receive payment for their services while certain patients' visual welfare depended on the collection of money. They offered to hand over the proffered amount for the benefit of those patients, but the question of the avoidance of paying tax on this offered money proved difficult. After nationalisation the question arose whether the expense of sending patients abroad would be a proper charge on public funds. In 1949 the idea arose of taking over a hospital in the country for the purpose; this was stimulated by the expressed opinion of tuberculosis experts that a patient was considered to have as good a chance of recovery in this country as abroad. It was in this way that interest centred on White Oak Hospital, Swanley, with a view to taking it over as a Hospital Annexe for the treatment of those suffering from ocular disease associated with tuberculosis. Though it was to be a national unit, the intention was that Moorfields should be responsible for the admission of all patients and for their nursing and medical care.

The project had developed in the early part of 1951 so far that the hospital was ready for occupation in May of that year; the hospital was under the jurisdiction of the South East Metropolitan Regional Hospital Board, and 22 beds would be available, augmented by a further 12 if the balconies were used. Nursing staff had been seconded to the unit, and housed in a nearby house; A. G. Cross was appointed Medical Officer in charge, to visit about once a fortnight. A Registrar was appointed, D. P. Choyce, to attend twice a week, and a Physician, Dr Gavey, was to be available to undertake visits as necessary. The unit was opened on 7 June by Mr Arthur Blenkinsop, then Parliamentary Secretary to the Ministry of Health. All patients for admission were to be seen first at one or other branch of the Hospital by a member of the Consulting Staff. As these words are written comes the announcement of the death of Brigadier H. L. Glyn Hughes; an able and versatile character, he was at this time Senior Administrative Medical Officer of the South East Metropolitan Regional Hospital Board, and was most co-operative and helpful to the Hospital in its early days under the Health Service, not only in the matter of the hospital at Swanley.

Some perturbation was caused to the organisers in 1952 by the suggestion that the premises might be required by the

Regional Board, with the result that the unit would have to be accommodated in some adapted near-by buildings called "The Cottages", considered quite unsuitable by those in charge. It was with relief that they heard in September 1953 that the Regional Board did not in fact require the premises. The opportunity to exploit the situation was taken; it was proposed to acquire "The Cottages", and thus 20 additional beds, for the Medical Officer in charge had expressed the opinion that a unit of 50 to 60 beds was required if it were to serve a national purpose. At a conference with the Ministry it was learnt, rather surprisedly, that the necessary capital funds were available to cover this plan. Though Cross confessed that the accommodation was not ideal—the buildings were some 150 yards apart—nonetheless he approved the scheme, which would, in addition to providing the beds, allow the provision of the necessary day rooms and a games room for which he had already asked in a survey recently submitted to the Board.

Choyce was succeeded in the post of Registrar by Redmond Smith in 1954; John Whitwell was appointed two years later, and J. H. S. Martin in 1957.

In April 1955 notification was received from the Ministry that the South-Western Metropolitan Regional Hospital Board had decided to vacate White Oak Hospital, Swanley within 6 months. Since the Eye Sanatorium was dependent upon the main hospital for certain necessary services, this meant that the former would have to be transferred elsewhere. The Hospital Annexe at Highgate was being used for squint and short-stay female treatment cases; it was now suggested that long-stay uveitis treatment cases should also be admitted there. Cross gave his opinion that the nursing of short stay and long-stay patients at the same institution was undesirable, and further that Highgate was lacking in some facilities necessary for the latter type of case. A unit was therefore established at St Anne's General Hospital, Tottenham, which situation, though not considered ideal, was satisfactory; 25 beds were opened initially with extension of up to 40 if necessary—which was of course more than Swanley afforded.

The unit was closed down in 1959 and the patients transferred to Highgate. Improved means of treatment enabled a reduction of beds from 40 to 16, for many cases could now be treated as out-patients or in their own homes. At first space for recreation for patients staying as long as three months was a problem, but the King Edward's Fund came to the rescue with a generous grant of £1850. A recreation hut was built, connected to the Annexe by a covered way, and equipped with light, heat and water.

Facilities for the supply of Contact Lenses had been inaugurated in February 1937 by the establishment of a centre, on a research basis, with Miss Mann in charge. In 1938 "another ophthalmic hospital announced that it was starting such a centre, and contemplated press publicity" (to quote from the contemporary minutes); Moorfields decided to do the same. An assistant medical officer was appointed in 1938 and began tuition; the Royal Westminster Ophthalmic Hospital, who had considered the question of establishing a joint Clinic in connection with the Centre, decided against the project. In January 1939 the Committee of Management agreed that as an emergency measure 25 urgent cases, on the hospital waiting list, should be transferred to the centre and paid for at the rate of five guineas per lens.

The centre continued to function on this sort of basis until the inauguration of the National Health Service, when the establishment of a centre on a national basis was proposed. Frederick Ridley was asked to draw up a relevant memorandum; it was decided to set up the centre at High Holborn, at all events in the first instance. The surgeon in charge of the present department, Miss Mann, was in fact resident in Australia, and at this stage she sent in her resignation.

Frederick Ridley was appointed medical officer to the newly planned Contact Lens clinic in June 1950, graded Consultant. The Ministry agreed to purchase his production method and equipment for £2500 on the condition that he became responsible for the development of Contact Lens work at the Hospital; his technician was also transferred to the Centre.

The department was ready for the reception of patients in September 1951. In October three assistant medical officers, part-time—$3\frac{1}{2}$ hours per week—were appointed; a trainee technician, full-time, was to be appointed on 1 April, 1952.

The fitters were state registered nurses holding the ophthalmic certificate. It was found that dental technicians were best suited for the preparation of lens blanks from moulds taken from the patients' eyes; the optical work was done by technicians with experience in the working of optical plastics as well as of glass.

By 1953 the department had developed to its full capacity; 438 cases were sent to the department in a year, of which 352 were supplied with contact lenses. The director was assisted by three part-time medical officers and 11 non-medical staff. It was soon found, however, that demand was outstripping supply. The waiting list lengthened; to remedy the situation, at least in part, the Ministry, in October 1955, agreed to finance the referral of seven patients per week to commercial suppliers for the period to 31 March, 1956. In the meantime, premises adjoining the department at 177 High Holborn became available for extension, and structural alterations were begun in February 1956. The arrangement for sending patients outside did not prove satisfactory; the time taken for fitting was up to three times that taken at the clinic, and the standard achieved was in many cases not as high as that reached in the clinic. When the director reported in January 1957 it was learnt that in fact referral had ceased in July 1956, at which date the extension in the St Giles' building was occupied, resulting in an increase in work of over 25 per cent. It provided facilities for 10 fitters and accommodation for two medical clinics, with three units for moulding and other special procedures, and a large fitting room. Those cases which were still in outside hands were returned to the clinic, where their fitting was completed.

The uncertainty surrounding the tenure of the lease of 177 High Holborn was temporarily resolved in October 1963 when the Ministry informed the Hospital that they were prepared to recommend an extension of the hospital's occupancy of No. 177, and of the Laundry Block in Dudley House, for a further ten years. They further made an offer for the hospital to take over additional accommodation on the ground and second floors—and this on terms which were acceptable to the Board.

Ida Caroline Mann, whose resignation has just been referred to, was the first and so far the only woman to be elected to the

161

Ida C. Mann

honorary staff of Moorfields—a remarkable and well-merited distinction, achieved in 1927. While holding this office she published two authoritative and valuable books—*The Development of the Human Eye* (1928) and *Developmental Anomalies of the Eye* (1937) both profusely illustrated, almost entirely by her own beautiful drawings. She retired from the Hospital in 1949 —but not from work. After a few years she migrated to Australia where she kept herself extremely busy studying ophthalmic conditions in this new field and travelling widely to little visited parts. Her interest turned in the direction of the influence of climate and geography on morbid ophthalmological conditions, a facet which was admirably developed in the Bowman Lecture which she delivered in 1961 entitled "Climate, Culture, and

Eye Disease". This aspect of ophthalmology has promoted increasing interest since, and has indeed given rise to the formation of the International Society of Geographical Ophthalmology, for which Miss Mann was largely responsible. J. E. M. Ayoub was appointed to the Staff in her place.

It is of interest to note in passing that women were first declared eligible for the post of House Surgeon in 1917, and as members of the Committee of Management in 1923.

In May 1950 the Medical Committee expressed to the Board the desirability of the presence of a Dermatologist on the Staff. The proposition met with unexpected opposition from a lay member of the Board, who persuaded them to ask for full details from the Surgeons which should justify their suggestion. These they gave, and put their case fully and firmly; the appointment was agreed. Dr Peter Borrie was appointed to the post, which he still holds today.

During the war the dental clinic at City Road had been discontinued. It was re-established in November of 1950, and John Winter, the previous holder of the appointment for many years, was re-appointed as Consultant Dental Surgeon: the Department was discontinued in 1963, and John Winter once again joined the consulting Staff. Patients at High Holborn requiring dental treatment continued to be referred to the Royal Dental Hospital.

At that branch, also, the increasing work in the Orthoptic Department demanded more space. The Department was previously housed in the basement, and it may be recalled that the protracted negotiations for alternative space caused the authorities to decide to expand in that situation, unsuitable as the location was known to be. Developments intervened, however, to enable the space on the first floor previously occupied by lecture hall and laboratories to be appropriated for the purpose; and the Department moved in to this convenient area which was equipped with all the latest and necessary facilities.

CHAPTER 13

Building and reconstruction – The future
Ten Year Plan – Surgical Trends – Corneal Grafting
Nursing Staff and accommodation
Ophthalmic Nurses Association – Children's Visiting
E. Wolff

THE current financial stringency caused a disappointment to the Board in their plans for development of the site adjoining the Hospital in City Road, for late in 1950 they were asked to make a material modification to the scheme; an alternative plan was therefore submitted to the Ministry, who had set an upper limit of £50,000 for the project. Some £15,000 to £20,000 was expected from the War-Damage Commission, which would make available a total of some £70,000, to be spread over the financial years 1952/3 and 1953/4. The same depression was apparently the cause of even further delay; but the situation began to clear in April 1956 when a letter was received from the Minister authorising the Board to enter into the necessary contract to acquire the sites (7/15 Cayton Street, 3/4 Cayton Place, and 1/36 Peerless Buildings) in his name in accordance with the terms of the District Valuer's report, the cost not to exceed £22,983. The House Governor reminded the Board that between £50,000 and £60,000 had been promised by the Ministry for the extension, and that they—the Board—had agreed to augment this sum by an allocation of £25,000 from the Endowment Fund. Wistful conversations were continuing with the Ministry over the scheme for rebuilding further west near a general hospital—two sites were being looked upon in March 1957, one in the neighbourhood of the Scala Theatre and the other in Titchfield Street—but, wisely, those who knew things kept their eye on local improvements. Sir Francis Lascelles in February had, with the Matron and House Governor, met Ministry officials and confronted them successfully with the necessity of providing in the scheme for additional accommodation for nursing staff. The Ministry had agreed that some extra accommodation for nurses should be included in the scheme and had suggested the allocation of the sum of £10,000 for this purpose. This was a considerable achievement on the part of the delegates.

In the meantime, in the summer of 1952 a major work of reconstruction was carried out at High Holborn. An area formerly covered by three small consultant's clinics, six refraction cubicles and part of the waiting hall was converted into three larger clinics and a physician's clinic. Appropriation of part of the waiting room space was enabled by the appointments system. The new clinics were provided with five refraction cubicles and a dark room, and had the advantage of allowing the team of surgeon and assistants to be accommodated in one area; the three clinics were inter-communicating. Soon afterwards further improvements were carried out. The basement, no longer needed for the extension of the Orthoptic department (to the relief of those concerned), was altered to provide a large canteen for the non-resident medical and lay staff—an amenity hitherto very meanly represented. The main kitchen was completely re-equipped with modern apparatus, a project which was much helped by the advice of the Hospital Catering Advisory Service of the King Edward's Fund; and the Physiotherapy Department was enlarged and provided with a new treatment room. A year or so later it was found necessary to provide a second lift at the High Holborn branch. This was a major undertaking and involved closing the in-patient department for two months. As far as possible patients were accommodated at the Highgate Annexe, while room was found for some, including private patients, at City Road. The emergency arrangements worked smoothly and the work proceeded expeditiously, and in two months the wards were reoccupied.

In spite of the persistence in many minds of the desire to move and rebuild near a general hospital, in politic fashion negotiations proceeded for the extension in City Road, especially as the assurance of the Ministry had been obtained that developments here would not be allowed to prejudice the long term policy. Plans were completed by August 1959 and work began; it was hoped that the work would be completed by April 1961. Abeyance and attention continued to alternate over the matter of a move westwards, and the accommodation of Hospital,

Institute, and Medical School under one roof. In 1960 a working party was set up to consider the possibility of moving the Institute and Hospital to the site of the Western Hospital in Fulham; Moorfields was of course consulted, and the Institute agreed to the proposal in principle, subject to certain conditions. Nonetheless, work on the extension continued and at one time it was stated to be three months ahead of schedule. Though the original plans had to be modified for financial reasons there was some augmentation of the very restricted ones agreed by the Ministry, affording a reasonable compromise. The question of nurses' accommodation could not, however, be satisfied at once, but provision was made for this extension later by strengthening the foundations and walls of the structures undergoing modification so as to enable the later addition of higher floors. As it was, the extension included thirteen nurses' bed-sitting rooms on the first floor, and a pleasant common sitting room. The two new clinics were not of a traditional pattern but consisted (as can be seen today) of separate rooms for Consultants and assistants, dark rooms and perimeter rooms. Opinion was divided among the Consultants as to the desirability of this relative isolation, some preferring the old open clinics where all worked together; those who chose took over the new clinics, those who preferred stayed where they were. The Casualty Department was designed to effect a compromise between the need for maximum supervision by the sister in charge and the necessity for privacy for the patient. There were included a minor operating theatre, sterilising bay, recovery rooms and a large treatment area. The Architect's solution was successful and went a long way towards reconciling these two largely incompatible aims.

Equally successful was the treatment of the basement on its conversion to the new Orthoptic department; the result justified the house agents' euphemism of "lower ground floor", looking out as it does on to a pleasant garden and patio. The orthoptic staff played a large part in the planning, and were entirely responsible for the decor. There were a large treatment room, a consulting room, vision testing room, lecture room and study room, private offices, reception room and record offices; again a very successful result of careful and intelligent planning which pleased the users and has been the admiration of many visitors.

On this level a new central linen department was also built, which enabled all sorting and counting of linen to be done away from the wards. The Finance department took over new and specially designed premises, and marked the occasion by installing modern machine accounting apparatus. The Records department was enabled to expand into a considerably increased space; similarly the Works department was allocated an area which gave much more comfortable and spacious working conditions, and enabled the installation of new apparatus.

In the end the total cost was rather more than £150,000, and the work done embraced little more than half the original intention—nonetheless it was a considerable and highly creditable accomplishment—and the Ministry gave reason to hope that an additional allocation of funds might be forthcoming to cover the amount spent in excess of the estimate, having already provided an extra sum of £20,000, the amount by which the lowest contractors' estimate exceeded the original capital allocation.

As already mentioned when dealing with the Royal Patronage, the Princess Margaret had consented to perform the opening ceremony, but circumstances at the last moment prevented this. Nonetheless, by Her Majesty the Queen's command, the new wing was named the Princess Margaret Wing; H.R.H. the Duchess of Gloucester stepped into the breach, and delighted everybody by the gracious manner in which she performed the ceremony. The occasion was combined with the Nurses' Prizegiving which again Her Royal Highness undertook with grace and apparent pleasure.

Just as the major rebuilding and extension scheme of the 1930s seemed to stimulate those in charge to continue the good work in other areas, and to modernise parts of the hospital hitherto accepted without comment, so the opening of the Princess Margaret Wing in 1969 carried further reconstruction in its train. The former Orthoptic Department was converted into the School of Nursing. The Pharmacy was enlarged and refurnished, and the old out-patient clinics were reconstructed, four being converted into two larger ones and a fifth being transformed into a vestibule and a new entrance to the Outpatients Department. A new external lift was built, primarily for the transport of goods but adapted for passenger traffic;

Her Royal Highness the Duchess of Gloucester after opening the Princess Margaret Wing and presenting the Nurses' Awards, 1 June, 1961; with Miss MacKellar (Matron), Frank Law, C. J. Malim (Chairman), and Sister Pugsley.

this eased the pressure on the other lifts to a marked and welcome extent.

The question of a move westwards and the establishment of a Hospital and Institute as a unit in the vicinity of a General Teaching hospital arose again in early 1958. Plans developed very quickly; an area in Fitzroy Square was the first objective, but it transpired that it was scheduled as a residential area and unlikely to be available; the London County Council suggested another site. While fully sympathising with the aim of concentrating on specialisation within ophthalmology, of developing teaching more fully, and of close liaison with general hospitals, some members of the Medical Committee, including the writer, had misgivings that a not fully justified sense of urgency was tending to spur the enthusiasts into precipitancy. He expressed this view at a Board Meeting, and incurred very grave displeasure from his colleagues on the Board who did not share his view. He felt almost at one with the Ancient Mariner: "Ah! well a day, what evil looks had I from old and young!" Eventually, as it turned out he had no cause to regret his action, and could not but take it as a vote of confidence when he was, shortly afterwards, elected chairman of the combined medical committee.

By mid-1961, just before the production of the "Ten Year Plan for Hospitals" by the Ministry, a further scheme for development evolved. It was reported that the Royal Free Hospital was to be moved, and that the hospitals and institutes in the Bloomsbury area—Great Ormond Street, The National Hospital for Nervous Diseases, The Royal National Throat, Nose and Ear Hospital, and the Eastman Dental Hospital— should remain and be developed on their existing sites, and that Moorfields should be associated with this group and be re-established, together with its Institute, on the Royal Free site in Gray's Inn Road. The obvious objection to this scheme was that it did not meet the previously expressed requirement that the new Moorfields should be intimately associated with and adjacent to a general hospital. In an attempt to circumvent this defect the suggestion was made to include a professorial medical unit within the new hospital.

The Ministry's Ten Year Plan excited much interest and provided some encouragement when it first appeared. It was hoped that it would enable those responsible to look forward in confidence to the future development of the Teaching Hospitals. It originated from the deliberations of a Study Group containing representatives of the Ministry, the Regional Hospital Boards, the Postgraduate Medical Federation, the University of London, and the University Grants Committee. A committee was subsequently established charged with the task of reporting on the advantages to Medicine and to Postgraduate Medical Education of the proposed grouping; Sir John Pickering was

Chairman. The rebuilding of Moorfields and its Institute did not appear in the first stage of the plan; nonetheless a Planning Committee was hopefully set up, and proceeded to work in the expectation that building might begin in 1971. Inevitably, any development of the Hospital in the meantime which involved building and expansion was eliminated or at least minimised, and those in charge settled down to careful long-term planning. A month or two later the Minister wrote to the Chairman regretting that it had not been possible to include Moorfields in the Ten Year Plan, but that it was hoped . . . *etc.* This caused a change of attitude on the part of the Board, who resolved against any further postponement of the plans for development of the existing buildings and facilities, while continuing with their plans for the new Hospital and Institute.

Let us take a glance at the surgical trends observable in the period following the passing of the National Health Service Act. General anaesthesia continued to increase in popularity; in 1949 the figures were 21 per cent over those of 1948. The practice of removing a cataract in its capsule—intracapsular extraction—was becoming more frequent than the alternative method of extracapsular extraction; in 1948 there were 263 intracapsular operations against 682 extracapsular, while by 1952 the majority were done by the intracapsular method.

1949 showed a strange increase of 40 per cent over the previous year's figure for intraocular foreign body operations; cases of buphthalmos—infantile glaucoma—went from 11 in 1948 to 34 in 1949. One would expect the number of cases of retrolental fibroplasia (blood vessel formation in the eyes of premature infants) diagnosed to increase at this time, and this was so; there were 9 in 1949 compared with one in 1948. Resection of the sclera for detachment of the retina jumped from 1 to 16, goniotomy for infantile glaucoma from 9 to 27. The drainage operations for blocked lacrimal sac or duct strangely diminished in number, while the operation of removal of the sac increased by roughly the same extent. In squint surgery, the simple operation of dividing a tendon, so common in the past, was rarely seen; the practice of increasing the purchase of a muscle by advancing its insertion was giving way to anatomical shortening (resection). It was becoming much more usual to implant a prosthesis in a socket to replace the eye after removal; 43 per cent of sockets were so treated in 1950 compared with 8 per cent in 1947, enabling much greater natural mobility of the artificial eye. The incidence of implantation of a plastic lens inside the eye after removal of cataract (see page 260) increased from 2 in 1950 to 19 in 1951. Greater public interest in the possibilities of corneal grafting was the probable cause of an increase in the number of corneal opacity cases in this period from 2 to 25, and of corneal graft operations from 16 to 37, rising to 92 in 1950, despite the difficulty of finding donor material at that time.

The Corneal Grafting Act was passed in September 1952, and it was hoped that it would go far to relieve the shortage of donor material. Publicity was given at this time to the possibility of bequeathing eyes for therapeutic purposes after death, and welcome co-operation in this matter was provided by many hospitals. Unfortunately the permission given by the provisions of the Act to remove eyes after death for therapeutic purposes was largely negatived by a letter circulated by the Ministry of Health which made it necessary to obtain the consent of relatives before the eyes could be removed. This proviso practically restored the *status quo*, and incidentally presented an unhappy task to whoever had to approach relatives with an awkward request at a time of sorrow and distress. Further, the Act was repeated in 1961 by the passing of the Human Tissue Act (9 Eliz.-2).

At this time a valuable and helpful step to relieve the situation was taken by Patrick Trevor-Roper at the Westminster Hospital, who set up an eye-bank there, with hopes of supplying donor material for most, if not all, the corneal grafting in London. At the outset a charge of £1 for each pair of eyes was levied to cover the cost of collection. This eye bank was transferred to the High Holborn branch in 1966, and by affiliation with the Eye Bank at East Grinstead (under the direction of T. Casey) became the British National Eye Bank in 1968. The turnover is in the region of 1000 eyes a year, which is sufficient to supply London and some of the home counties, to distribute to some developing countries whose local supply is insufficient, and to provide material for experimental use at the Institute.

In the early 1950s the seriousness of the shortage of nursing staff was such that in spite of a formidable waiting list, 14 beds were closed in February 1953 as a temporary measure, because of the shortage. At this stage Matron approached the Board with the suggestion that Nursing Auxiliaries be appointed in an endeavour to relieve the situation. The Board was naturally sympathetic towards any suggestion which might help, but was apprehensive lest the implementation of this one might lower nursing standards and efficiency in the Hospital. Nonetheless the posts were advertised; there were 30 applicants but only two accepted employment, on account of the inadequate salary offered. An approach to the Ministry to authorise an increase in the salary was met by the reply that the question of salary scale for this grade was under consideration by the Nurses and Midwives Whitley Council, and an interim increase was refused. In an attempt to stimulate nursing recruitment a Certificate of Proficiency for State Enrolled Nurses after two years satisfactory work was instituted, and to relieve the nursing difficulty there it was resolved in January 1954 to appoint a ward clerk to the Children's Ward. Originally there were four, but the Ministry had declared the posts redundant; this ban was relaxed for a period of one year.

In July 1955 the question was raised again. When the Ministry of Health Administrative and Clerical Staff Review visited the Hospital and declared ward clerks to be redundant, it was put to them that ophthalmic patients had special claims which would justify a relaxation of this ruling; as a result the appointment of 3 ward clerks was sanctioned, and later a fourth, supernumerary to establishment and subject to review.

In 1958, the situation still pressing, an extra 8 agency nurses and 32 ward orderlies were recruited. By 1961 it was necessary to request the Ministry to sanction the employment of 43 agency nurses for three months; the number was increased to 50 for the following three months, and by July 1962 had reached 100. It was pleaded by Matron, and quite acceptably, that the necessity for this expensive and not altogether satisfactory arrangement derived ultimately from the lack of accommodation for resident nurses. The Chairman at the meeting where this was discussed reminded the Board that a scheme (which we have already noted) for the extension of the Princess Margaret Wing within the next three years to provide nursing accommodation had been submitted to the Ministry as part of the Ten Year Plan. Temporary relief from the embarrassment caused by the shortage of nurses' accommodation was constantly being sought. In January 1962 fifteen rooms were reserved in the Mount Pleasant Hotel to accommodate trained nurses; the cost was to be £9000 per annum exclusive of meals. The timing for this step was happy, because it coincided with the rewiring and redecorating of Stuart House, which demanded the closing of 20 rooms at a time. Further relief of the situation was offered when the Royal Northern Hospital enquired whether we would be interested in acquiring Thoresby House, in City Road and conveniently near the Hospital; there were 28 rooms but the Royal Northern would need temporarily to retain between 10 and 12 for their own use. The Regional Board informed the Ministry of the plan; the Board of Governors accepted the offer, and suggested the transfer of 19 Brunswick Square (12 rooms) to the Regional Board in exchange. A month later the Regional Board changed its mind and withdrew its offer; the hospital's hopes were deferred. Nonetheless, as we shall see, the premises in Brunswick Square were given up in June 1965, which was the opening date for the new premises taken over in Guilford Street. The Housekeeper at Brunswick Square moved into the basement flat at Guilford Street; twelve members of the catering staff had to be housed elsewhere.

In 1954, with the object of increasing the prestige and influence of the ophthalmic nursing profession, the Ophthalmic Nurses Association was founded, largely at the instigation of Miss MacKellar. By January 1955 there were 346 members, of whom 180 were members of the nursing staff of the Hospital; a grant of £100 was made to the Association by the Board of Governors. The inaugural meeting was held on 14 May, 1955 when the Hospital entertained the members of the new association; the first general meeting of the Association was also held at the Hospital in March 1956. The Association was destined to expand into a very important body; it interested international membership, changed its title to the International Association of Ophthalmic Nurses, and acquired its own Armorial Bearings.

The Medical Committee was very concerned over a directive from the Ministry concerning the visiting of children in hospital. They represented to the Board in very strong terms their fears of unfortunate results which might arise from a relaxation of visiting hours, and some even said that they were doubtful whether the visiting of children should be allowed at all. The Board passed their views on to the Ministry, who replied that the relevant memorandum was intended to apply to Hospitals where a rule existed forbidding any visiting of children, and urging discretion. Further representations being made by the Ministry, it was decided in January 1954, despite misgivings from both the surgical and nursing staff, to implement the Ministry's suggestion of permitting daily visiting to children for an experimental period of 6 months, the Matron to report each month on the effects of the arrangement.

In June 1954 the Matron and the Sisters in charge of the Children's Wards reported unfavourably upon the observed effects of daily visiting by parents. Those who were visited suffered distress, they said, as did those who were not visited. They pointed out that ophthalmic patients were in a special category in this context; that inflamed eyes, and those recently operated upon, could sustain damage from emotional weeping, with the consequent rubbing of the eyes and possible removal of protective dressings; that most of the children were physically well immediately after operation, and that duration of stay was short. They added thoughtfully that it had not been possible to assess the effect on a child of a stay in hospital deprived of parental visits. Great Ormond Street disagreed with these views and invited the Sisters to visit the Hospital, where daily visiting was allowed. It was decided to continue the practice for six months and await a further report.

The matter remained finally undecided in the following years. An enquiry was received from the Ministry in 1963 whether unrestricted visiting in the Children's Wards, as prescribed by them, was in operation at the Hospital. The hours of visiting at

City Road were then 2.30 p.m. to 6.00 p.m. and at High Holborn 2.00 p.m. to 4.00 p.m. and 6.00 p.m. to 6.30 p.m., while visiting was allowed at other times on special request, at the discretion of the Ward Sisters. The House Governor put it to the Ministry that this constituted unrestricted visiting, but the Ministry did not agree. The resisters were compelled to modify their views, a concession facilitated by consideration of modern paediatric practice, and indeed almost compelled by the harrowing stories of the psychological harm risked by the adoption of any other routine; unrestricted visiting in the Children's Wards became the rule, with the proviso that it was not practicable until cloakroom facilities were available for the parents visiting.

In July 1964 the Ministry were apprised of a note which had been devised for the information of parents. It told them when they could visit, and when they should not, and added that appeal to the Ward Sister for any concession was always available. It is interesting to note that in 1968 a trial scheme for "open visiting" in the adult wards was instituted, and at the end of the year was pronounced a success, and much appreciated by the patients.

The Hospital lost a trusted and loyal servant, and many lost a valued colleague and dear friend when Eugene Wolff died on 25 February, 1954. He was a notable figure in Ophthalmology and a very charming personality. Coming from his birthplace, South Africa, as a boy, he went to University College School, University College, and University College Hospital. A short period in uniform in 1918 was followed by 10 years as demonstrator of anatomy at University College, during which time he wrote his well-known book *Anatomy for Artists*. He was house surgeon and registrar at University College Hospital and clinical assistant at Moorfields; for a time he was on the staff of the Metropolitan Hospital, resigning this post when appointed to the Royal Northern in succession to Basil Lang in 1928. He also relinquished his demonstratorship in anatomy on becoming pathologist to the Royal Westminster Ophthalmic Hospital in 1930, which post he retained even after election to the honorary staff in 1936, and after the amalgamation in 1947 he continued

175

E. Wolff

to work at his pathology at the newly created Institute of
Ophthalmology. He left all ophthalmic students and ophthalmologists for ever in his debt on account of his books, the
Anatomy of the Eye and Orbit and the *Pathology of the Eye*, and by
his many articles on these and kindred subjects in the ophthalmic journals. He died in office in 1954, and was succeeded by
S. J. H. Miller.

CHAPTER 14

Anniversary – Special Funds – A. S. Philps
C. L. Gimblett – J. G. Milner – A. J. M. Tarrant
B. S. Clarke – Sir Allen Goldsmith – G. G. Penman
R. C. Davenport – J. H. Doggart – J. D. M. Cardell
Specialisation – Armorial bearings

THE year 1955 marked the 150th anniversary of the founding of the Hospital, which was greatly honoured by a visit from Her Majesty the Queen in celebration of the occasion. This gracious lady spent a long time in the Hospital and visited many departments and wards, including the children's wards, and the theatres. She talked with patients and members of the staff, and with many of the surgeons, almoners and nursing officers while taking tea afterwards in the Board Room. Here she was reminded of an incident which occurred during the visit of the Duke and Duchess of York to open the King George V

150th Anniversary, City Road. 17 March, 1955. The Queen arrives, escorted by E. P. Carter, Chairman of the House Committee.

177

Extension in 1935. At that time, before the Hospital acquired its Coat of Arms, the cover of the annual report was decorated by a picture of a small attractive girl with a bandaged eye. While being shown over the physiotherapy department by the assistant medical officer in charge, the Royal Duchess brought a message from "her little girl" who hoped the patient on the cover was doing well. He replied asking her to tell her daughter that she was indeed doing well and hoped to return home quite soon. Her Majesty was amused to realise that the "little girl" was, of course, herself.

Three years later the hospital was again privileged to entertain Royalty when the Princess Margaret came in May 1958 to present the annual prizes and awards to the nursing staff. She afterwards visited wards and departments and took tea in the out-patient department, leaving a very proud and happy memory behind her. The occasion was broadcast to the wards at both branches.

In 1956 there were 12 special funds belonging to the Hospital and it was realised that they needed organisation and legal clarification. The Treacher Collins Pathological Memorial Fund was one; it was created at his death in 1933 and had not been applied to any particular purpose by the time nationalisation came along—an event which rather negatived its purpose. Another Fund was the Lister Fund; this had started as the Convalescent Home Fund, but since this project never reached fruition (as we have seen) and since Sir William and Lady Lister had contributed so generously to the Fund in 1943 it was decided to rename it and apply it to other purposes. At this time, then, it was decided that the income from the two funds be paid over to the Institute for research purposes; the first payment amounted to £4784.

The funds had a capital value of some £28,500 producing an annual income of about £1100. Some were vested in the Board of Governors and thus were at the disposal of that Board; some were not, and the Hospital solicitors were asked to draft certain resolutions which the Board might submit to the Charity Commissioners with the object of regularising the position, since in some cases the original intentions of the donors were no longer possible of fulfilment. A Board of Trustees was appointed for each relevant group of Funds, to administer them according to the following resolutions. The Gifford Edmonds Prize Fund (there had been but 10 awards on 15 possible occasions, the last 12 years before) was to be amalgamated with the Cruise Clinical Research Scholarship, together with the H. W. Kolle Fund and the Archer Prize Fund, to form the Moorfields Clinical Research Scholarship of an annual value of some £400. The Samaritan Fund was to be augmented by the Mary Elizabeth Edwards Fund and the Mayfield Children's Convalescent Fund, and the income paid to the Samaritan Fund at the City Road branch, to be administered "in aid of patients leaving or having left the Hospital in a manner conducive to their recovery or betterment". The Lister Fund, as has been already described, had already suffered a modification of object; its annual income of £400 was now to be devoted to ophthalmic research, whilst the income from the Treacher Collins Pathological Memorial Fund was to be passed to the Institute for a similar purpose. Suitable disposition was found for the few remaining minor Funds; the Commissioners found legal reasons for making the modifications in the suggested distribution.

The Hospital lost three of its surgeons this year, one by death at a sadly early age, one by retirement, and one by resignation. The death of Seymour Philps was reported on 26 April, 1956; G. L. Gimblett retired in August (and died but 5 months later), and J. G. Milner resigned in the same month. They were succeeded by C. A. G. Cook, J. R. Hudson and K. C. Wybar; the first assumed duties at City Road and the other two at High Holborn. In this year also the Rt Hon. the Viscount Mersey died. He had been Chairman of the Royal Westminster Ophthalmic Hospital from 1932 to 1946 and had played an important part in the negotiations which preceded amalgamation.

The death of Alan Seymour Philps occurred at the early age of 50. Educated at Aldenham School and St Bartholomew's Hospital, he was House Surgeon to the Royal Westminster Ophthalmic Hospital, out-patient officer at Moorfields, and chief assistant in the eye department at St Bartholomew's. He

A. S. Philps

was elected to the staff of the Royal Westminster in 1944, and of St Bartholomew's in 1947. In the war he was appointed to the Colchester Military Hospital, became adviser on Ophthalmology to the War Office, and then served abroad, taking part in the Normandy landing. His forte was in Surgery, and this feature was consistent with his manual dexterity and artistic ability outside his speciality, for he was a beautiful draughtsman and painted in water colours and oils. This gift found most acceptable expression in his book, *Ophthalmic Operations*, illustrated by himself. He was a charming character, a very human being, understanding and generous; a thoroughly integrated personality who was devoted to his work, enjoyed his fishing and loved his fellow men. He was a wise and sympathetic clinician and an excellent teacher; his early death from an incurable malady of which he was fully aware was a real loss to Ophthalmology.

Charles Leonard Gimblett was at Clifton College and Caius College, Cambridge, and qualified at St Thomas' Hospital in 1914. Following war service he held house appointments at his Hospital, and was elected to the staffs of the Royal Northern and the Royal Westminster Ophthalmic Hospitals in 1923; he was senior surgeon at the latter hospital at the amalgamation in 1947, serving for nine years as surgeon to the combined Hospital. While clinical assistant he acquired from Claud Worth a keen interest in squint and orthoptics, which resulted

C. L. Gimblett

in his establishing the orthoptic department of the Westminster in 1930; he was the first Chairman of the British Orthoptic Council, formed in 1934, and was medical officer in charge of the Orthoptic Department of the Westminster from 1932 till 1945. He played a large part in the development of the department, and also in securing the recognition of orthoptists as medical auxiliaries. In the year following its foundation the

Council was renamed the British Orthoptic Board, but it has in fact since reverted to its first title. It is an Examining body, and is concerned with the control of the activities and with the welfare of orthoptists.

John Giddings Milner, from Marlborough and Trinity, Cambridge, qualified from St Bartholomew's Hospital and was appointed to the Staff of the Royal Westminster Ophthalmic Hospital in 1936; he was also ophthalmic Surgeon to Charing Cross Hospital and St Andrew's Hospital, Dollis Hill. He served

J. G. Milner

in the Royal Air Force in the war, and continued to work at the High Holborn branch of Moorfields after the amalgamation. He resigned from Moorfields early, in 1956, while continuing on the staff of Charing Cross to retiring age. From 1948 to 1953 he was Surgeon-Oculist to the late Queen Mary.

In 1957 Arthur Tarrant, the House Governor, decided to retire after a notable period of service to the Hospital of 33 years. Though only in his early sixties, he had been contemplating retirement in the near future, and his ideas were crystallised by the offer of the post of London Executive Representative of the University College Hospital, Ibadan, an important appointment, though less demanding than his present one, and likely to last the convenient period of two to three years. No one could dispute the appositeness of this offer and his resignation was accepted, though with great regret by all at the Hospital, lay and medical alike. He returned in due course to enjoy full retirement in the South Country; he was succeeded by John P. Heming, with G. de B. Pleydell as Deputy House Governor. It would be difficult to overstate the value of the services Arthur Tarrant rendered to Moorfields as Secretary and House Governor. He was always available, always co-operative, and always enthusiastic. The growth in size and status of the Hospital during his term of office was in no small measure due to his devotion and application to his task, and his qualities were never better applied than during the amalgamation period and the conversion from voluntary status to part of the National Health Service; though one could sense an aversion to the intrusion of bureaucracy, he gave his very best to his duties and played a valuable part in the smooth transition. None has served the Hospital more effectively and more successfully. Moorfields should remember Arthur Tarrant.

B. S. Clarke, Ph.C., M.P.S. also retired this year. He was appointed assistant pharmacist in 1920 and became chief in 1927, thus serving the hospital for over 36 years. He was a well qualified and enthusiastic pharmacist who carried out useful research, and enabled substantial economies to be effected. He was succeeded by A. W. Baker, who retired in 1973; the deputy chief pharmacist, R. Watkins, was appointed in succession.

The year 1958 saw the resignation of two members of the surgical staff and the retirement of another. Sir Allen Goldsmith resigned in January on the grounds of ill-health, having been advised to reduce his professional commitments. G. G. Penman resigned from the Westminster Branch in September; and R. C. Davenport retired from City Road, and also from the office of Dean of the Medical School. He had been on the staff for 28 years and Dean for 21 years, which latter office he held through all the first years of the Institute. He was succeeded as Dean by Keith Lyle.

Allen John Bridson Goldsmith was elected to the staff of the Central London Ophthalmic Hospital in 1937, at the same time holding the post of pathologist. He had been through the

Sir Allen Goldsmith

house at Moorfields and served as Pathologist and Curator for 3 years; he was yet another Middlesex man to be Surgeon to Paddington Green Children's Hospital. He continued on the Staff of Moorfields after the amalgamation, but retired before reaching the age limit, in 1958. He was appointed Surgeon-Oculist to the Household in 1952, succeeded to the Royal Appointment in 1965, and received the honour of Knighthood in 1970. He has recently retired as ophthalmic surgeon to the Middlesex Hospital to which he was appointed in 1946. He produced *Recent Advances in Ophthalmology* in collaboration with Duke-Elder. S. J. H. Miller was appointed to the Household on Sir Allen's promotion.

Gerard Giles Penman came from South Africa to receive his education at Sherborne School, Pembroke College, Cambridge

G. G. Penman

and St Thomas' Hospital, and was duly elected to the staff of that hospital. In 1927 he joined the Honorary Staff of the then Royal Westminster Ophthalmic Hospital, and continued in office there after the amalgamation until 1958 when he retired. He was also for a time on the staff of the Royal Northern Hospital and the Hospital for Sick Children, Great Ormond Street. He served for two years with the Royal Field Artillery in the first world war. He remains a member of the Joint House Committee of the Hospital.

Robert Cecil Davenport was one of the best loved ophthalmic personalities of his time. Born in China, where his father was a surgeon, he came to England to go to Mill Hill School, then to St Bartholomew's where he qualified in the middle of the first world war. He served in Mesopotamia and returned to hold house appointments at St Bartholomew's where he was also demonstrator of Physiology. In 1922 he came to Moorfields as clinical assistant, won the Lang Research Scholarship, and

Robert C. Davenport

attained the Staff in 1930, having been for a time on the Staff
of the East London Hospital for Children, the Western Ophthalmic Hospital, and the Central London Ophthalmic Hospital.
He was a member of the Committee of Management and then
of the Board of Governors from 1937 onwards, and served the
hospital as a devoted and talented clinician and a well-informed
and reliable adviser till he retired in 1959. This long service was
broken by his appointment to St Dunstan's, the institution
which tended the blinded servicemen, where his sympathy and
understanding was of inestimable value to his patients; he
remained Principal Medical Consultant until his death, which
took place two short years after his retirement.

Apart from his clinical and administrative occupations,
Davenport took his full share of the academic and political
activities of his specialty, and was honoured by election to the
highest posts. But perhaps the milieu in which his genius found
the fullest scope was in the Dean's office where he succeeded

Goulden, first at Moorfields until the amalgamation, and then at the Institute, until 1959. His knowledge of and solicitude for the students, more especially those from abroad (the majority) was phenomenal, and he must have felt rewarded when he saw the gratitude of his charges and their obvious affection for him. On his retirement, hundreds of his old students from 63 countries subscribed to make him a gift, and the accompanying letters of appreciation told their own story. A devoted servant of Moorfields, a brilliant Dean—and a great gentleman.

In January 1960 J. H. Doggart resigned from the Consultant Staff, a little before retiring age. A. G. Cross was appointed to

James H. Doggart

follow him as Medical Officer to the Orthoptic Department at City Road. In this year also Sir Francis Lascelles resigned from the Board when he moved to Yorkshire. He joined the Committee of Management of the Westminster in 1933 and became Chairman of the High Holborn House Committee on the amalgamation. He was also Chairman of the Nursing Committee and a member of the Finance and Staff Committees. He rendered most valuable service to the Hospital.

James Hamilton Doggart was a colourful personality and a master of clear, lucid, entertaining prose, which he employed in many books and contributions to books, mainly on the medical aspects of Ophthalmology and the nursing and treatment of children's eyes. This latter trend was evidently the outcome of his appointment to the Hospital for Sick Children, Great Ormond Street, for 27 years, during which time he was also Surgeon to Moorfields and St George's Hospitals, having retired from the staff of the Central on appointment to Moorfields. Considering his many appointments and busy private practice his literary output was quite remarkable; he found time also to be an Examiner in Ophthalmology, a co-opted member of the Council of the Royal College of Surgeons, President of the Faculty, and Honorary Secretary to the Editorial Committee of the *British Journal of Ophthalmology*.

A month later J. D. M. Cardell also retired from the staff on reaching the age limit. John Douglas Magor Cardell was elected to the Staff of the Central London Ophthalmic Hospital in 1927 and joined the roll of Moorfields Consultants in 1947 after the Central was converted into the Institute; he worked at City Road. At the time of the amalgamation he was senior surgeon at the Central, and his counsel and advice were most valuable in the delicate negotiations which amalgamation and transformation involved. It does not fall to the lot of all of us to be pioneers; Cardell was able, straightforward, devoted and honest—maybe, *per contra*, the sort on which the reputation of a great hospital is built.

On the previous two or three occasions the retirement of members of the Consultant Staff had not been immediately followed by the appointment of successors. Attention had been lately given to the desired Consultant staffing of the hospital and the medical committee had acquainted the Board with the results of their deliberations. It was decided in September that three new Consultants be appointed immediately, the staffing at this stage being 11 at City Road (plus the Reader and Senior Lecturer who were under the aegis of the University of London) and 6 at High Holborn; at the time of the amalgamation these numbers had been 12 and 9. Redmond Smith, D. P. Greaves, and P. D. Trevor-Roper were accordingly appointed in January 1961; the two former to work at City Road and the last at Holborn. On the appointment of these surgeons an innovation in staffing was introduced. They were each attached to already existing and fully staffed clinics. Redmond Smith went to

J. D. Magor Cardell

Cardell's, Greaves to Stallard's, and Trevor-Roper to Frederick Ridley's. They were to be responsible primarily for the out-patient work, and had 4 beds each allotted to them. In the senior consultant's absence they were to take over his whole duties and assume the use of his beds.

It was at about this time that the idea of specialism within the specialty began to be cultivated. There had been signs of this development already; the retinal detachment unit and the ocular T.B. unit provide examples of the trend. The Medical Committee made a proposition to this effect to the Board, asking for the provision of extra sessions for consultants where necessary. The suggestion was also made that consultants, especially when senior, might be allowed to assume charge of such special clinics and give up, in whole or in part, their work in a general clinic.

Cyril Shapland decided in December 1961 that he would prefer to relinquish both his out-patient sessions and confine his work to the Detachment Clinic and detachment surgery; such a change, if made, would put him in a position on the staff comparable with that of H. B. Stallard, who a little before had given up his out-patient work in order to concentrate on radio-therapy. It was decided to appoint an additional Consultant to undertake two out-patient sessions and one operating session per week. A statutory Advisory Appointments Committee was set up, with Frank Law representing the medical staff of the Hospital; Derek Ainslie was duly appointed in March 1962.

The tendency towards specialisation received further recognition in a report on future consultant staffing, submitted in September 1963 by the Medical Committee to the Board. There was no suggestion that the total number of consultants be altered, but it was suggested that the next vacancy at City Road might be filled by a part-time Reader, to take over a clinic and to supply material for the 40 professorial beds. The report admitted that "full specialisation at Moorfields is at the present time impracticable", but suggested that teams of surgeons should be formed to undertake responsibility for review and follow-up of special subjects, and to have access to all such cases and records of Moorfields' patients, whoever might be in actual charge of such patients. Additional sessions were to be allocated as necessary; in cases where these were not practicable, Surgeons were to be free to delegate "at least one" out-patients session weekly to assistants led by a "Chef de Clinique" —though they were, rather strangely, to retain responsibility for all their patients. The suggestion was also made that some senior consultants might be "rewarded" by renaming them "Acting Consultants". A somewhat puzzled Board referred the report back for further consideration and clarification. In their reply the Medical Committee reiterated their opinion that it was desirable for most of the surgeons on the staff to hold consultant posts at general undergraduate and postgraduate hospitals, and that specialisation within ophthalmology should be encouraged. The recommendation which included the ideas of a "Chef de Clinique" and "Acting Consultants" was considerably modified—extra sessions were recommended where necessary, and if these were not available, the surgeon might give up one of his general clinics in favour of special work, while full resignation of the more senior Consultants from general clinics was again counselled.

In March 1964 a memorandum on the treatment of malignant disease by Professor Barrie Jones and a letter from Professor Ashton on cancer follow-up led to a re-arrangement of specialist clinics. The Skin and Virus Clinics had been integrated to form an External Diseases Clinic, followed by a Radiotherapy Clinic on the same afternoon. At the same time a Genetic Clinic was established as part of the Professorial Unit. This unit was to be established on the second floor, and entailed the conversion of the lecture room there. Diplomatic negotiation was required to adjust matters so that the Palmer Lecture Room could serve for use by both the Consultants and Students and the Nurses. The unit was accordingly established on the second floor to Professor Barrie Jones' at least temporary satisfaction, and 40 beds allotted to him in compliance with University requirements. An immediate effect of this measure, which reduced the bed complement of the other surgeons to 8 or 9, was an increase in the waiting list which in September 1967 stood at 1478 at City Road. The Medical Committee were concerned over this, and it was largely as a result of the situation that they recommended no replacements after the retirement of E. F. King and C. Dee Shapland, due in November and December respectively. They recommended also that King's waiting list be transferred to the Professor's and that all other beds be pooled, recalling that Shapland had in fact been replaced in anticipation by Derek Ainslie's appointment to the staff, when the former gave up his out-patient clinics 2 years before.

In 1958 the Board of Governors decided that it would be consistent with the dignity of the Hospital and the trend of the times to exercise the right to carry armorial bearings. Details were entrusted to Frank Law who was understood to have considerable interest in and some knowledge of such matters. He consulted Mr Colin Cole at the College of Arms, then Portcullis Pursuivant and now Windsor Herald, who was, as usual, enthusiastic and co-operative, and refreshingly receptive of any suggestions as to design. The result was graciously approved by the Board and certainly received with enthusiasm by all concerned with the Hospital. The arms are reproduced in colour opposite page 194; the text of the Grant reads as follows:

To All and Singular to whom these Presents shall come, the Honourable Sir George Rothe Bellew, Knight Commander of the Royal Victorian Order, Garter Principal King of Arms and Sir John Dunamace Heaton-Armstrong, Knight, Member of the Royal Victorian Order, Clarenceux King of Arms, Send Greeting! Whereas Christopher John Malim, Chairman of The Moorfields Eye Hospital hath represented unto The Most Noble Bernard Marmaduke, Duke of Norfolk, Knight of the Most Noble Order of the Garter, Knight Grand Cross of the Royal Victorian Order, Earl Marshal and Hereditary Marshal of England and One of Her Majesty's Most Honourable Privy Council that in the year 1804 an hospital for diseases of the eye was founded in Charterhouse Square in the City of London and called the London Eye Infirmary. That the said hospital was later moved to Moorfields in the said City and was then known as the Royal London Ophthalmic Hospital and was incorporated by Royal Charter dated the Seventeenth day of December 1890. That the said hospital was amalgamated with the Royal Westminster Ophthalmic Hospital and the Central London Ophthalmic Hospital and the three combined hospitals were created one body corporate by the name of Moorfields Westminster and Central Eye Hospital by the Moorfields Westminster and Central Eye Hospital Act 1946. That by an order made by the Minister of Health under the National Health Service Act 1946 on the Sixteenth day of August 1956 the name of the said hospital was changed to The Moorfields Eye Hospital. That the Governors of The Moorfields Eye Hospital being desirous that Armorial Bearings should be granted to the hospital with lawful authority, he hath requested the favour of His Grace's Warrant for Our granting and assigning such Arms and Crest and in the same Patent such Supporters as may be proper to be borne and used by The Moorfields Eye Hospital on Seals or otherwise according to the Laws of Arms

And forasmuch as the said Earl Marshal did by Warrant under his hand and Seal bearing date the Twenty-sixth day of June 1957 authorise and direct Us to grant and assign such Arms and Crest and such Supporters accordingly know ye therefore that We the said Garter and Clarenceux in pursuance of His Grace's Warrant and by virtue of the Letters Patent of Our several Offices to each of Us respectively granted do by these Presents grant and assign unto The Moorfields Eye Hospital the Arms following that is to say: Per pale Or and Sable a Sun counterchanged on a Chief Azure a Leopard's Head Argent crowned with an Eastern Crown Gold between two Fleurs de lys also gold And for the Crest On a Wreath Or and Sable An Elephant's head couped proper holding in the trunk a Fleam Or as the same are in the margin hereof more plainly depicted And by the Authority aforesaid I the said Garter do by these presents further grant and assign unto The Moorfields Eye Hospital the Supporters following that is to say: On either side a Peacock in its pride holding in the beak an Ophthalmoscope proper the dexter gorged with a Chain pendant therefrom a Portcullis Or the sinister also gorged with a Chain pendant thereform as Escallop Argent as the same are also in the margin hereof more plainly depicted the whole to be borne and used for ever hereafter by The Moorfields Eye Hospital on Seals or otherwise according to the Laws of Arms. In Witness whereof We the said Garter and Clarenceux King of Arms have to these Presents subscribed Our names and affixed the Seals of Our several Offices this tenth day of July in the Seventh year of the Reign of Our Sovereign Lady Elizabeth the Second by the Grace of God of the United Kingdom of Great Britain and Northern Ireland and of Her other Realms and Territories Queen, Head of the commonwealth, Defender of the Faith and in the year of Our Lord One thousand nine hundred and fifty-eight.

G. R. Bellew, Garter.   J. D. Heaton-Armstrong, Clarenceux.

It may be of interest to follow this by an explanation of the heraldic description (the "Blazon") contained in the terms of the grant.

ARMS

Per pale:	Divided vertically
Or and Sable:	Gold and black
A Sun counterchanged:	A sun divided and coloured as described on a background of the same colours transposed
On a chief Azure:	In the upper third of the shield coloured blue
A Leopard's Head Argent:	A leopard's head in silver
Crowned . . . etc.:	*Idem.*

CREST

On a Wreath Or and Sable:	The wreath, in the "livery colours" sits on the helm (looking like a piece of twisted rope) and carries the crest
. . . couped proper:	. . . cut off at the neck; in its natural colouring
. . . a fleam Or:	The ancient form and name of a surgeon's lancet, in gold

SUPPORTERS

. . . in its pride:	With tail displayed
. . . the dexter gorged with a Chain pendant therefrom a Portcullis Or:	The right-hand one (on the left-hand side as you look at it) having a chain round its neck carrying a gold portcullis
The sinister . . . an Escallop Argent:	The left-hand one (on the right-hand side as you look at it) similarly bearing a silver escallop

The other elements are those which appear on any achievement—the helm, the mantling or lambrequin, and the compartment. The mantling, depicted, like the wreath, in the livery colours, derives (according to some theorists) from the pugaree, slashed in the heat of battle, and is expanded as a decorative feature at the whim of the artist. The compartment is anything which gives foothold to the Supporters and a resting place for the Shield.

The Coat of Arms

[*face page 194*

Though armorial bearings had originally an essentially distinctive and decorative function, there is a modern tendency for their design to be more allusive in character; on this ground they may be largely "explained". Many of the allusions in the Hospital arms are obvious and need no reference, *e.g.* the sun counterchanged, representing darkness giving way to light, the fleam, the peacocks with their multiple "eyes", and the ophthalmoscopes. The leopard's head and the fleurs-de-lys are found respectively in the arms of Guy's Hospital and St Thomas's Hospital and allude to the fact that it was members of the staffs of these Hospitals who first suggested the founding of an eye hospital. An elephant's head appears on many Saunders arms, because the name is said to derive from Alexander, and one of that name, called the Great, had a deal to do with elephants. It appears here in reference to J. C. Saunders, the founder of the Hospital.

The former Westminster and Central Hospitals are referred to in the supporters. The portcullis has had a heraldic connection with Westminster since Tudor times. The escallop, a charge appearing on the arms of the Dukes of Bedford, brings in the Central London Ophthalmic Hospital, for this has in its various locations always occupied a site in territory owned by this family.

The compartment, the form of which may be a matter of artistic taste and design, and is often a mound of earth or grass, appears here as a stone plinth in reference to the urban situation of the Institution whose arms it supports. On it is carved the motto—"Let there be light."

Various references to the Achievement have subsequently been made. There is an attractive tie for past and present Residents which bears the crest; another for members of the administrative staff consisting of the shield—with its sun counterchanged, and its two fleurs-de-lys in chief with the leopard's head in the honour point. Money-raising and social functions, such as the "Peacock Ball" have been named after some features of the achievement, which had added dignity to the Hospital and refers happily to the amalgamations of 1945 and 1946.

14B

CHAPTER 15

Out-patient arrangements – Board Room
General anaesthesia – Progress – Professor
Retrolental Fibroplasia – Institute research
Nurses' Training and accommodation

THE political authorities, on nationalisation of the Medical Services of the country, demanded an appointment system for out-patients and a reorganisation of records. It was thought that the installation of these two facilities at once over the whole Hospital would be financially and administratively impossible; accordingly one clinic at each branch adopted the new recommendations, and after six weeks it was considered possible to extend the innovation to another clinic at each branch. In due course it was adopted in every clinic. In connection with the Ministry's requirements in the establishment of a Medical records department, an officer in charge was appointed in April 1949 in the person of Lt Col. J. A. L. Powell. One suspects that in the Ministerial mind was the hope that an appointments system would not only regularise attendance times and reduce waiting but also relieve the staff of some of the burden of the enormous work load which they had to bear. This was an ever present trouble. Usually uncomplaining, the surgeons and their assistants sometimes felt compelled to draw attention to the fact that not only were they asked to do too much for their own comfort, but that the turnover unquestionably compelled the work to drop below the first-class standard which should have been obtained. In April 1959 the attention of the Board was again drawn to the question, and attendances on a recent day in that month at one clinic quoted, which numbered 36 new patients and 130 old. This produced some temporary response and a sub-committee was set up to "study the problem and report to the Board", though it was difficult to see what remedy could relieve the situation short of a strict limitation of numbers, from which would emerge an enormous waiting list and a breach of the proud edict of the Hospital that no patient was to be sent away unexamined. So patients continued to come at the wrong time —and were seen; to come without Doctor's letters—and were seen; to come on the wrong day—and were seen. The hope expressed so often by the instigators of the National Health Service, that peripheral clinics of all kinds should deal with the routine out-patient turnover locally, and the central hospitals receive none but referred and special cases, never materialised—Moorfields was Moorfields (and for that matter Bart's was Bart's and Guy's was Guy's) and that was where the central figure of the whole business was determined to go. And who shall blame?

A definite effort to relieve matters was made, however, after the sub-committee reported. An augmented Casualty Depart-ment was set up, to whom were to be referred all patients except those with appointments (except temporarily those with personal letters to surgeons). The department was to be staffed from the clinic out-patient officers; no patient was to attend there more than once (except minor treatment cases). Urgent cases were to be referred at once to a clinic; others were to be quickly examined and referred to a clinic by appointment. The scheme was good in intention and looked well on paper; in fact, the Department soon became, to all intents and purposes, an autonomous extra clinic.

Only for a time, however, was the matter settled, for it was thought necessary to reopen the subject in 1963, and a sub-committee was set up in August to consider organisation and staffing in the out-patient clinics. They produced a long and detailed report, covering appointments, nursing staff, secretarial staff, casualty work, clinic reception offices, portering staff, and financial considerations.

It had long been the intention to do something to improve the appearance of the Board Room—in itself an imposing and pleasant room but not equipped and decorated in a manner complementing its possibilities. The wish became capable of immediate and ample fulfilment by the receipt in 1960 of a gift of £4000 specifically for this purpose, and for a similar purpose in the House Governors' room, from Mr Trevor A. C.

Bowen, D.L., J.P. The result is considered to have been a complete success; Moorfields has a Board Room which will compare with that of any hospital in the country, and which vindicates the aim of the donor, whose generosity is commemorated by a panel over the doorway. Mr Bowen died in 1964; two years later his daughter generously gave a further £500 to complete the furnishing of the Board Room.

Shortly afterwards one of the Consulting surgeons gave a pair of Georgian torchères to stand on the door side of the Board Room carrying each a candelabrum of early 19th century date and French origin, and provided shades throughout of uniform design. The appearance was pleasing and the lights provided the illumination hitherto lacking on that side of the room.

As mentioned before, general anaesthesia was gradually becoming more popular, and the services of the anaesthetists attached to the staff were being increasingly called upon. In 1958 46 per cent of operations at City Road, and 53 per cent at High Holborn were performed under general anaesthesia. In the transition period between the almost exclusive use of local anaesthesia and that of general anaesthesia, the value and possibilities of a combination of local anaesthesia and deep sedation were being exploited. Until well after the second world war local anaesthesia was almost universal; later more control was obtained, and less call made upon the co-operation of the patient, by the addition of lid akinesia and retrobulbar injection. Then enzymatic zonulysis followed; though not without its hazards, in properly selected cases its use certainly facilitated extraction. The contrast between the attitudes and opinions of the different surgeons at the time of the changes in routine is very interesting. When general anaesthesia was introduced the expressions of relief were many, and the advanced techniques which practically eliminated post-operative vomiting converted the majority of surgeons. The other side of the coin is significantly revealed in a passage from Collins History, page 165. "The substitution of local for general anaesthesia in cataract operations aided materially in their safety and success. The dreaded effects on the eye of vomiting and reaching on the recovery from the administration of ether or chloroform were avoided, and the aid of the patient in turning the eye in any direction did away with the necessity of dragging it into suitable positions, which was frequently requisite when the patient was unconscious. The immediate result was a considerable decrease in the number of cases in which the vitreous humour escaped, and the possibility of greater precision in the adjustment of parts after the removal of the cataract." Thus yet another cycle was completed.

In a record such as this it is impossible to note each change, each advance, each indication of progress as it occurs. Small in themselves as they may be, their added effect produces profound changes in the routine of the Hospital; their significance is obscured by their inevitability. The whole attitude towards hospital service began to change soon after the first world war, and of course suffered a violent and fundamental change in the mid-forties. One of the more important innovations was the habit of frequent travel. It is probably true to say that in the twenties, not two of the surgical staff had travelled abroad in a professional capacity, indulging in lecture tours and visits of inspection, while enjoying what was later officially termed "study leave". After 1948, gradually, but with increasing momentum, things began to change, and after the second world war it became increasingly common for surgeons, usually those of middle seniority, to travel abroad to lecture and learn something of the ways and methods of foreign colleagues. Names such as Ridley, Lyle, Doggart, Law, King, Stallard and many others occur in the records, reporting their visits to the Board. So it has gone on until now it is practically routine for a resident to undertake a foreign visit at the end of his period at the Hospital. A trend in a similar direction was encouraged by the Faculty of Ophthalmologists when they instituted study tours. By this date the list of these tours must be a formidable one; starting with tours for consultants, the Faculty began to organise tours for Registrars—perhaps an even more important venture; and the reciprocal welcoming and entertainment of visitors from abroad naturally followed.

Equally difficult is it to record—short of making a tidy and tiresome chronological list—the modifications of technique and habit which were equally unobtrusive in their sequence but equally important in their results. The gradual invasion of general over local anaesthesia; the sequence of techniques in surgery, as intracapsular replaced extracapsular extraction of cataract; diathermy replacing cautery puncture and caustic application, to be followed by scleral resection, circlage, indentation, cryotherapy and the laser beam in the treatment of detachment of the retina; the enormous forward step made in the control of ocular infection by the antibiotics, which replaced such heroic and destructive manoeuvres as Saemisch Section, and virtually eliminated such confessions of defeat as evisceration of the globe; the list is endless. The thought of "the inevitability of gradualness" everywhere obtrudes. To one in practice at the time, the introduction of dry sterilisation was but an incident, however important; a study of its effect has probably never been made and would in any case be extremely difficult. Equally difficult would it be for a researcher into such matters—one could list them by the score—to amass his material; if he were successful in this particular matter he would learn that it was introduced into Moorfields in 1957 at a cost, in "two sterilising ovens" and extra instruments, of £1660. However, one has, in the accepted phrase, to "draw the line somewhere", and confine oneself to the broad picture of the Hospital's progress and advance as a whole, however personally interesting and important these individual items may be.

Many other features contemporary with this would appear antiquated, if not antediluvian, to the present generation. The writer as House Surgeon was the first to suggest the wearing of caps in the theatre, his theory being that, provided silence was kept, there was at least as much need in the interests of sterility to wear a cap as a mask. The illustration of the original theatre in City Road as it was in his time as house surgeon is of interest. After removing his coat and, sometimes but not always, his collar and tie, the surgeon put on mask and gown, having washed up, and proceeded. Notice that the nurses wore no masks; notice that the audience are completely unprepared, and that their outdoor shoes are approximately at the level of the trolley bearing the drops and dressings.

His suggestion was at once adopted. A few years later, when on the honorary staff of the hospital, he brought a cricket shirt, white trousers and canvas shoes to the hospital into which he

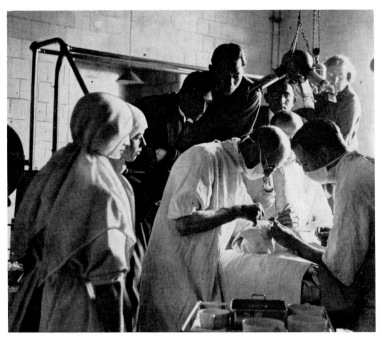

The Old Theatre at City Road

changed before operating. A senior colleague meeting him thus garbed on the way to the theatre, said in friendly but faintly sarcastic tone: "Dear me, are you going to play ball?"

The status of various medical officers who were on the staff of the Institute, and paid by the Institute, but who nonetheless undertook work on behalf of the hospital, was constantly under review. For instance, in January 1952 an Honorary Contract of Service (Consultant Status) was conferred upon Dr (later Professor) Ashton, Dr Greer, of the Pathology Department, Dr C. H. Smith, senior lecturer in Bacteriology, and Dr Peter Hansell, Director of the Department of Medical Illustration. Many more honorary contracts have been conferred since these early days.

In the following year the Board of Governors received a memorandum from the Institute concerning the desirability of securing the appointment of a professor. This stemmed partly from the reflection that the Dean would reach the age limit for hospital service in five years time and the Director of Research—holding a specially created unpaid post, unique in the University hierarchy and probably unfillable when the holder retired—would probably be wanting to reduce his responsibilities at about the same time. In view of the very special qualities desirable in a Professor of Ophthalmology it was thought that there was no one in the country at that moment who satisfied the criteria. It was therefore suggested to the Board, on the advice of the medical committee, that the Senate should be approached with the suggestion that a Readership be established; the holder would automatically become an honorary member of the Hospital consulting staff and would have a preferential claim to the Chair when it was established. The Board agreed and authorised the Committee of Management of the Institute to approach the University; in due course —in April 1954—E. S. Perkins was appointed Reader in Ophthalmology at the Institute.

It was at about this time that Norman Ashton, University Reader and Director of the Department of Pathology, began to see the light at the end of his important researches into the cause of retrolental fibroplasia. This blinding infantile disease, which had shown an alarming increase in incidence of late years, was causing grave concern to surgeons all over the country. Doubtless the condition had been seen over the past many years; equally doubtless the eye affected had been excised as malignant or had been given the totally inadequate and equivocal diagnosis of pseudoglioma.

The condition was first described as a recognisable clinical entity in 1942 by T. L. Terry, then Assistant Professor of Ophthalmology at Harvard University. He named the condition, noted its occurrence in premature infants, and made some suggestions as to aetiology, including reference to a persistent vascular sheath of the lens. In 1951 Dr Kate Campbell of Melbourne suggested the presence of a connection between the occurrence of the condition and the administration of high concentrations of oxygen to these infants. The suggestion was taken up eagerly by pathologists in various parts of the world, including Sweden, Israel and America, and in this country by Ashton. In his experiments he used kittens—animals whose eyes are immature at birth, and thus provided admirable material for the enquiry. After diligent and careful experimentation over some four years Ashton was able to affirm the connection; his researches provided much new knowledge on the connection between hyperoxia and hypoxia and retinal vascularisation, and indeed vascular behaviour elsewhere. He found that oxygen in high concentrations could cause complete obliteration of ingrowing retinal vessels in the immature eye; restoration to normal oxygen tension, especially if rapid, could cause reopening of vessels not completely occluded; it could also cause a prodigal revascularisation, with the formation of an abnormal vascular network and the occurrence of haemorrhages, and (in the human eye) organisation and fibrosis. The importance of the discovery and the publication of the knowledge cannot be over-estimated; the flow of blind premature babies ceased like the turning of a tap, and an important cause of infantile blindness was eliminated.

Parallel with this line of enquiry, Ashton was pursuing another in the field of corneal vascularisation in its relation to low oxygen tension in the normal corneal tissue and a decrease in the compactness of the limbal tissues. Redmond Smith and Kenneth Wybar were studying the ocular circulation in general; equatorial anastomoses between the anterior and posterior arterial group were demonstrated, and it was found that practically the whole of the choroidal circulation could be injected through a single short posterior or anterior ciliary artery. Further, no pecularities could be found in the choroid subjacent to the macula; no structural nor morphological differences between the choroid situated there or anywhere else at an equal distance from the disc could be detected.

In the Department also Charles Cook was investigating diabetic retinopathy and its experimental production, and Dr C. Smith was directing his virus research towards the study of the aetiology of uveitis, and also co-operating with the clinical research unit in the treatment of ocular infection, especially of corneal ulcers due to *Ps. pyocyanea*. Further investigations into uveitis and its connection with toxoplasmosis were being made by J. Hudson, and C. H. Greer was studying 62 cases of malignant melanoma of the choroid in an attempt to correlate the histological structure and prognosis.

With this brief description of the research activities in the Pathological Department it would be appropriate to give an outline of the work proceeding in other departments of the Institute; in this way an indication may be given of the stage of development and progress in this its fifth year of existence. The Ophthalmological Research Unit (Medical Research Council) was working on the properties of the blood-aqueous barrier, Dr M. E. Langham taking the most prominent part; some of his work was done in conjunction with Professor Bárány at the University of Uppsala. A study of the rate of flow of the aqueous humour had just been started, connected with investigations into the control of the intraocular pressure. The metabolism of the cornea was still being investigated, and the pharmacology of the eye was occupying other workers. Dr Katherine Tansley was investigating the production of cataract by neutrons, and comparing the results with those produced by X-rays.

Another department under the aegis of the M.R.C. was that concerned with the physiology of vision. Here Drs H. J. A. Dartnall, G. B. Arden, and R. A. Weale amongst others were investigating the electro-physiology of single optic nerve fibres; the photochemistry of the visual pigments; the measurement of the absorption of light in the dioptric mechanisms of the eye; *in vivo* measurements of accumulation of photosensitive pigments in the eye during dark adaptation; and subjective observations in vision. Dr Katherine Tansley, Wernher Research Fellow, was also studying normal retinal histology, and evolving new staining techniques, as well as investigating the retinae of a strain of rodless mice.

The Glaucoma Research Unit was active in many areas of its own field. P. L. Blaxter had evolved the bulbar pressure test; A. C. Higgitt was studying the dark room test, and J. H. Dobree diurnal variations of tension. W. E. S. Bain was investigating the pressure in the episcleral veins, and Langley the alterations in the osmotic concentration of the blood and its possible influence on ocular tension. H. E. Hobbs and Redmond Smith were concerned with gonioscopic studies, and S. J. H.

Miller with the behaviour with the optic disc in the evolution of glaucoma, which he was studying by photographic means. Research proceeded on the action of cortisone, on the value of various antibiotics (Derek Ainslie, A. G. Cross, and D. P. Choyce); on factors influencing the transparency of corneal grafts (A. Lister, A. G. Leigh, D. P. Greaves); while A. S. Philps and L. G. Fison were studying the many problems associated with detachment of the retina. Peter Borrie the dermatologist was investigating rosacea, and R. C. Davenport and R. H. Rushton myopia. Miss Pugh in the Orthoptic Department continued her analysis of foveal vision in the amblyopic eye, while Edgar Fincham was working on the accommodation reflex. H. C. Weston continued his general studies in occupational optics.

This is a formidable list of research projects. In many departments, of course, there was regular routine work to be done. In the Pathology Department, for instance, the staff, as well as reporting upon over seventeen thousand histological and bacteriological specimens in the year, carried out over seven thousand blood, serological, biochemical, and other tests. The Department of Medical Illustration under Dr Peter Hansell—now the Department of Audio-visual Communication —was developing at a great pace, and meeting success. In 1951 every member of its staff gained distinctions in examination results or diplomas, and the department was awarded the Hood Medal of the Royal Photographic Society. This was the first time that the medal had been awarded to a group, and the first time it had been gained in a medical field. In the year under review nearly 5000 photographs were taken, and 1000 slides and transparencies made; nearly 300 drawings or paintings made, and 2300 feet of cine film exposed. Demonstrations were arranged and exhibitions mounted. The library was expanding rapidly; 16 periodical journals were added to the existing long list, and 130 volumes. And, over all, the courses of study proceeded and the numbers of students increased; a tutorial system was instituted for the F.R.C.S. Diploma. In the two examinations for the D.O., of 72 entrants from the Institute 31 were successful; two passed the F.R.C.S. in November and eight in the following May. Interchange with other academic bodies was free and increasing; the countries of the Institutes involved included Sweden, the U.S.A., Belgium and Pakistan. Perhaps the most important visitor was Professor Alan Woods, who took a great interest in the work of the Institute, and gave many lectures here and at Guy's Hospital; his visit under the exchange scheme was returned by Frank Law, who spent two months of the following year at the Wilmer Institute of the Johns Hopkins Hospital and elsewhere in the States. Lastly, hospitality was extended to many scientific bodies with associated interests; these included the Colour Group of the Physical Society, the medical section of the Institute of British Photographers, the Ophthalmological Society of the United Kingdom and the Pathological Section of the Royal Society of Medicine.

In 1959 the University had conferred upon Norman Ashton, then Reader in Pathology, the title of Professor. On 1 March, 1965, they established a Chair in that subject to which Professor Ashton, not surprisingly and very deservedly, was appointed.

The tendency in other hospitals and specialties was towards the shortening of training time for nurses in training for the Hospital Certificate, the main object being to improve recruitment. In accordance with this trend it was decided, in October 1962, to reduce the training time of postgraduate nurses from 12 to 9 months, and to reduce the training period in the case of state enrolled nurses from 15 to 6 months, eliminating theatre and out-patient experience, but providing for these nurses to take a three months course in either of the latter spheres after their full training experience was ended. Student nurse training was to be reduced to 18 months as a minimum, which would carry a remission of 6 months when they commenced their general training.

In 1963 a disconcerting letter was received from the Ministry of Health revealing the proposals of the General Nursing Council to discontinue the associated training between ophthalmic, orthopaedic, chest hospitals and general hospitals as from January 1965. There was, however, an alternative proposal, amounting to a concession, for ophthalmic hospitals. A nurse eligible to receive the ophthalmic nursing diploma on registration was to be granted six months reduction in general training provided certain requirements in her previous training were satisfied. In this year also, reductions in the period of nurses training under the associated scheme were announced. Postgraduate training was reduced from 13 to 12 months, student nurses' from 2 years to 18 months, and state enrolled nurses' from 15 months to 12 months. Again the hope was that these measures would encourage applicants. Comments on these matters were requested by the Ministry, and the Nursing Committee duly prepared and submitted them.

Further adjustments of training time were made as circumstances demanded. In 1967 the time for post-registration nurses aiming at the Moorfields' certificate and medal was reduced from 9 to 6 months, and in 1970 the same period was adopted for state registered nurses doing the full post-registration course. Student nurses, entering at age 17, were required to take an 18 months' course, which secured them a relief of 6 months in their full general training.

In 1969 it was learnt that the General Nursing Council had decided to lower the age of entry for nurses' general training to $17\frac{1}{2}$ years. This caused some consternation, for it was naturally thought that it would adversely affect the recruitment of student nurses to special hospitals for pre-registration training; there being but six months' difference in the age of entry, a prospective nurse might well not wish to spend a preliminary eighteen months in a special hospital before commencing her general training. Some mitigation of the situation, it was thought, might be afforded by the secondment of nurses to special hospitals during their general training. At the same time the Director of Nursing announced her proposal to introduce a pilot scheme for selected nurses to train in ophthalmic procedures for a period of six months only. These nurses would form part of the hospital's existing establishment and would perform only specialist nursing duties. The Nursing Committee agreed to the trial, which, if successful, it was suggested, might be adopted generally, on the recommendation of the Ophthalmic Nursing Board.

The constant search for more nursing accommodation led the authorities in 1963 to consider the conversion of St Matthew's Hospital in Shepherdess Walk for this purpose, and careful attention was given to this possibility. It emerged that the scheme would cost some £90,000, which made some think that it would be no more expensive to extend at City Road, and attention veered to this alternative. An approach to the Ministry met with a rebuff, and interest was rekindled on the St Matthew's project. The situation was not made any easier by the attitude of the Ministry towards resident nursing accommodation; they held the view that residence was required only "when the needs of the service made it necessary", and thought that the resident proportion need never exceed one third of the total.

So concerned were the authorities over the question of nursing accommodation that in November 1963 a special meeting was called of the Nursing Committee with co-opted members of the Board of Governors. It is a little daunting to note that there were six attenders against seven who apologised for absence. The Joint Committee recommended that two houses in Guilford Street, the property of the National Hospital and at present used as a hotel, be acquired and converted at a cost of some £20,000. This plan was adopted and work commenced which it was hoped would be completed by the end of the year; accommodation for 20 nurses would be provided.

The premises were opened on 1 June, 1965, and the nearby house in Brunswick Square was closed. Completely redecorated and refurnished, it made an attractive and most valuable addition to the extramural accommodation.

A study of the hospital records of the 1960s leads one inevitably to detect a change in attitude towards, or at least atmosphere surrounding, the question of accommodation for nurses. The sense of urgency seems to pale, the enthusiasm to fade. Whether this was attributable to the expressed opinion of the ministerial authorities, who favoured the housing of nurses outwith the hospital walls, and set a percentage desirable upper limit for those resident within; or whether it was due to some antecedent over-estimations and misplaced enthusiasm, the fact emerged that a change had occurred. One actually reads in 1966 of a suggestion to cut down the occupancy at Stuart House and accommodate nurses from other hospitals. Even more amazing comes the suggestion, a little later, after spending £20,000 on the conversion of the Guilford Street premises but 15 months before, to vacate the buildings and sublet the rooms to Orthoptic Students. A month or two later the proposition arises for the hospitals of St Peter, St Philip and St Paul (genito-urinary hospitals now incorporated together with the Shaftesbury Hospital) to rent some accommodation there. It is all very mysterious, and impossible to explain so long after. A final wonder is the pathetic plaint of the Board a week later—they hoped that some accommodation for nurses as well as for the domestic servants already there might be found at Guilford Street. And it was for nursing accommodation that Guilford Street had been acquired. As a matter of fact the proportion of accommodation in Guilford Street which was given over to nurses was nil, or practically so. This emerged in July 1969 when the hospital received six months' notice from the National Hospital, who wished to take over the property in January 1970. The records state that at that date, most of the occupants were from the hospitals of St Peter, St Paul and St Philip, but that alternative accommodation would have to be found for some domestic staff in residence there. At this stage the North West Metropolitan Regional Hospital Board wished to hand over Thoresby House (see page 258); there were other authorities who had an eye on this property, which fact stimulated Moorfields to increase its efforts to negotiate the transfer.

CHAPTER 16

Resident Staff – Medical School anniversary
Institute – Professorial appointments
Fellowships of the Institute – Institute appeal
Sir Stewart Duke-Elder – Trachoma
Barrie Jones' work – V.D. Department – F. W. Law
P. McG. Moffatt – C. D. Shapland – E. F. King
J. P. Heming

WITH the aim of meeting the need for more and better trained ophthalmologists both in this country and abroad, it was decided to increase the number of House Surgeons from six to twelve at City Road and from four to six at High Holborn, and to extend their period of training from two to three years. The scheme was initiated in November 1959 by the addition of three medical officers at City Road and one at Holborn. The total complement was to be reached in June 1960; the cost would be £8000 in a full year. The suggested grading was: House Surgeons twelve to five—Registrar; House Surgeons five to one—Senior Registrar. The senior was entitled Senior Resident Officer; Numbers two to six Resident Surgical Officers; the remainder, House Surgeons. The augmented period of training now included six months at the Institute and also a period at the Detachment Unit and the Ocular Tuberculosis Unit at Highgate.

Before very long further developments occurred. In February 1963 the Board approved the recommendation of the Medical Committee that the number of House Surgeons be once again increased, this time to 21 at City Road and 9 at High Holborn. The allocation of their duties was an extremely complicated business, but was adequately executed by the sub-committee appointed for the purpose; careful planning was also needed to initiate the scheme, which could not be done immediately. It was introduced in June 1963, the appointments being made at appropriate moments and the resignations arranged, one every three months, so that every House Surgeon served his full three years; at City Road the number of House Surgeons was to be built up to the full 21 over a period of three years. A comparable scheme was devised for the Holborn branch where the complement would be similarly built up over three years. Partly as a consequence of this development, it was hoped that the employment of *locum tenens* medical officers in the clinics to replace medical staff on annual leave would be wholly or largely avoided.

Up to this time the Cancer Registrar, J. M. Mallett, had been responsible for the cancer follow-up, devoting to it one session per week. It was now resolved to place that responsibility in the hands of the Director of the Department of Pathology, with a full-time secretary; the medical supervision of the follow-up was to be in the hands of the staff of the department, while one House Surgeon at each branch was to supply the clinical abstracts.

Further increase in the Resident complement occurred in 1964 with the Ministry's approval; four additional posts were created, three at City Road and one at High Holborn, and the resulting new training arrangements were fully implemented.

The year 1960 marked the 150th anniversary of the foundation of the Medical School. On 12 April, 1961 an open day was held at the Institute and at both branches of the Hospital; many demonstrations and exhibitions were given at the former and operations were televised at the latter. In the evening a reception was given to members of the staff, and civic and academic dignitaries in London, at the Senate House of the University. The most important absentee was Robert Davenport who had served the School as Dean since 1938 at Moorfields, continuing as Dean of the Institute until he retired in 1959—a period of 21 years of devoted and assiduous attention to this important office. His health had begun to deteriorate soon after his retirement, and prevented his attending the reception where literally everyone missed him; his death followed a year later. It was sad that the enjoyment of so well earned a leisure was denied him.

This year was marked by a dramatic acquisition by the Institute indicating once again a step ahead in the increase of its potentialities. The Wellcome Trustees gave an electron microscope to the Medical Research Council for use in the Institute. It was not long before it began to make valuable contributions in this new field.

Professor Ashton continued to add to his list of distinctions and thus to further the prestige of the Institute. He gained the degree of D.Sc. (as did Dr Dartnall); he gave the Banting Memorial Lecture in London and the Doyne Memorial Lecture at the Oxford Congress in 1959. He was awarded the William Julius Mickle Fellowship in 1960; this is awarded every five years by the University of London to the most prominent contributor to advances in medicine, art and science. Sir Stewart Duke-Elder had been awarded a Fellowship bearing a similar name—the Charles Mickle Fellowship— in 1959, by the University of Toronto, and crowned his career in the following year by being elected a Fellow of the Royal Society. Many other honours fell to other members of the staff —too numerous (with apology) to list *in toto* here, but all duly recorded in the appropriate places in the Institute reports. And a large and increasing number of members of the Hospital and Institute staffs continued in their work of visiting and lecturing abroad, playing prominent parts in the activities of Congresses, Societies and Academies all over the world.

In 1961 it was brought to the notice of the Board that the grant to the Institute of £10,000 per annum for five years was due to terminate in December. The Finance Committee had expressed the view that it would be possible to allocate the sum of £42,500, to be drawn upon up to the figure of £10,000 annually for five years. It added that a second instalment of the Shepherd gift was also available in the sum of £5000, together with a further sum of £700 recently received. After discussion concerning the state of the Endowment Fund, the policy governing disbursements therefrom, and an estimate of what might be expected in the future from legacies, it was decided to allocate the sum of £42,500 to the Institute from the Endowment Fund for the next quinquennium, and to add to this the sum of £5700 from the Shepherd Fund. On reviewing the situation in 1965 the Board accepted the recommendations of the Finance Committee, to the effect that the immediate annual grant to the Institute should be £6000 supplemented by what could be spared from the Endowment Fund income. All legacies were to be secluded and added to the corpus of the Endowment Fund for investment. In 1968 the grant was £9000; in 1974, £13,500.

In 1966 the Ministry decided to place some exchequer funds at the disposal of hospitals for the purpose of financing what they called "locally organised clinical research". Moorfields received £8000 for 1966/67; the Research Committee agreed the allocation of the sum. At the same meeting the valid point was made that research projects tended in due course to become routine treatment, and care would have to be taken that when this occurred the expense involved would have to be met from other sources than research grants. Representations made to the Ministry on this point met with a favourable reception, and an additional revenue allocation of £5000, over and above the original £8000, was made to enable the hospital to take over research projects which had become routine clinical treatment. In 1971 the grant for locally organised clinical research was £12,500.

An important modification in the structure of work at the Institute occurred in 1961. When first formed in 1948, a unit of the British Postgraduate Medical Federation, it was primarily a Teaching School. Then the Medical Research Council transferred from University College London a group of research workers who were concerned with ophthalmic research, and also created a Vision Research Unit; amalgamation to form the Ophthalmological Research Unit soon followed. At this time the greater part of this Unit was incorporated into the structure of the University as a mature and self-dependent concern, while the Medical Research Council kept its interest in the Institute by continuing to sponsor the more academic part of the project by recreating the Vision Research Unit and remaining responsible for its finances.

The idea of appointing a Professor of Ophthalmology to work at the Institute and Hospital persisted and developed, and in due course the University established the post. At the first meeting of the Appointments Committee the members were unable to come to a satisfactory decision between the two candidates, and the appointment was postponed. Very soon after this it was announced that the Sembal Trust had founded and endowed a Chair of Experimental Ophthalmology, and to these Chairs two Professors were appointed: Barrie Jones to the Chair of Clinical Ophthalmology after serving for the previous six years as whole time Senior Lecturer while doing clinical work and research with both the Reader and the Director of the Pathology Department, and E. S. Perkins to that of Experimental Ophthalmology. A Ceremony of Inauguration following these appointments was held at the Institute on 1st April, 1963; both the new Professors gave inaugural addresses which are duly recorded in the Institute's Report of the year.

In the meantime the routine teaching work of the School continued, with T. K. Lyle as Dean; courses were added for Ophthalmic Consultants and Senior Specialists and for general practitioners, and short courses on orthoptics, contact lenses and refraction were included. In 1967 A. G. Cross succeeded as Dean; under his direction the School proceeds with unabated vigour, ever with an eye to modifications and improvements which will enable it to preserve the high standard upon which its reputation deservedly rests.

The Committee of Management of the Institute decided in January 1966 to acknowledge openly the debt which it owed to certain gentlemen for outstanding services to the Institute. The title of Fellow of the Institute of Ophthalmology was created, and six fellowships were immediately conferred; those thus honoured were Sir Stewart Duke-Elder, the Rt Hon. The Earl of Rothes, Mr N. E. Behrens, Mr Charles Hayward, Mr Kenneth Wood and Dr C. P. Stevens. The Fellows were robed at a dinner in the Senate House, where Professor Norman Ashton gave the speech of honour.

The year 1963/64 was an outstanding one for the Institute in respect of gifts towards its work. The Sembal Trust—which had been responsible for establishing the Chair of Experimental Ophthalmology—made a grant of £50,000 to support research on Trachoma and to finance a field trial in the Middle East; the Wolfson Foundation made a grant of £7000 a year for five years to support work on Glaucoma; the Worshipful Company of Armourers and Brasiers endowed a Research Fellowship of £2500 a year; and the Medical Research Council established the Oculogenital Virus Research Group which, as we have noted before, evolved from the Departments studying TRIC virus infection of the eye and genital tract. These munificent gifts enabled the continuance of many research projects which would otherwise have had to be abandoned; nonetheless they were regarded only as short term expedients to carry the organisation over a crisis, and it was thought necessary to provide for the future in an even larger and more permanent manner. As a result, in the following year a completely new appeal was launched in a big way. Called the "Fight for Sight Appeal" it started with a press conference at the Institute where the representatives were shown some of the work in progress. Radio and television gave further publicity; a representative appeal committee was appointed under the Chairmanship of Sir John Gutch.

The Electrodiagnostic Clinic, with Dr Geoffrey Arden at its head, at this stage transferred its routine clinical work to the hospital under the care of John Kelsey. The accounts of the activities of all the various departments of the Institute, both routine and research, make enthralling reading, and give ample evidence, if any were needed, of the healthy flourishing state of the organisation and the astonishing position in the world of ophthalmology which it had acquired, largely through the drive and initiative of its main instigator and its Director of Research, Sir Stewart Duke-Elder, whose time for retirement arrived in the following year. With what satisfaction he must have been able to lay down his task in 1965 and reflect upon the organisation which he had seen grow to such splendid maturity. The Committee of Management passed a most laudatory resolution of farewell, of which an illuminated copy was presented to him at a special meeting at which the title of Emeritus Director of Research was also conferred upon him, and at which he was elected the first President of the Institute. A dinner in honour of Sir Stewart and Lady Duke-Elder was held in September at the Apothecaries Hall attended by a most distinguished company; the Dean, T. Keith Lyle, made an informal and entirely felicitous speech proposing their health; the Chairman of the Committee of Management, Lord Rothes, presented to Sir Stewart a portrait of himself by Edward Halliday which had been subscribed to by a large number of past and present staff, students and friends—altogether, Sir

Stewart departed trailing well-deserved and appropriate clouds of glory. And further, the Institute could congratulate itself that his interest and wise counsel were still to be available in his new capacity as President.

Work continued at home and abroad on the attempt to devise means to control Trachoma and modify its ravages. Charles Smith was working on the problem in Jerusalem, and it seems likely that he would have succeeded in isolating the causative organism (which proved to be not a virus but of the Clamydia group) had he not, in the course of his culture work, used penicillin, to which it was sensitive. In a parallel project on the other side of the world T'ang, Chang, Huang and Wang, using Streptomycin instead, to which it was not sensitive, succeeded in being the first to isolate the organism. Similar research proceeded at the Institute in connection with ocular and genital inclusion blennorrhoea; the first strain isolated was L.B.1; L.B.2 and L.B.3, followed from investigation of babies with neonatal disease. These were morphologically indistinguishable from Trachoma virus; the disease was reproduced by inoculation into baboon eyes after serial egg passage. Human volunteers were used in investigating the properties of G17 strain; it was proved that the cultivated virus was the cause of Trachoma.

As work proceeded in this clinic, from an examination and classification of new cases of TRIC Virus infection it was confirmed that they may be separated into three categories: Trachoma, Inclusion Conjunctivitis, and a third labelled TRIC Virus Punctate Kerato-conjunctivitis and representing an intermediate syndrome. It was further found that one strain of virus isolated from the genital tract could cause Trachoma; investigation into this discovery led the enquiry into the field of Reiter's syndrome, which it was thought was a separate entity from the TRIC virus infection.

In November 1965 a team of seven, headed by Professor Barrie Jones, visited Iran to study the natural history of Trachoma. In the following May a team of 3 under the same leadership took part in the first follow-up examination of children in Iran who had been vaccinated under the scheme developed by the Medical Research Council's Trachoma Unit under the direction of Professor Collier; over 500 children were examined.

The Department for the treatment of patients suffering from Diseases of the Eye associated with venereal disease was opened in 1920, following the provision of a grant of £1000 from the Ministry of Health and the London County Council. It is likely that this act was prompted by an increase in the incidence of these diseases, which is common following a war. Dr S. H. Browning was appointed medical officer in charge; an assistant was appointed six months later in the person of Mr E. Biddle. The grant was discontinued in 1932, a period when measures of economy were being introduced in all directions. This loss of revenue did not close the department; the Medical Board recognised the valuable service that the department had rendered, recalled that there had been nearly 8000 attendances in the past year, and expressed its desire that it should continue. This it did, though in a modified form, becoming in time a reference clinic only. In 1956 it is recorded that "the progress of medicine is exemplified by the closing" of this department on 31 December. The attendance figures had remained steady until the second world war, when evacuation and mobilisation considerably reduced the population of London, and the activity of the Department decreased. On the return of peace the usual and expected increase in the incidence of venereal disease did not take place. Statistics showed that the spread of syphilis, here and in other civilised countries, appeared to be coming under control, and congenital syphilis, which manifestation had provided a large proportion of the work of the department in the past, was becoming rarer. Penicillin, "and the enlightenment of the general public" are quoted as being responsible for this reduced incidence; the work became insufficient to justify the continuance of the clinic, and it was closed. The medical officer in charge, by coincidence, reached retirement age at this time.

Public enlightenment would not appear to have continued to exert its beneficent influence, for on 1 October, 1964 a consultant venereologist was appointed; the department was re-opened and renamed, with some delicacy, the Diagnostic Clinic. This clinic continued at the Hospital; activity on a parallel line has commenced at the Institute, in which the newly appointed venereologist is involved. Investigation of TRIC virus infection of the eye and genital tract were being investigated by a team under the aegis of the clinical professorial department, and in 1964 the oculogenital Virus Research Group was established by the Medical Research Council. The work entailed clinical investigation and treatment and laboratory research; the importance of TRIC agent and related members of the Bedsonia group became more and more obvious. In 1967 the work had extended to include a systematic study of the ocular and systemic features of syphilitic Kerato-uveitis, and at this stage the Institute assumed responsibility for the M.R.C. Research Group as originally formed, which was renamed the Sub-Department of Virology.

Frank Law retired in August 1963 under the age limit, and was succeeded by Lorimer Fison. In that same month P. McG. Moffatt died suddenly while on a fishing holiday in the North; I. M. Duguid succeeded him at the Holborn branch in January of the following year, and took over the supervision of the Visual Aid Clinic. It was held at the Holborn branch on Monday and Thursday afternoons concurrently with his out-patient clinics.

Paul McGregor Moffatt came on to the roll of Consultants of the Moorfields, Westminster and Central Ophthalmic Hospital, later to be renamed "Moorfields", on the amalgamation in 1947, having been appointed to the staff of the Westminster in 1938. After qualifying from Guy's he entered general practice in Lancashire for four years, then returned to London and studied for and obtained various high degrees and diplomas, becoming House Surgeon at the Westminster and Registrar both there and at Guy's. He was an excellent clinician, and devoted to his specialty; he did some pioneer work in vitreous replacement, and established the first Visual Aid Clinic at Moorfields after that subject had emerged, largely as a result of the researches of Charles H. Keeler. His long association with

P. McG. Moffatt

the National Institute for the Blind, and with Blind Certification, and the experience gained from these interests, made him particularly suited to supervise and develop this clinic.

Frank William Law[1] was one of the most popular and colourful members of the staff of Moorfields; from the time he became a house surgeon in 1927 until he retired from the consultant staff on reaching the age limit, he participated enthusiastically in all its activities. He occupied the post of pathologist and curator after his time in the House, and was medical officer in charge of the Department of Physical Therapy for many years. He served on the Committee of Management (later the Board of Governors) for 23 years, and at the same time played a prominent part in the time-consuming committees which guide the intricate life of the Hospital such as the Finance Committee and the House Committee,

[1] Biographical note by Sir Stewart Duke-Elder.

Frank W. Law

of which latter he is still a member. An astute physician and a gifted surgeon with a penchant for plastic surgery and trephining for simple glaucoma, for many years he undertook the lectures on operative surgery; at this time the commoner operations were performed by the students upon pigs' eyes. He made more than 100 contributions to the literature. His other main ophthalmological post was at Guy's Hospital.

Law was educated at St Paul's School, and St John's College, Cambridge. Here his main athletic activity was rowing. He captained the College Boat Club and gained his Blue in his last year, rowing 2 in the University Boat, having been spare man the year before. He came down to the Middlesex Hospital where he was impressed, rather unwillingly, into the Rugby Team, and endured several cup-ties which are rather better known for their boisterous energy than their high skill. He left his last game rather thankfully on a stretcher. His early student course was interrupted by the first World War during which he served as a combatant officer in the Royal Field Artillery in France and Flanders (1917–18). It is interesting that he maintained his active interest in the Army throughout his professional life, becoming Consultant Ophthalmic Surgeon to the Army and consultant to the Queen Alexandra Military Hospital, Millbank, the Royal Hospital, Chelsea, and the King Edward VII Hospital for Officers.

Of all his manifold activities one of the most important was the prominent part he played in ophthalmological life in this country. An enthusiastic member of the Ophthalmological Society of the United Kingdom, he has been its Treasurer for 25 years, was its Secretary for 8 years, and its President in 1960–62. He has served for many years on the Council of the Oxford Congress and was Master in 1953–54. Equally important was his work on the Faculty of Ophthalmologists; he was its first Secretary and four years later its President, and to him is due much of the efficiency of this organisation. To these should be added his work on the Ophthalmic Nursing Board of which he was Chairman since its inception, the General Optical Council, the Court of the Worshipful Company of Spectacle Makers of which he became Master, and on the Hospital Committee of the Order of St John, for his services being made a Knight of the Order. He was examiner for the Fellowship in Ophthalmology at the Royal College of Surgeons of England, for the D.O., and for the Orthoptic Board.

This would seem enough, but to this multitude of national activities should be added the part he played in international ophthalmology. He was the Secretary General of the XVI International Congress held in London in 1950; this was the first international congress to be held after the second World War, and the arrangements for its undoubted success entailed four years of arduous work and the creation of many precedents; it was probably the most onerous task he ever undertook. Thereafter he represented Great Britain on the International Council, the Council of the European Ophthalmological Society, and the International Association for Prevention of Blindness of which he was Vice-President; he became an honorary member of six foreign ophthalmological societies, received the Van Duyse Medal from the Belgian Society, and was an exchange Professor at Johns Hopkins.

This is surely a rich, useful and full life's work, much of it spent in 47 years' service in the social and professional life of Moorfields.

Nevertheless, Frank Law had time to extend his early activities in rowing and rugby to the enthusiastic pursuit of fishing and shooting. He and his wife were excellent hosts; one of his greatest loves was music and he would often entertain their guests by playing the organ in his drawing room, or with two-piano music with his wife.

C. D. Shapland retired from the staff in November 1964, and E. F. King in December of the same year. Cyril Dee Shapland was appointed to the staff of Moorfields in 1938, having already been surgeon to University College Hospital for five years, and served on the staff of both until retiring age. He had already been through the House at Moorfields and held the office of Curator and Pathologist for 3 years, thus treading a path followed by so many in succession. He served in the R.A.M.C. during the war, holding many important posts. It was during his time as House Surgeon at Moorfields that the operative treatment of detachment of the retina commenced; at the

C. Dee Shapland

International Congress in 1929 in Amsterdam Gonin had introduced his operation for the sealing of the hole which resulted in replacement of the separated retina. Shapland was the House Surgeon to assist Sir William Lister at the first cautery puncture performed in this country, on 27 December, 1929. His interest in the condition and its surgical treatment never waned; in 1950 he introduced his lamellar modification of Muller's scleral resection operation of 1903, which was a considerable step forward in this field.

Edgar Frederick King, a Bristol graduate, was House Surgeon at Moorfields before being appointed to the Staff in 1937 where he served for 27 years; he was for a similar period on the Staff of the Westminster Hospital. He was an outstanding clinician; his acumen was remarkable and his diagnoses, though always reasoned, seemed at times inspired and even

E. F. King

uncanny. This, combined with a flair for teaching, made him an invaluable member of the Staff of a hospital, especially in the out-patients department. He was at home alike in teaching undergraduates or postgraduates, and equally enthusiastic in either field; his pupils had reason to be grateful for their good fortune in coming under his influence. He was a most valuable committee man, expressing his balanced judgements deliberately and clearly.

The House Governor, J. P. Heming, decided to retire in November 1964. He was appointed Secretary of the Royal Westminster Ophthalmic Hospital, as it then was, in 1946; he became Deputy House Governor of the combined hospitals a year later, and House Governor on Tarrant's retirement in 1957. His tenure of office was thus short compared with some of his predecessors, but nonetheless it was quite long enough for him to make his mark and to render the hospital deeply in his debt for his initiative, devotion and hard work. Just at the time of his retirement the status of the Hospital, due to the repeated representations of the Chairman, was raised from "Postgraduate Group B" to "Group A", in the bureaucratic jargon then obtaining. The change actually occurred after the post of House Governor had been advertised, and because it affected salary values of administrative staff might well have affected the quality of applications for the post. Accordingly the post was re-advertised, and Heming kindly agreed to continue in office until the situation was resolved. Luckily his abilities were not immediately lost to the organisation which he had so loyally served, for he became Secretary to the Appeals Committee at the Institute, and performed a most useful service to this venture in the opening stages of the "Fight for Sight" Appeal. He was succeeded at Moorfields by Arthur Gray who was formerly Secretary to the North London Group Hospital Management Committee.

CHAPTER 17

Progress and improvements – Liaison Committee
H. B. Stallard – High Holborn anniversary
C.S.S.D. – The theatres – Catering redevelopment
Paediatric Ophthalmology – C. J. Malim

It soon became apparent that the Government's scheme for the development of the Postgraduate Teaching Hospitals and Institutes was falling behind schedule, and hopes of a start in 1971-2 began to recede. It seemed likely that no move was probable within 15 years, and this made a fundamental difference to the attitude of the hospital authorities towards their more immediate plans and aims. The Medical Committee had on many occasions drawn attention to the urgent need for revolutionary reorganisation of the operating theatres in the interest of progressive surgery, the surgical reputation of the hospital, and even of actual safety itself. The kitchens at City Road were also in great need of replanning—and the assistance of the King Edward's Hospital Fund was here invoked for advice on the matter; it was readily forthcoming and very helpful. The X-ray Department was in need of replanning and modernisation and the need for safety precautions against radiation hazards was pressing.

Modern methods of technology were taking their place in hospital routine on the administrative as well as the surgical side. A computer was established in the Finance Department and demonstrated there both its potentialities and its vagaries. Professor Perkins began the organisation necessary to transfer the diagnostic index of patients to magnetic tape preparatory to computer analysis. Much attention was given to improving the standard of asepsis, and the surgeons and the pathologist and his staff produced recommendations of importance which were implemented as soon as conditions—and, indeed, finances —permitted. Surgical development proceeded and evolved in many directions. The Light Coagulator came more into use and proved its worth; soon the Laser Beam added its help in the same milieu, and received lay publicity when surgeons of the hospital used these methods in the treatment of the Duke of Windsor in London. Low temperature applications—Cryosurgery, involving the use of liquid nitrogen, the invention of Professor Krwawicz of Poland—was making its way with increasing usefulness. Deep freeze techniques for the storage of human eyes as donor material for corneal grafting were being successfully exploited, and the establishment of an eye bank at the Hospital was planned.

At High Holborn the development of No. 177 had proceeded. The top floor had already been completely renovated at a cost of £13,000 to provide a new corneal lens unit and hospital lecture room. A works study team was asked to advise on the establishment of a Central Sterile Supply Department. The Professorial Unit was completed and occupied. A new buffet for the out-patients department was designed and presented by a patient at the hospital. The nurses were given a roof garden; redecoration, rewiring, cleaning and modernisation proceeded in all departments of the hospital. In a word, there was evidence on all sides that those in charge were determined to keep abreast of the times on their present site, and not postpone progress and improvement in the interests of a vague and receding future.

The Postgraduate Hospitals Work Study Team on outpatient routine reported in 1965 and the hospital decided to implement their report and recommendations on waiting time, at first on a localised and experimental basis.

A constructive innovation in the interests of the management of the hospital routine was the inauguration of a Medical and Nursing Staff Liaison Committee, which was to consist of six representatives from each side and to meet informally. Matters of mutual concern would form the subjects for discussion, which would be particularly concerned with the care of patients in the wards. The timing of this venture, though incidental, was happy, for the Salmon Report had just been published and was already causing considerable concern in medical and nursing quarters.

In April 1966 H. B. Stallard retired from the consultant staff; the Medical Committee decided not to recommend his replacement by another appointment, at any rate in the immediate future. His beds were distributed amongst the other surgeons; the Professorial Unit continued his follow-up and research work in malignant disease.

Hyla Bristow Stallard—"Henry"—had the unusual though not unique experience of two spells on the Staff of Moorfields—one as an honorary surgeon from 1933 to 1938 (after being

H. B. Stallard

Pathologist and Curator) when he retired for private reasons, another as Consultant under the National Health Service regime from 1947 to 1966, when he retired under the age limit. He had a most distinguished student and academic career, gaining many prizes and giving many eponymous lectures including, in this country, the Doyne at Oxford and the Middlemore at

Birmingham. He was elected President of the Ophthalmological Section of the Royal Society of Medicine in 1967. His great metier was in operative surgery; at Moorfields, whilst not going as far as some overseas colleagues in setting up a regular operative team and concentrating on surgery to the exclusion of most other duties, he nonetheless enjoyed a certain degree of autonomy at one end of the theatre block and established a reputation there, by his operative skill and faultless technique in many branches of ophthalmic surgery, which attracted students and observers from all parts of the world. His special interest was in the treatment of intraocular tumours by radio-active implants, which formed the subject of his Doyne lecture. Here he was doubtless stimulated by the previous work in this field, and revolutionised current thinking; as a result a large number of patients have avoided enucleation with apparently no adverse effect upon the vital prognosis, and often of course with retention of vision. His main publication was *Eye Surgery*, a comprehensive manual describing fully the details of surgical operations, illustrated largely by himself. "Henry" established an international reputation in another field, that of athletics; an Olympic runner, he represented this country and the Empire many times, having of course earned a "Blue" at Cambridge; he won the mile in the University Sports three years in succession. In the years 1923, '24 and '25 he performed the astonishing feat of being A.A.A. champion for the mile, half-mile, and quarter mile successively. His characteristics were enthusiasm, energy and a worship of physical fitness; a non-smoker and practically teetotal, he must have been one of the fittest men in the country throughout his life. His academic career was crowned by his election to the Presidency of the Opthalmological Society of the United Kingdom in 1973.

And now, even before these words reach the printer, he has left us. Just before assuming the Presidency he was struck down by an evil malignancy which attacked, with unseemly irony, a part of that magnificent skeletal mechanism which had enabled him to be the supreme athlete that he was a half a century before. He was actually receiving daily and heavy radio-active dosage at the time of the Congress in April 1973; with superb bravery he conducted the Congress and even presided at the dinner. He attended a Council meeting in June where he tendered his resignation; this was accepted with the utmost regret, and Henry left the meeting in the hands of his senior vice-president. At the next meeting in October he attended again and many remarked his brave and cheerful demeanour; he installed his successor Louis Werner and stayed throughout the meeting. Ten days later he was dead. A grand man and a great friend. How truly did Thomas Hughes say: "It is no light thing to fold up and lay by forever a portion of one's life, even when it can be laid by with honour and thankfulness." It is no light thing—indeed, it is a heavy thing—to be denied the reward of a little subsequent contemplation of that portion, in this case so deserved and justified.

The High Holborn branch of the hospital celebrated the 150th anniversary of its foundation in 1966. A service in the adjacent St Giles in the Fields Parish Church, which has for so many years been associated with the hospital, was followed by a party. A reception was also held in the House of Lords, attended by the Minister of Health, Mr Kenneth Robinson, and by many distinguished guests from the hospital service and associated professions.

This anniversary year was a busy one for High Holborn. An ambitious and ingenious plan for the provision of office space comprised the erection of a mezzanine floor in the out-patient hall; this enabled transference of some ground floor offices, freeing space for enlarging the Casualty Department, and also for the detachment and glaucoma units. The enlargement and re-equipment of the Contact Lens department was completed, and the conversion of Dudley House, a contiguous building already referred to, rehoused the Medical Records Department. The Board Room was redecorated and refurnished; and all attention was then focused on the projects of the new theatres and the new lift. The Orthoptic department was completely redecorated and rewired, and was admired by many visitors to the First International Congress of Orthoptists, some of whose sessions were held at the hospital. This was an important and enjoyable congress, appropriately and efficiently presided over by Miss Barbara Lee, the Head Orthoptist at High Holborn.

150th Anniversary, High Holborn. Reception, House of Lords. Professor Ashton, C. F. Seath (Secretary to the Institute) and J. P. Heming (formerly House Governor of the Hospital, then Secretary of the Appeal Committee at the Institute).

In November 1965 Lord Derby attended at the High Holborn branch and officially presented a cryo-surgical unit to the Hospital. This was provided by friends and relatives of the late Mr Irvine Aitchison, and presented by Messrs Dolland and Aitchison. This same firm made another generous offer to the Hospital in 1971 which was gratefully accepted. It consisted of a seven-year covenant of £3000 a year for a research fellowship in ophthalmic optics; Montague Ruben was made Clinical Director of the fellowship.

The Central Sterile Supply Department came into operation at the end of 1966; all sterilisation in the wards was eliminated, and it was only a matter of time before the service was supplying both branches, including the new theatres. It was interesting that this department was placed in the hands of a member of the nursing staff, Miss G. Smith; she had travelled and studied

the work involved with Miss Sinclair the Theatre Superintendent, and the efficiency of the service provided by the unit
amply justified the choice.

150th Anniversary, High Holborn, 1966. Reception, House of Lords. The
Earl of Arran receives Mrs Kramer and L. G. Kramer (Treasurer of the
Hospital).

The Board were able, in mid 1965, to respond to the pleas of the Surgeons for better operating theatre accommodation in full fashion and free of all financial worry. Through the good offices of the Chairman, Mr C. J. Malim, a munificent gift of £152,000 was received from the Hayward Foundation for the specific purpose. All idea of restricting development on the site was abandoned, and attention was given to maintaining the position and condition of Moorfields as the premier eye hospital for the next 20 years. Though the prospect disappointed some, the position was at least clarified and the tentative and uncertain basis of planning was changed for something more stable and reliable. It was a most encouraging and stimulating moment; plans were speeded up, representatives, medical and lay, travelled abroad inspecting theatre layouts, and tenders were sought. With City Road thus provided for, it was a great relief to learn that High Holborn could also plan in similar fashion; for the Ministry agreed to provide the money to furnish that branch also with a new theatre suite. A grant from King Edward's Hospital Fund of £5000 was earmarked for improvements in the out-patient department at City Road, and plans went ahead for a new X-ray department there, reorganisation of the casualty department at High Holborn, and reorganisation at both branches of the kitchen and dining room services, and modernisation of those wards not already thus treated. A spirit of progress and enthusiasm had been reawakened, which had wilted a little under the uncertainty and frustration of the recent past; nonetheless the horizon was by no means clear, for staff shortages and budget difficulties continued to cause worry and anxiety. Every effort was made to raise funds; the hospital once again appeared on television in November 1965 when a Light Coagulation manoeuvre was shown, and the Children's Ward appeared to the public eye when Sir Brian Horrocks appeared on TV for the "Fight for Sight" Fund of the Institute. The personal appeal of this great man was undiminished; the result was the astonishing sum of £34,000. A year later the Appeal benefited from the proceeds of a Film Première—Charles Chaplin's "A Countess from Hong Kong" at the Carlton Cinema. It was a cheerful occasion, graced by the patronage and the presence of H.R.H. Princess Alexandra, accompanied by Mr Angus Ogilvie. Chaplin himself and many

Film première in aid of the Fight for Sight Appeal—"A Countess from Hong Kong"—January 1967. Sir John Gutch, Chairman of the Appeal Committee, and the Earl of Rothes, Backs to the camera—H.R.H. Princess Alexandra and Lady Ogilvie.

of the celebrities of the Cinema world attended; the evening yielded the excellent return of nearly £16,000.

On 1 April, 1965 a change of boundary between the North East and the North West Regional Hospital Boards caused a transfer of the hospital to the latter. Although the teaching hospitals are not under Regional control, there is nonetheless much co-operation required and exercised; the association with the North East Board had been most happy for 17 years. At this time also a Royal Commission on Medical Education was set up, and a sub-committee elected for the purpose submitted a memorandum of evidence.

Work began on the theatres at both branches at the end of 1966 and it was hoped that a year would see it completed. The estimated cost for the project was soon found to be insufficient for the purpose—and this at both branches. The University Grants Committee came to the rescue in gallant fashion. There was of course an important teaching element involved in the project; the Committee agreed to meet the cost of this in the sum of £16,000 at City Road and £7000 at High Holborn.

In July 1967, while good progress was being made on the theatre construction project, Mr Charles Hayward and other Trustees of the Hayward Foundation were invited to lunch at the hospital. This was a very pleasant and successful occasion; lunch was taken in the Board Room, a representative few of the lay and medical members of the hospital committees being present. It was clearly enjoyed by Mr Hayward, who was taken to see the stage which the buildings had reached, and could appreciate the size and importance of the project for which he was financially responsible.

Another visit was paid by Mr Hayward, this time in the evening, for cocktails, on 12 December. Members of the Board and the medical and nursing staffs were present, as were also members of other staff departments who had been particularly concerned with the new theatres. Mr Hayward was able to see the work rapidly approaching completion. Perhaps the most exciting visit for this benefactor was made in November 1969, when he and other members of the Hayward Foundation, after lunching in the Board Room, were able to see the theatres in full working order and in action, and to listen to the commentaries. They were immensely impressed with all they saw and heard, and decided to pay regular visits to the hospital in future.

As is usual in such ventures, the estimate of cost was below what was necessary to complete the work. The Hayward Trustees gilded their original gift of £155,000 with a further £22,000 and thus removed all financial worries.

The theatres at High Holborn were ready for use before those at City Road. The first operation was performed there on 22 January, 1968, and this branch dealt with any emergency surgery arising at City Road during the period between the closing of the old theatres there and the opening of the new. The sterilisation of surgical supplies for the theatres at both branches was undertaken by the C.S.S.D.

The story of the theatres is a memorable one and marks a peak of progress in the history of the hospital. From the Hayward Foundation, the Ministry of Health, and the University Grants Committee combined came the sum of £362,980; the first meeting of the City Road Planning Committee, under the able and enthusiastic chairmanship of Mr Francis Cumberlege, met first in September 1965—work started in December 1966 and was completed in January 1968; and the hospital is the richer by the provision of six theatres built on the Honeywell plan which are the best of their kind in the world, and which ever since their completion have been the subject of admiration and envy from interested visitors from all over the world. On 28 March, 1968 the suite was officially opened by Her Majesty Queen Elizabeth The Queen Mother, whose visit was conducted with her characteristic charm and grace on a day memorable for all concerned.

The hospital was fortunate in being able to place the theatres in charge of Miss Sinclair, who had been theatre superintendent for some years. Her experience and application were invaluable in the task of initiating the working and routine of the unit. She retired at the end of 1968 and was succeeded by Miss Watkins, who had already been her deputy for some years.

The work involved in building the theatres was long and complicated, and its successful completion was a triumph, not the least for those who had to contend with the routine running of the hospital during the period of dislocation and strain. The Central Sterile Supply Department was another triumph, for it was soon supplying all wards and theatres at both branches. Other works, only relatively minor because of the outstanding importance of the theatre project, had proceeded and were proceeding. The main lift at High Holborn was replaced and extended to the eighth floor in time for the opening of the new theatres there; the whole catering service and amenities were in process of complete reorganisation at both branches, the site of the old theatres at City Road being used as temporary dining rooms in the meantime. The out-patient department was modernised and refurnished following a grant of over £5000 for the purpose from the King's Fund. The new waiting hall made a pleasant background for the nurses' prizegiving ceremony,

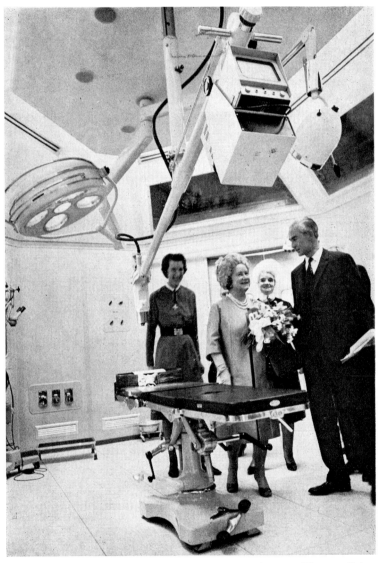

Her Majesty The Queen Mother after opening the new Theatre Suite, 28 March, 1968, with Sister Sinclair, Matron and the Chairman, F. M. Cumberlege.

enhanced on this occasion by the gracious presence of H.R.H. Princess Alexandra.

Inevitably, envious eyes from many sources were cast on the area vacated by the moving of the theatre suite. The Professorial Unit thought they could very conveniently make use of the space; the resident surgeons thought new consulting rooms there would be very agreeable. Many different interests were involved, and all got together to devise a scheme which would make the most profitable and equitable use of the area. In the end, after serving a useful purpose as temporary dining rooms during reorganisation of the catering and dining room services, the old theatre area was converted at one end into new consulting rooms for the resident staff to replace the old ones on the first floor. At the other, quarters for fluorescein photography, electrodiagnosis, the Argon laser and other special diagnostic and therapeutic facilities were provided.

To close the theatres chapter, one little financial aftermath is worthy of record, if only to emphasise once more that financial transactions so commonly "draw a serpent's tail behind", and perhaps even more forcibly to emphasise the value of the Endowment Fund and the goodwill of those who administer it. There was a "contingent liability" of £9000 which the Fund was asked for and cheerfully honoured, throwing in for good measure a further £1000 for equipment which had just been mentioned as an afterthought. And then was added a further request, with a similar title, for £6000 relating to the 1959/60 extension scheme—an eventuality eight years old which the Fund might have been expected to forget by now. But it met the situation—with good grace, as usual. Some folk wonder why an Endowment Fund should be necessary with a National Health Service in a welfare state.

It was natural that after so large an enterprise as the installation of new theatres at both branches at a cost of some £363,000 was successfully concluded, developments should be on a smaller scale. Nonetheless in the following year a considerable redevelopment programme was carried out in the catering department. Numerous kitchens and dining rooms made the set-up awkward and uneconomical, and it was decided to

237

spend most of the capital allocation for the year on a project for their improvement. Helpful advice was given at City Road by the Catering Adviser of King Edward's Hospital Fund, and at High Holborn by the Minister's advisers. Further, these same bodies, pleased with the progress of the Board's plans, came forward with gifts of £5000 and £3000 respectively, which enabled the work to be completed satisfactorily. It was possible to implement the Ministry's scheme of "pay as you eat" for nursing staff, which was announced at this time, with the minimum of inconvenience; the change over was smoothly carried out, and the nurses welcomed the alteration from a fixed deduction from their salaries which the scheme introduced.

A Fellowship of Paediatric Ophthalmology was established in 1967 through the generosity of the Variety Club of Great Britain, with a gift of £15,000. This was the first of its kind in the world; Brian Harcourt was elected to the fellowship, to work at Moorfields and the Institute with connections with Hammersmith Hospital and Great Ormond Street; Kenneth Wybar, Surgeon to the children's hospital, was to have overall charge. The holder threw himself into this important and valuable duty with great enthusiasm, and was almost overwhelmed by the number of problems which were at once referred to him.

The following year we saw the retirement from the Chair of the Board of C. J. Malim on grounds of increasing professional commitments. He had been a member of the Board for 12 years and Chairman for eight, and had rendered most valuable and devoted service to the Hospital. Outside his brilliant committee work, perhaps his most remarkable achievement was his responsibility for the obtaining of the munificent grant from the Hayward Foundation for the building of the new Theatre Suite. In his time of office a considerable programme of modernisation and redevelopment was accomplished; he takes his place in a line of Chairmen who leave the Hospital deeply in their debt. He was succeeded by Francis M. Cumberlege.

CHAPTER 18

N. E. Behrens – Abbey Service – Covent Garden
Todd Report – Green papers – The Hospital's future
Retinal unit – Micro-surgical workshop
Statistics

A NOTABLE lay figure left the scene in 1965 in the person of N. E. Behrens, when he resigned from the City Road House Committee—his last official position in the hospital. He was appointed to the Council of Management of the Central London Ophthalmic Hospital in 1933 and became its Chairman in 1942—thus holding the key position at the time of the negotiations for amalgamation. After that he was appointed to the Board of Management of the combined hospital in 1947, and in 1948 to the Board of Governors, where he served until 1962. He had been a member of the Finance Committee, for some years as Chairman, and held the office of Treasurer; he continued his association as a member of the House Committee. He served the hospital faithfully and well, and saw with co-operative dignity his hospital lose its identity and then cease to be a hospital at all. He was big enough to sublimate his personal feelings in what he could see was a larger cause.

On 20 April, 1967 a "special Service for Ophthalmology" was held in Westminster Abbey; it was indeed a memorable occasion. Representation was very full indeed, and included that of the ophthalmological societies, the eye hospitals, overseas ophthalmologists, ophthalmic nursing, orthoptists, opticians, blind organisations, the University of London, city companies, colleges and medical societies, the armed forces, the Order of St John, The British Red Cross, the Churches, and the chaplains of Moorfields Eye Hospital. The officials of the Abbey were present in strength, the choir was superb; 12 resident surgical officers acted as stewards and conducted the processions into the Abbey in solemn and dignified fashion; Professor Derrick Vail and Sir Tudor Thomas read the lessons. A major part of the inspiration and of the organisation could be traced to Professor Norman Ashton; for him it must have been one of those rare occasions when a man sees his idea implemented and carried out faultlessly to the enjoyment and inspiration of everyone concerned. The service was in part intended to further the welfare of the "Fight for Sight" appeal, and as a thanksgiving for the £430,000 already contributed; a retiring collection was taken by members of the nursing staff and resulted in a sum of £430 being given to the appeal.

At one time it looked as though the hospital might be concerned in the developments planned for the Covent Garden area. Representatives of the Hospital and Institute met the principal planner for the project at High Holborn in October 1969. The plan included the site for a hospital which was originally intended for St Peter's, St Paul's, and St Philip's and although not now required for these hospitals the planners were anxious to have a hospital on the site, though no action was intended before 1980. The matter was discussed in some detail but of course no conclusions were reached at this stage.

At this period the Board of Governors were much concerned over the future of teaching hospitals in general and the Postgraduate ones in particular. The Report of the Royal Commission on Medical Education (The Todd Report) was published, and two "Green Papers" on the future of the Health Service emerged from the Ministry. The strong feeling of the Board and the medical staff was that, though close collaboration with Undergraduate Hospitals and their medical schools was in every way desirable, independence of administration, thought, and spirit must remain with the Postgraduate Hospitals, and nothing must be allowed to detract from their position as leaders in their own specialties.

Just as the main concern of the Hospital authorities, when the future of the postgraduate hospitals was being considered, was for the preservation of its autonomy, so, when the question of rebuilding the Institute arose, their concern was for the geographical propinquity of Hospital and Institute as a primary consideration rather than the association of the Institute with a general hospital. It was once suggested that the Institute might be rebuilt near Charterhouse Square, and thus satisfy the Todd requirement of association with a general hospital—in this case the amalgamated St Bartholomew's and the London. There seemed a possibility that Moorfields might one day be rebuilt near St Bartholomew's Hospital—but there seemed no guarantee of proximity to the Institute in this idea. There was little to recommend the Charterhouse Square scheme as envisaged other than the thought of the Institute finishing up where Moorfields had started—a romantic conception of no validity.

The indecision clouding the above questions prevented the Institute from proceeding with the scheme of converting the Cayton Street building, acquired the year before and intended for the Pathological Department.

The period of uncertainty was unfortunately prolonged because of a change of Government in 1970, and a new policy statement was predicted. The hospital authorities were still awaiting the answer to such a fundamental question as to the number of ophthalmic beds which were considered desirable for London, and—even more important to them—how many were to be located at Moorfields. Until the answers to such questions were known, no long term planning was possible. However, one could not stand still, and the working party of the Hospital and Institute, set up to make plans for the future, with Lord Rothes as Chairman, decided to build a new nurses' training school at City Road, to be sited over the new theatres, together with a new Professorial Unit. They planned to convert the existing school into a ward, and close the High-gate Annexe. Further, since nurses' accommodation was to become available at High Holborn as part of a new hotel and office block to be built next door to the Hospital, it was planned to transfer thither all the nurses' accommodation in Stuart House and to close that home as well. The execution of these plans would at least concentrate the hospital on two sites instead of four; but the ideal of having the whole Hospital and the Institute in close contiguity, and in association with a general hospital, still seemed a very distant hope. In the Institute at this time the feeling was strong that the future of the Hospital and Institute lay in expansion on the City Road site.

A recommendation of the Todd Report was that Moorfields should be amalgamated with the London and St Bartholomew's hospitals. The reaction to the operative word was immediate and sharp. While the medical and academic staff had for years discussed the desirability of association with a general hospital, the idea of such a union as would destroy the financial, administrative, academic and surgical freedom of the hospital, and erase its identity and individuality, was anathema to them. The Green Paper published shortly afterwards provoked almost equal criticism. The creation of Area Health Boards which would control the teaching hospitals was an unacceptable idea; would this not again destroy their independence, and remove their right of direct access to the Ministry? The reaction generally to the Green Paper was such that the Minister decided to prepare new proposals.

Some of the recommendations in the Green Paper caused considerable concern and the reaction was immediate. An *ad hoc* committee was appointed under the chairmanship of Mr Francis Cumberlege. It considered notes made by the Chairman, comments prepared by the House Governor, including a memorandum prepared by a group of House Governors, and the findings of the Teaching Hospitals Association. This committee advised the Board to support the retention of Boards of Governors, the retention of direct contact with and financing by the Central Department, the retention and control of Endowment Funds, and of responsibility for the employment and appointment of staff. The London Postgraduate Committee had prepared and submitted a detailed memorandum to which this committee also subscribed. It was learnt that already the Secretary of State was setting up a working party to consider the problems of Inner London and the reaction of postgraduate teaching hospitals to the proposals in the Paper.

Probably owing to the change of Government in 1970, the immediate result of the Todd Report and two Green Papers in 1968 was just nil. In 1971 a new policy statement on the Health Services was awaited. This did nothing to decrease the difficulties of the Board; the future size of the Hospital, its location, its connections and its administration after a host of projects and tentative suggestions, were still undecided, and long term planning was still not possible. The Institute authorities were so concerned over the lack of available accommodation that they decided that the Institute should move, to be adjacent to the City Road branch. In October 1971 the Dean announced that he had heard from the Vice Chancellor of the University of London that the bed allocation for Moorfields had been reduced to 217, to include patients from the London Hospital. This was in contrast to the 300/350 which had been recommended by the Working Party of the Board of Studies (under the Chairmanship of Professor Barrie Jones), this to include patients from the London and St Bartholomew's hospitals. The suggestion caused considerable concern, and immediate action was taken in an attempt to remedy the situation. As a result the Board received the assurance that no final decision would be made without consultation.

Representatives of the Hospital and Institute, the University Grants Committee and the Department of Health met on 21 February, 1972 in the Senate House. They decided that owing to the decline in population of Inner London, the total number of beds in the capital allocated to ophthalmology would be 750, and thought that 450 of these should be allowed to hospitals in Inner London. It was expected that, of these, 275 would go to Moorfields, with a few extra for private patients from overseas; the final decision has not yet been made.

It will be recalled that the Institute had acquired property in Cayton Street, near to the hospital and previously in the possession of the Metal Box Company, in which to house the Pathology Department and the Dean's Department. This idea was subsequently modified, and consideration was given to using it for the Department of Experimental Ophthalmology and, possibly, that of Clinical Ophthalmology, together with a lecture theatre. In the early part of 1972 the Haslemere Estate, who it will be remembered were building the hotel adjacent to the High Holborn branch in which provision was being made for nurses' accommodation, had purchased property on the other side of Cayton Street, and were willing to sell some part of it to the Hospital. Eventually 27,000 sq. feet of it changed hands at the remarkable figure of 50 pence per sq. ft. Since it was shortly to become necessary to surrender the accommodation occupied by the Contact Lens Department at High Holborn, it was decided to transfer the department to these new Cayton Street premises, and to occupy the rest of the building with the Finance Department and nurses' rooms, of which space could be found for 47.

Thoresby House (see page 258) was already in occupation by nurses and domestic staff. In March 1970 the proposal had been made to transfer the Nurses' Training School to Highgate, but there were many objections to this idea and it was dropped in favour of converting Highgate into a Nurses' Home. When this new accommodation for nurses had been achieved, Stuart House was to pass to Charing Cross Hospital. A nurses' new training school was built over the new theatre block, together with the new Professorial Unit, which provided greatly improved premises for both units.

There was no cessation on the almost infinite variety of suggestions made and plans formulated for the future siting and development of the Hospital and Institute. In mid-1972 the Department of Health enquired of the London Hospital whether the authorities there thought that Moorfields and the Institute could be accommodated on the London Hospital site; this was in line with the recommendations of the Todd Report. Much enquiry was devoted to this suggestion; in October came an offer from St Bartholomew's Hospital for the rebuilding of Moorfields and a part of the Institute within the curtilage of St Bartholomew's, and for the erection of a new building to house the non-clinical parts of the Institute in Charterhouse Square adjacent to their Medical College. The authorities did their best to cope with and to assess the relative values of these rather bewildering offers, ever mindful of the urgency of the need to transfer some part of the Institute to the already acquired Cayton Street site. The University naturally did not wish to finance an interim move, and expressed their preference to rebuild on one or other hospital site. At a meeting of the Joint Committee of the Academic Board of the Institute and the Joint Medical Committee of Moorfields, a resolution was passed recommending the adoption of the scheme for rebuilding on the St Bartholomew's Hospital site; the University Grants Committee and the Department of Health have both approved the scheme in principle. The rebuilding of the Institute may begin by the end of the present University quinquennium; hopes are entertained that a start may be made on the new hospital as part of the Department's next ten year hospital building programme—1980 to 1990. It seems unlikely that Moorfields will move for 15 years or so; there is compensatory satisfaction in the reflection that all the improvements and additions—and they are many—which have been undertaken will be justified. The past attitude and decisions of those in charge of the interests of the hospital have been vindicated.

In January 1959 a retinal unit was established, to be centred in the first instance at Highgate. Four male and four female beds were set aside; C. D. Shapland was put in charge of the unit, with another consultant at each branch in liaison. A Zeiss Light Coagulator was purchased at this time at a cost of £3000. This instrument was kept at City Road and soon began to show its potentialities in use. This unit continued, after Shapland's retirement, in the charge of Lorimer Fison, and closed down in 1974 when it was decided to convert the nurses' old training school at City Road into a ward, and to transfer thereto Lorimer Fison's Retinal Unit from Highgate, naming the new unit the Stallard Ward.

The influence of the advent of microsurgical techniques on ophthalmic surgery and its teaching was so profound that Professor Barrie Jones considered that a portion of the Hospital should be devoted to teaching and research in this field. His idea was that his old unit be adopted and adapted to this end, under the faintly whimsical title of a "Microsurgical Workshop"; the authorities agreed to this suggestion. Preliminary arrangements were made to use this area for the Diabetic Clinic prior to its conversion for microsurgery.

Apart from being frequently misleading, statistics are notoriously dull. Nonetheless, it is interesting to note the changes in numbers treated from time to time, which consideration excuses the inclusion here of figures arbitrarily chosen from the years 1900 (the first full year in the new Hospital), 1928 and 1970.

	1900	1928	1970
In Patients	1871	2581	8409
Total O.P. Attendances	99,821	121,804	186,598

As well as the general and ever-present pitfalls inherent in the study of statistics, however, there are special pitfalls here which compel the utmost caution in analysis. Every now and again a different system of recording attendances is introduced. A patient who has attended before may be recorded as a new patient if the interval between attendances be five years— or two, or one. Every attendance at a special department— there were over 5000 in 1928, excluding those at the Bacteriological Department—may be recorded as an attendance at Hospital, as well as that at the clinic. And so on; it is essential to be fully informed about the system in use at the relevant time before drawing conclusions or making comparisons.

A comparison in expenditures is interesting. Adverse comment is recorded in 1863 because the drug bill had risen in five years from £191 to £415. The expenditure on drugs and dressings a hundred years later was £29,000; today the figure is nearly double that.

CHAPTER 19

A. G. Leigh – Orthoptic Department
Contact Lens Department – T. K. Lyle
F. T. Ridley – Institute – Coming of age
Pocklington Unit – Refractive Keratoplasty

ALL his friends—and they were found all over the Hospital and all over the world—were shocked and grieved to hear of the sudden death of George Leigh on 11 August, 1968 at the age of 59, and while he was Chairman of both the Branch and the Joint Medical Committees. A memorial service was held at St Giles in the Fields, Holborn. This year also saw the retirement of Keith Lyle and Frederick Ridley. The former was succeeded as head of the Orthoptic Department at High Holborn by Kenneth Wybar, the latter as Director of the Contact Lens Clinic by his assistant Director Montague Ruben, who was to have a maximum part time contract, with access to beds and the right to operate in cases arising from work in his department, but was not to hold a general clinic.

To fill the vacancy at High Holborn Barrie Jay was elected and R. K. Blach was appointed to City Road.

These two departments (the orthoptic and contact lens) had developed into most important sections of the hospital. The Orthoptic Department owed a very great deal to Sheila Mayou, who was made head of the School of Orthoptics at its foundation at the Central in 1932, and who gave 38 years continuous service to its welfare; she played a leading part in its development and indeed in that of orthoptics itself. Miss Mayou retired in December 1970; she at City Road and Barbara Lee at High Holborn had the satisfaction of seeing the departments in their charge develop into important fields of investigation, treatment, teaching and research. There were 4589 new patients referred in 1970, and total attendances were over 56,000. The intake of students was some 20 a year; the Schools were recognised as training centres for teachers and demonstrators, and as examination centres for these teaching grades. Discussion sessions are regular and frequent, some being conducted by the

247

surgeons in charge. Refresher courses are held, and ophthalmologists attend the routine work; two intensive courses a year are held for ophthalmologists preparing for the D.O. and the F.R.C.S., and the residents attend as part of their training. General practitioners, medical students, and nurses are also provided for.

Similarly the Contact Lens Department may be said to owe its development and success to Frederick Ridley, whose activities in its early days have already been described. By now there were some 1400 new cases a year, and 18,000 total attendances. Courses for postgraduates and opticians are held, the residents attend to learn fitting, and in 1970 eleven honorary fitters were attached to the department, anxious to acquire the technique. Research is undertaken, and a preformed corneal lens bank has been created. Keratoprosthetic procedures form an important side of the work. The success of this department was undoubtedly due to the expertise and application of Frederick Ridley; and he must have been gratified to be able to hand over to such a skilled and enthusiastic successor as Montague Ruben.

Arthur George Leigh was one whom Moorfields could ill afford to spare so soon—he died in office six years before retiring age. He came from Liverpool to be House Surgeon at Moorfields in 1938. After war service he was elected to the staffs of St Mary's Hospital and Moorfields. His great interest, of course, was in the cornea; his research, teaching, writings, and results in corneal transplantation are common knowledge. He was a good companion, a valuable and staunch colleague, and though such an outstanding authority—and he knew it—a modest man. He would justifiably be called a clubbable man—though whether in fact he enjoyed the membership of any clubs one does not know, other than that of his golf club, where he was a regular attender and a doughty opponent. In his earlier days he played a good game of hockey and was capped for Lancashire. Had he been spared he would surely have brought to Moorfields even more credit and fame than he did.

Thomas Keith Lyle rendered most valuable service to ophthalmology in many ways—and indeed continues to do so

A. G. Leigh

after retirement from active hospital work. Son of an ophthalmic surgeon, he went to Dulwich College and Sidney Sussex, Cambridge, then to King's College Hospital whence he qualified in 1928. He held three important and strenuous hospital posts for over 30 years—King's College Hospital, The Royal Westminster Ophthalmic Hospital (continuing at Moorfields after the amalgamation until 1968) and the National Hospital, Queen Square. Later in his career he became Dean of the Medical School at Moorfields, succeeding Davenport in 1959 and holding the office until 1967. Further, he directed the orthoptic department at the Holborn branch from the amalgamation till he retired, examined in ophthalmology for many years, and added to what one would consider an already full programme the duties of President of the Faculty, co-opted member of Council of the Royal College of Surgeons, President of the Ophthalmological Society of the United Kingdom, Master of the Apothecaries' Society, Deputy Hospitaller of the Order of St. John (later Hospitaller), member of the International

T. Keith Lyle

Council of Ophthalmology—to name but a few; not all
simultaneously, admittedly, but it is a formidable list. He was
awarded the Nettleship Medal in 1959 and gave the Doyne
lecture in 1953, choosing as his subject "The prognosis and
treatment of ocular palsy". It was ocular muscle balance and
imbalance, and the problems of binocular vision, which
particularly engaged his attention; he made many important
contributions to the study of these subjects, and wrote exten-
sively on them.

Frederick Thomas Ridley, a Birmingham graduate, having
been pathologist to the Central London Ophthalmic Hospital,
was elected to the staff of that hospital in 1928 having served
for a short while on the staff of the Western Ophthalmic
Hospital. Three years after the amalgamation with Moorfields

Frederick T. Ridley

he was appointed Director of the Contact Lens Department situated at the High Holborn branch, and it was there that he was able to apply his great scientific and administrative ability and create a department of first class importance throughout the country; he has contributed much to this specialty within the specialty. He gave many important lectures, including the Doyne, "Contact Lens theory and practice" forming the subject for this; he won the Nettleship Prize in 1963. He, of course, carried out the routine duties of surgeon to the Hospital as well, and this in enthusiastic and devoted fashion. He was President of the 2nd International Corneo-Plastic Conference held in London in 1967.

On the coming of age of the Institute in 1969, its annual report contains a summary of its history appropriately contributed by

Sir Stewart Duke-Elder, most of the contents of which have already received notice in these pages. The progress which the Institute has made and the position it has achieved in world ophthalmology are indeed remarkable to contemplate. The writer makes some interesting comparisons; the initial research staff of 29 and secretarial and technical staff of 16 had increased to 81 and 89 respectively, together with some 25 ancillary staff (1969); the budget in 1948 was £31,811 and in 1969, £435,000.

Though some of the departments listed could be more properly considered departments of the Hospital, the connection between the two institutions is so close, and the collaboration so fundamentally necessary, that their inclusion is justified. Four fully staffed and equipped departments operate under a Professor (one has two Professors); other departments have their Readers and Directors. The computer section undertakes routine and research work, the library expands and progresses, and courses of study—basic, advanced, clinical, special—proceed in constant succession; consultants, general practitioners, examination students and research students are all catered for. Prizes, Fellowships, and Research Scholarships are offered, research projects into the basic and applied aspects of the specialty proceed in practically every department, needing some fifty pages of the report for their bare recital. Behind all this the routine administrative and financial background exists as it has to in any comparable organisation, all controlled by various Boards and Committees, special and general, guided by the President, Sir Stewart Duke-Elder, its Chairman, The Earl of Rothes, its Dean, A. G. Cross and its Treasurer, Mr L. G. Green, and operated and co-ordinated by its indefatigable and devoted secretary, Clifford Seath. The evolution and maturation of the Institute of Ophthalmology is a phenomenon the like of which has not been seen before in this field, and one feels it will be a long time before such an event is repeated.

The coming of age was celebrated in ample fashion. Three open days were held, and the staff received and entertained and enlightened such a bevy of visitors that some of them must have found the duties more strenuous and tiring than their routine work! The open days were preceded by a splendid birthday dinner at the Apothecaries Hall on the evening before, and many distinguished guests honoured the gathering. Further, an evening was spent in the Great Hall of B.M.A. House at a party attended by all the present staff and as many of the past as could be summoned.

The question of working space continued to obtrude, and relief was felt when negotiations for more proved successful. With the help of the Fight for Sight Committee, a building adjacent to the City Road branch, offering 1500 square feet of space, was acquired and with further financial help from the University Grants Committee it was hoped to adapt the building without delay and transfer some departments to their new site within a year. We have seen how circumstances interfered and postponed this aim.

The annual report of the Institute mentions that adverse comment had in the past been made on the nature of its contents, as being unintelligible to those of its readers who were neither doctors nor scientists. The report therefore included a brief explanation of the work in hand in lay terms. It seems to one that the same comment might be applicable to some parts of the contents of this book. In the following ten paragraphs therefore we reprint *verbatim* the explanation given by the writer of the introduction to the annual report in question, with acknowledgements and thanks.

"The Department of Clinical Ophthalmology has a special responsibility for teaching the resident surgical staff, who are the consultants of the future. It also has responsibility to exploit the closed-circuit television system for teaching and to organise regular clinical seminars. It provides a clinical service within the Hospital, through the Professorial Unit, and has associations with other hospitals which can provide special expertise. It organises and runs special clinics dealing with particular eye problems. It is responsible for the research on the role that viruses play in eye disease. Trachoma, the major cause of blindness in the world, is under intensive investigation and important results of practical benefit to the patients have been achieved. New scientific techniques have been developed to undertake this work which will have an application in other branches of medicine. Advances have been made in the techniques of corneal grafting which have had direct and beneficial results for numbers of people who could not previously be helped.

The Department of Experimental Ophthalmology undertakes

253

laboratory studies and organises research clinics to investigate certain particular eye diseases. It is mainly concerned with glaucoma and uveitis and provides an opportunity for scientists working in the laboratory to aid doctors investigating clinical problems, leading to a better understanding of these conditions and to improved treatment. From the laboratory new methods of diagnosis and new pieces of apparatus are developed and subsequently produced commercially. The follow-up of relatives of patients with glaucoma has shown the importance of the hereditary nature of this condition. It is the aim of this department to bridge the gap between the scientist and the doctor and apply knowledge gained in the laboratory for the benefit of the patient.

The Department of Neurophysiology is concerned with the understanding of the mechanism by which we see. As a result of the work of this department highly sophisticated electronic methods have been developed which aid in the diagnosis and understanding of some types of eye disease and eventually lead to improved treatment of these diseases. Here again intensive and time-consuming laboratory work is being undertaken for the long-term benefit of the patient.

The Department of Anatomy uses an electron microscope to investigate the complex structure of the eye and in particular of the retina. It is in this way and by this detailed study that abnormalities can more readily be recognised and understood. It also investigates the structure of the eye in a number of different species of animals and fishes. From all this work more knowledge is gained and so our understanding of the function of the normal eye is improved. The department has made a special study of the effect of laser damage on the retina which is particularly important now that lasers are becoming more frequently used in industry as well as in universities.

The Department of Physiology and Biochemistry is concerned with laboratory investigations into the way in which the normal eye functions, with particular reference to its blood supply and nutrition. It is also concerned with the effect on the eye of certain drugs which may lead to new advances in the treatment of some eye diseases. From this basic work flows clinical benefit to the patient.

The Department of Physiological Optics is particularly interested in the ageing of the eye. It is concerned with research on the retina in relation to vision and the various changes in the visual pigments resulting from exposure to light. The department also studies some of the effects of laser light on the eye and the damage that this might cause. Certain visual aids which might be used for teaching complicated procedures, and new diagnostic methods for vision testing, are also being investigated.

The Department of Pathology is concerned with the diseased eye and is responsible for the laboratory investigations which are required on patients attending Moorfields Eye Hospital. It also provides an expert reference laboratory for histological examination of the eye for hospitals in the United Kingdom and overseas. It is concerned with problems of cross infection and sterilisation within the Hospital. Its research programme has included an intensive study of the retinal vessels; of the problems of the blinding disease called diabetic retinopathy, occurring in some people with diabetes; and of the effects of oxygen on the developing eye, an extension of the work done in previous years on the disease of the premature baby known as retrolental fibroplasia. The department studies problems of eye disease in all its aspects and uses both light- and electron-microscopy in these studies. It is also responsible for the Cancer Follow-up Department wherein all cases of malignancy are reviewed routinely. Research work in chemical pathology has increased with the acquisition of electronic apparatus which has helped considerably in many clinical and research investigations.

The Orthoptic Department is sited at both branches of the Hospital and, in addition to its important work of teaching both the postgraduate students and orthoptists studying for the Diploma of the British Orthoptic Board it undertakes research into visual anomalies. It is mainly concerned with squints in children but more recently an increasing number of adults with abnormalities of the ocular muscles has been investigated.

The Department of Contact Lenses and Prosthetics is located at the High Holborn Branch of the Hospital and in addition to organising courses for postgraduate students it undertakes research on the way in which contact lenses may be used in certain eye conditions and on new techniques and new materials.

The Department of Audio-Visual Communications concerns itself with graphic and photographic problems and provides a photographic service for Moorfields Eye Hospital and for other hospitals in the London area. The medical artist provides impressions of the retina which cannot easily be photographed. The department maintains a library of slides of all eye diseases which may be called upon by lecturers when necessary. The television section is concerned with the exploitation of the closed-circuit television system located in the operating theatres at both branches of the Hospital and it now has a considerable library of video-tape recordings for the benefit of students. It operates regular live transmissions from the theatres which have proved of great benefit to both the students and to the nurses.

The Library does not require a great deal of explanation except to say that the range of books provided in our subject is the most extensive in Europe. The intake of journals has been increased so that a wider range of subjects is now covered and both staff and students may have access to up-to-date information."

In 1970 the Pocklington Eye Transplantation unit was transferred to the Institute from the Royal College of Surgeons and was integrated with the research programme there, naturally intensifying the work on the cornea. Another aspect of this field appears in the work on refractive keratoplasty by Derek Ainslie. This pioneer work consists in modification of the refractive power of the eye by means of alteration in the shape of the cornea; it demands great surgical expertise, careful calculation, and fine precision lathe-work. A problem was presented by the change which occurs in the corneal volume on freezing; a solution may offer in introducing a corrective factor in the calculations. The notable feature of this work in its experimental stages was the meticulously ethical approach made by Ainslie; for all the benefits—and one could confidently predict there were many—which could accrue from the work for patients in the future, none was imperilled in the present.

CHAPTER 20

More modernisation – Miss MacKellar
Guilford Street – Thoresby House – A. Lister
N. H. L. Ridley – Norman Ashton
Visits of Secretary of State – Specialisation
A. F. Gray – The Earl of Rothes – Cayton Street
Institute reorganisation – House and Medical Committees

IN 1970 many items of building, extension, and modernisation were undertaken, some on a larger scale than was previously hoped for on account of unexpected allocations of money from the Department of Health. A new passenger lift was installed, in the space intended for it when the area was built 40 years before, by the west staircase at City Road, and the goods lift was reconditioned. At High Holborn the Casualty Department was improved, and Bernhard Baron and Swinburne Wards were remodelled. Although the Pharmacy at City Road had been enlarged very recently, further work was begun here and measures were taken to cope with the more efficient production of the great quantity of sterile eye drops which are used at the hospital. When the scheme is completed the pharmacy will be in a position to supply the whole hospital, and other nearby hospitals as well. This work was facilitated again by a special grant from the Department of Health. The strike in the electric power supply industry speeded up the project for standby generators, which were installed at both branches.

On 31 July of this year Miss Margaret MacKellar, O.B.E. retired after serving the hospital for 28 years—as principal tutor, assistant matron and matron. Her title of Director of Nursing was conferred by the Board—the rank of Principal Nursing Officer 9(b) came to her under the Salmon structure—but Matron in fact she was and matron in name she will remain. One could not calculate and tabulate all she did for Moorfields, and indeed for Ophthalmic Nursing at home and abroad—and in the latter field notably for the Ophthalmic

Hospital of St John in Jerusalem, in which she took the greatest interest. She was largely responsible for the formation of the Ophthalmic Nurses Association which developed into an international body, and for the ophthalmic Nursing Board the conduct of which the writer shared with her for over 20 years. Nobody could have had the interests of her charges and their work more closely at heart; her single-mindedness in committee when pursuing a project had to be experienced to be appreciated. In her retirement she may look back on her career with completely justifiable satisfaction. She was succeeded by Miss Marion Tickner, who in fact received her ophthalmic training at the Central London Ophthalmic Hospital, after qualifying from the Kent and Canterbury. She was matron of the Royal Northern Hospital before coming to Moorfields.

In 1970 the Guilford Street Hotel had to be returned to its owners. Just previously a second offer had been made by the North London Group Hospital Management Committee to transfer Thoresby House to the Board. It will be recalled that the hospital had received an offer of these premises a few years before. The Regional Board was then acting as intermediary between the North London Group Hospital Management Committee and the Ministry, and after a month of negotiation withdrew the offer. Thoresby House had been in the past the Midwives' Home of the old City of London Maternity Hospital, which was situated on the corner of City Road and Old Street until destroyed by bombs in the war. The house was conveniently near the City Road branch, and the Hospital was glad to accept this second offer. It was a useful acquisition, providing room for staff, and offices for the Group Engineer.

Arthur Lister retired from the staff under the age limit in 1970, and was succeeded by N. S. C. Rice, who had been appointed in 1969 and took over his duties in March 1970. At this time also Dr Lerman and Dr Shippard, the anaesthetists, retired. The one had been appointed to the Central, and the other to the Westminster, in 1947; both had thus made a

Arthur Lister

notable contribution to the hospital in a period of service of 24 years. Harold Ridley retired in July 1971, and Peter Fells was appointed to the vacancy. On his retirement Ridley announced the establishment of the Ridley Foundation by himself and Mrs Ridley. The object of this far-sighted and generous act was to assist staff in studying in any teaching hospital in the United Kingdom, to assist charities, and to further research at Moorfields, the Institute and St Thomas' Hospital and School.

Arthur Lister, nephew of Sir William (see page 84), was educated at Lancing College, Trinity, Cambridge, and the London Hospital. He was elected to the staff of both Moorfields and the London in 1939, but did not settle fully to the duties involved until he returned from war service in 1945. He made a special study of gonioscopy and goniotomy, and pioneered the development of the operation in this country, contributing largely to the knowledge of the angle of the anterior chamber and its functions, and making many original observations. His stereoscopic photographs of the angle are superb. An unassuming character, he was conscientious to a degree, and his work throughout was of the very highest standard. In his spare time he indulged his great pleasure in walking; until lately one of his main leisure interests was a beautifully kept car of very respectable age which he drove with consummate skill at a considerable speed. The writer will not forget the dramatic account given to him by a colleague from Baltimore after a trip with Arthur Lister.

Nicholas Harold Lloyd Ridley was elected to the Staff of Moorfields in 1938 and to that of St Thomas' in 1946. It was at the latter hospital that he developed the idea of implanting a

Harold Ridley

plastic lens in the eye in place of an extracted opaque one—a procedure first suggested, it is said, by one of his dressers. The operation was regarded as an extravagant conception and had a mixed reception especially in the States where it was at one time openly condemned as dangerous and unjustifiable. *Per contra*, after hearing a paper by Ridley on the subject, an American colleague commented thus: "Mr Ridley described this epoch-making operation as if it were an ordinary commonplace affair; real British." In spite of opposition, it made its way, though with fundamental modifications; Ridley's original idea of implanting into the posterior chamber has been abandoned and these lenses are now all placed in the anterior chamber. The majority still feel that special circumstances are necessary before the attempt is justified, but there is no doubt that those who have concentrated upon the technique perform a large number of implants with dramatic results, and many patients have reason to be grateful for the innovation, the credit for which must go to Harold Ridley as the originator. His other main professional interest was in Tropical Ophthalmology, and he made valuable contributions to the literature on Onchocerciasis.

In the following year, Professor Norman Ashton was elected to Fellowship of the Royal Society. The award of this very high honour was warmly welcomed by his colleagues and friends as evincing due recognition not less of his highly competent directorship, extremely sound routine pathology and inspired teaching than of his brilliant achievements in the field of research. In September of the same year he was made President of the Ophthalmological Section of the Royal Society of Medicine —a cachet of lower calibre, but very distinctive, especially for a non-ophthalmologist. A further honour fell to him in 1973 when the University of Chicago conferred the degree of Honorary D.Sc. upon him.

Liaison and Communication between the central authority and the Hospital continued to be cultivated. In 1970 the Hospital was pleased to receive the Minister of State, Lord Aberdare, on two occasions, and to show him some of the work of the Hospital and the latest developments. In December 1971 the Secretary of State, Sir Keith Joseph, paid a visit to the

Visit of Lord Aberdare, Minister of State, High Holborn, 26 February, 1971. Left to right—T. G. Talbot (Chairman, House Committee), Miss Tickner (Matron), the Minister, J. R. Hudson (Chairman, Medical Committee), B. I. Sharp (Hospital Secretary), F. M. Cumberlege (Chairman).

Hospital and made an extensive informal tour. In the following year he made the presentation of the nurses' awards.

No better evidence of the swing towards individual specialisation within the specialty could be given than by a recital of the number of special clinics which had evolved by the time 1970 was reached. Of these there were ten—not to include the long-standing special departments such as Uveitis (Cross and Fison)

Visit of the Secretary of State, 1971. Left to right—Sir Keith Joseph, George Stanley (Deputy Chairman, and Chairman of the House Committee) and Arthur Gray (House Governor).

and the Radiotherapy at the Royal Marsden (Lederman and Wybar). Their titles as quoted in the Report on Research provided by the Chairman of the Research Committee (Professor Perkins) are: External Diseases, Corneal, Retinal Function, Orbital, Diagnostic (for sexually transmitted diseases), Genetic, Scleritis, Lacrimal, Radiotherapy, and Congenital Glaucoma. This is a remarkable list to have evolved within the professional lifetime of some surgeons still on the staff of the hospital. And further it should be carefully remembered that the research undertaken by the Institute staff is by no means confined to the basic, academic, and experimental; a dozen or more clinics are concerned with the examination and investigation and, indeed, the treatment of patients.

Just as there were many who deplored the demise of the voluntary system after the second war, so there were some who had misgivings over the advent of specialisation. There is no question that this latter innovation was given the most careful and impartial consideration by all concerned before it was introduced; it must be admitted that, taking the broad view, each development appeared desirable and indeed inevitable. This did not prevent second thoughts on the part of many, who perforce accept the changes in the light of unavoidable processes in the realm of social and scientific evolution. An interesting and relevant comment is made in another context by L. T. C. Rolt, when commenting on trends, towards the end of his biography of that great man Isambard Kingdom Brunel: ". . . just as the machines, by carrying too far the principle of division of labour, degraded the craftsman into a machine-minder, so, just as surely and far more subtly, the process of specialisation has by perpetual reduction destroyed that catholicity of intellect without which civilisation cannot survive." The question is puzzling and provoking; and there we must leave it.

The King's Fund College of Hospital Management were concerned with the provision of multidisciplinary courses designed to prepare senior officers for the administration of the new Health Service after its reorganisation; in this context the Department of Health had instituted Secretary of State Fellowships. In June 1972, the House Governor, Arthur F. Gray, was offered one of these Fellowships by the Department. The chairmen of the various hospital committees were favourably disposed towards this proposal, and agreed that the House Governor should accept the post and devote two thirds of his time to the task, the remainder to Moorfields. After a year or so he reduced the time given to one-fifth, and resigned from the post shortly afterwards. The acceptance of this appointment provided another example of the House Governor's interest in matters outside the Hospital. He always concerned himself with the hospital world in general, and belonged to, and indeed held office in, many relevant and associated bodies and organisations. Not only does such an attitude increase the interest of a hospital officer in his appointment, but it can do nothing but good in furthering the ultimate interests of his own hospital.

In 1972 the Rt Hon. the Earl of Rothes retired from the Chairmanship of the Institute, an office he had held since its inception 25 years before. He had indeed served the Institute well, and his experience, wise counsel, and devotion to its welfare were invaluable. A laudatory and appropriate resolution was passed at a special meeting of the Committee of Management; a dinner was given in his honour, when he was presented with his portrait. He remains as a co-opted member of the governing body; he was succeeded by the Chairman of the Board of the Hospital, Francis M. Cumberlege. In January of the same year the Librarian, Miss Mina Yuille, retired; she had served 24 years, and was instrumental in the development of the library from its start, with the hospital library as its nucleus, to become the important department it is today. She was also Technical Editor of the *British Journal of Ophthalmology* and *Ophthalmic Literature*.

At this time approval in principle was given to the scheme to adapt the Cayton Street building, and hopes rose again for the work to begin and for the transfer thither of the Pathological Department and the Dean's Department. Anticipating these changes, some reorganisation was made in the academic set-up at the Institute. The Department of Physiology and Biochemistry became associated with that of Experimental Ophthalmology; the Department of Anatomy and Neurophysiology became one with the Department of Physiological Optics to form the Department of Visual Science, Dr Weale, Director of the latter department, who had been created Professor in January 1972, becoming Director of the combined Departments with Dr Arden, previously Director of the Neurophysiology Department, as Reader. Within a couple of years the Reader himself achieved the distinction of Professorship, a due and proper elevation which increased still further the prestige of the Department. More attention was given, in the teaching programme, to consultants, and many successful courses were held; monthly staff meetings were initiated which promised to be valuable and popular.

One cannot but feel sympathy over the frustrations and disappointments encountered by the authorities at the Institute in their endeavours to develop and utilise the Cayton Street site. Time and again these plans were changed. Soon after the "go ahead" was given, some difficulties arose in the negotiations with the University Grants Committee over the question of grants. The first attitude of this body appeared to be that, if they contributed to the cost of adaptations, when the building was eventually sold they would claim the whole of the proceeds. That attitude was mercifully modified; the Committee offered to provide a grant of £100,000 provided that, on eventual sale, 25 per cent of the proceeds should revert to them. This proposition was agreed by the Trustees, and thus the way for proceeding with the conversion was opened.

The reorganisation at the Institute was followed by a change of significance in the teaching field. It was decided that as from the start of the academic year in 1973, the General Teaching Course should last for nine months instead of for two periods of four months each as in the past. The content was extended, and more time was allowed for clinical instruction.

An administrative change was also effected in the Hospital. The two separate House Committees, and the two Medical Committees were respectively combined. G. C. Stanley, Chairman of the City Road Branch and T. G. Talbot, Chairman of the High Holborn Branch, were appointed respectively Chairman and Vice Chairman of the new Combined House Committee. It is hoped to achieve in the future a similar unification of the training of House Surgeons at both branches.

CHAPTER 21

International links – Industrial action
The Hock Foundation – A. G. Cross – J. E. M. Ayoub
C. A. G. Cook – Professorial Units
Refraction Teaching Unit – N.H.S. reorganisation

Two reminders of the international reputation and overseas contacts enjoyed by the Hospital were received in 1973. A request was received from the University of Iowa for a stone from Moorfields, which they wished to incorporate in the new library of their Eye Department. It was appropriate that this library was to contain a considerable proportion of the library of a recently retired member of the consultant staff of Moorfields.

The second reminder came from the New York Eye and Ear Infirmary. Collins in his History (page 35) records the attendance at Moorfields of two newly qualified Americans—Dr Edward Delafield and Dr J. Kearney Rodgers. Their enthusiasm was such that, on their return to New York in 1818, they set about founding an eye hospital there on lines similar to those of Moorfields; and thus the New York Eye and Ear Infirmary was born. In April 1973 members of the Alumni Association of the Hospital, some 50 in number, came to this country to hold their annual meeting here. A week was spent in clinical discussion and entertainment, the chief places of interest to the visitors naturally being Moorfields and the Institute.

An unusual worry arose when the atmosphere of industrial unrest invaded even the hospital field—an area which one had begun hopefully to regard as almost sacrosanct. In the current inappropriate phrase, "industrial action" was taken at the instigation of the National Union of Public Employees, and their members were instructed to withdraw their labour for four days from 1 March, except for services to emergency patients. The effect was much mitigated by the decision of the General and Municipal Workers Union not to support this action; no more than a day's disturbance of theatre routine and domestic services to non-patient areas resulted. A more serious move followed in the refusal of the Public Employees Union members to continue their duties in the Private Patients area. The Medical Committee stigmatised this action as discriminatory; admission of private patients was stopped and the Lower Corridor closed, whilst use was made of the Top Corridor for some mothers with babies, and general ward patients. The inconvenience continued for about six weeks, when the strike was lifted.

In January 1973 the Chairman of the Medical Committee (James Hudson) reported the establishment of a Trust Fund—the Francis and Renee Hock Foundation—for the Retina Unit at High Holborn, and that he had been appointed a Trustee. The nominal value was £70,000. The author strongly suspects that Hudson himself played a large part in enabling the provision of this splendid sum. The income from the Fund would probably be used in the maintenance of a Research Fellow, who might spend some of his time in the newly established Professorial Unit of Professor Hill. In the early stages at least some of the income was used in the purchase of equipment.

This year saw the retirement under the age limit of A. G. Cross and J. E. M. Ayoub; and Charles Cook resigned for health reasons.

Alexander Galbraith Cross was another member of the staff who rendered most valuable service to the Hospital outside the routine duties. From King's College School and Caius, Cambridge, he came to St Mary's Hospital, where he was a University Scholar, and where he collected important prizes, and the Cheadle Gold medal in Clinical Medicine in 1933. He served his resident appointments at St Mary's and at Moorfields, at which latter hospital he was also Curator; his first honorary appointments were at the West Middlesex, Tite Street and Princess Beatrice Hospitals. He served in the RAFVR in the war with the rank of Wing Commander; on his return it was not long before he was appointed to the Consult-

A. G. Cross

ant staff of St Mary's and Moorfields. It was then that this enthusiasm and flair for the academic administrative side began to show; he was appointed Dean of St Mary's and served for some years, and in 1967 became Dean of the Institute after Keith Lyle. He was consultant to the Royal National Throat, Nose and Ear Hospital, the Royal Masonic Hospital, St Dunstan's and the Royal National Institute for the Blind, and held the important office of civilian Consultant in Ophthalmology to the Royal Navy, to which he was appointed in 1946. On retirement he was succeeded in this office by Stephen Miller.

In addition to the many duties inherent in these appointments Cross found time for many other activities. He examined in the Fellowship for the Royal College of Surgeons, in the

D.O., and in Ophthalmology for the University of Bristol; he was for five years co-opted member of the Council of the Royal College of Surgeons, Vice-President of three academic societies and on the editorial board of three important professional publications. He served as a member of the Board of Governors of both St Mary's and Moorfields and for eight years was on the Paddington Group Hospital Management Committee; a member of the Council of the Faculty of Ophthalmologists, he became Vice-President, and in 1968 was elected President. With a busy private practice, his routine hospital duties, and all these commitments in addition, one might well think that he was fully occupied; nonetheless he found time to write many articles in the ophthalmic literature, and produced a 12th edition of "May and Worth", managing all the while to appear unhurried and to have time for any new venture as it arose. He was, and indeed still is, a most efficient and popular Dean, worthily upholding the standards of his predecessors; he continued in office after retiring from hospital work. He had a great genius for this administrative milieu and the committee work which it involved; his judgements were as valuable as his approach was quiet and considered.

In his time Alex Cross was a distinguished Rugby football player. He played for Caius for three years and was secretary of the club; he played in the University side on a number of occasions. While up at Cambridge he was elected a member of the Hawks Club in recognition of his prowess in the field. His athletic activities were not confined to football, for he captained his college at lawn tennis. On coming down he played rugger for St Mary's for seven years, in four of which they won the Hospitals Cup.

On his resignation from the Hospital staff, he was succeeded by John Wright; Peter Fells took his place as Director of the Orthoptic Department at City Road. Cross, however, continued in office as Chairman of the British Orthoptic Council, and also as a member of the Orthoptists' Board of the Council for Professions Supplementary to Medicine.

John Edward Moussa Ayoub went to St Paul's School and Lincoln College, Oxford before entering as a student at St Thomas' Hospital where he qualified in 1933, took his B.M., and B.Ch. in the same year and proceeded to the Fellowship

J. E. M. Ayoub

two years later. He filled the Ophthalmic House Surgeon's post at St Thomas' and became Chief Clinical Assistant at Moorfields; he was on the staff of the West Middlesex Hospital before being appointed to the London Hospital in 1947 and to Moorfields in 1950; he became Consultant to the Royal Masonic Hospital in 1967, and is Consultant Emeritus in Ophthalmology to the Royal Navy; he had been succeeded as Consultant on retirement by Kenneth Wybar. He spent the war in the Senior Service as a specialist in Ophthalmology with the rank of Surgeon Lt Commander. He has been Vice-President of the Section of Ophthalmology, Royal Society of Medicine, and served his time as Councillor of the Faculty, where for long he was in charge of study tours which he arranged most ably; he continued in this capacity after resigning from the Council. He was for a long period on the Ophthalmic Nursing Board.

It is common to say that a man has the sea in his blood, but to say he has water in his blood is unusual and sounds a little awkward and indeed pathological (though for less good reason). Nonetheless, one would have so to describe John Ayoub if using such an expression, for his penchants included fresh water. His clubs reveal this—Leander, Royal Solent Yacht Club, Royal Cruising Club (this last by election). In his earlier days he was a very distinguished heavyweight oar. He rowed for St Paul's and became vice-captain; he won two oars while rowing for Lincoln, and rowed two years in the University trials, missing his Blue by the narrowest margin. He was captain of Boats at St Thomas' Hospital over a very successful period. He even won a whaler race in Alexandria Harbour between the hospital ships *Maine* and *Atlantis*. Such versatility on the water is almost unprecedented!

In due and natural course his interests centred more on his other aquatic medium, and the somewhat less strenuous occupation of sailing took up his leisure time. He had indulged in this all his adult life, not by any means always without adventure. It is true to say that he has sailed his own boat into nearly all the harbours lying in the triangle Glengariff, Brest, Texel. A worthy disciple, indeed, of Claud Worth. In his retirement in the Channel Islands (where he has been officially recognised as the Island Ophthalmologist by the states of Alderney) he is in the fortunate position of being able to cultivate even more intensely the interest of a lifetime.

The vacancy on the staff was filled by the appointment of Peter Wright.

Charles Alfred George Cook, M.C., G.M., resigned from the staff of Moorfields in September 1973 some five years before reaching retiring age. This was just when Professor Hill was taking up his duties at High Holborn; Barrie Jay, who had been elected surgeon in 1968 and worked at High Holborn, transferred to City Road to replace Charles Cook.

Cook received his earlier education at St Edward's School, Oxford, before coming to Guy's Hospital. He qualified in 1939, and after the war took the D.O.M.S. and his Fellowship. Throughout the war he served as Captain and then Major in the R.A.M.C., with very great distinction, especially in 1945 when he received his two decorations. Most of his specialist education had to wait for the war to finish; in 1946 and onwards

C. A. G. Cook

he was Clinical Assistant, House Surgeon, Senior Resident
Officer and Chief Clinical Assistant at Moorfields, and Senior
Registrar at Guy's Hospital. He was Moorfields Research
Fellow from 1951 to 1958, and worked at the Institute, where
he had been Junior Lecturer in the Pathology Department
practically from the outset. He carried out important research
work under the aegis of Professor Ashton, notably in the field of
diabetic retinopathy. He worked for a short while at the West
Middlesex Hospital before being appointed to the staff of
Moorfields in 1954 and Guy's in 1956. He soon established a
reputation as an outstanding teacher, especially of undergraduates; he examined in the Fellowship and the D.O.M.S.
and for the Orthoptic Board, and served as Secretary of the
Ophthalmological Society and as Vice-Dean of the Institute.
A freeman of the City of London, he was duly elected to the

Court of the Worshipful Company of Spectacle Makers; he most unfortunately had to decline, on grounds of ill health, the offer of the post of Warden which would have led to the Mastership. This ill health was the source of great sorrow and disappointment to his friends and colleagues; after a time he decided to give up his private practice and continue only at Hospital; even that proved more and more difficult, so that finally he resigned from both, to everyone's regret. His disability seriously interfered with his leisure interests which were mostly out of doors; but more recently all his friends were delighted to observe obvious signs of improvement and recovery. May this continue so as to enable him to enjoy his enforced retirement.

In 1973 the premises for the Department of Clinical Ophthalmology were completed and occupied. This new Professorial Unit occupies a complete floor above the operating theatres in City Road and provides consulting rooms, clinic rooms, seminar rooms and office accommodation; it is a worthy home for this important department. The Department was opened by H.R.H. Princess Richard of Gloucester, who also opened the new School of Nursing and presented the Nurses' Awards, on 6 June. Soon after this the arrangements were completed for the transfer of the Research Chair in Ophthalmology of the Royal College of Surgeons at the Royal Eye Hospital to the High Holborn branch, following the closure of the Royal Eye Hospital. Accommodation was provided for Professor Hill, who took up his duties in his new surroundings on 21 September, 1973.

It was at first intended to create a Department of Clinical Optics in the basement of the Cayton Street building taken over by the Institute. This idea was later modified and a Refraction Teaching Unit was planned. It was to consist of ten cubicles, a dark room and a tutorial room, to cost some £20,000; responsibility for it, financial and other, would rest upon the Institute. For long there had been some discontent and misgivings over the teaching of refraction at the Hospital; this unit would constitute a forward step and would go far to regularise what had been hitherto a rather neglected and unorganised field.

The reorganisation of the National Health Service, which

came into effect on 1 April, 1974, naturally concerned the Hospital, though the postgraduate hospitals as a group were less affected than others. This group was subjected to a survey by "Scicon" (a Management Consultant body with the title Scientific Control Systems Ltd.) in the previous year, and their report was considered by the London Postgraduate Committee of the Teaching Hospitals Association in January 1974. The report in its first part was factual; the second set out a number of possible solutions for the problems of the postgraduate hospitals in the reorganised service, and a concise statement of advantages and disadvantages. The Dean regarded the report as a basis for discussion and predicted that the postgraduate hospitals would have to fight for survival. It was a matter of great satisfaction to the Hospital that the Chairman, Francis Cumberlege had been appointed Chairman of the new Area Health Authority for the City and East London. The Teaching Hospitals Association had decided to disintegrate, but owing to lack of progress in forming a new association of Health Service Authorities, they postponed this until the end of 1974. The House Governor had acted as Honorary Secretary to the Association for Postgraduates. It was expected that the London Postgraduate Committee would continue in being and probably form part of the new association.

When the Act came into force, the London Postgraduate Teaching Hospitals were not fitted into the area pattern with the other hospitals. Their Boards of Governors were preserved, temporarily at least, which gave time for them to consider their positions in the new organisation, and to draw up plans for the future which might enable them to serve their purpose best in the new set-up and at the same time preserve for themselves a measure of administrative, academic and financial freedom.

The question of the bed complement is still not finally decided; the attitude towards this question is slightly modified by the latest trends in the specialty. In the last few years the average length of stay of a patient has been reduced from 12 to 7 days consequent upon changes in approach, surgical techniques and post-operative treatment. It began to seem likely that if the bed complement were to be reduced to, say, 250 beds, as much work and as brisk a turnover could be accomplished with that as with the present one of 345.

Postscript

And thus ends not by any means the history of Moorfields, but this account of the history of Moorfields up to date—one might well say, to its devotees, of our beloved Moorfields, for the influence of the Hospital on those who serve it engenders in them an undeniable loyalty and affection.

Collins in his "*History*" says that institutions, like individuals, if they wish to survive in the struggle for existence, have to obey the universal law of adaptation to environment, and indicated how this had been achieved in the first hundred years of the Hospital's existence. I am well sure that if he could read this account of the succeeding seventy years he would be able to say that the capability for adaptation had in no whit declined. It is further possible to say with some confidence that he would be satisfied with the scientific and the material progress of the hospital in this latter period. He could not fail to be impressed with the energy and foresight of the governing body in keeping the buildings adequate and up to date, and in caring for the financial, administrative and sociological welfare and progress of the hospital with such unremitting zeal. And on the professional side he would see on all hands ample evidence of enterprise, energy, foresight, and progress, and a devotion to the Hospital on the part of all who work there which would justify and satisfy those who laid so sound a foundation. It is always difficult to estimate whether changes, and the rate of change, have been more marked at one period of history than at another, and the more usual conclusion is that the greatest changes have occurred in one's own time. When one considers the fundamental change that has occurred in the attitude towards the activities of hospitals, and towards voluntary service; the political encroachment into hitherto domestic and social matters; the growth of the Social Services and the development of the Welfare State; the changes that have occurred in the practice of ophthalmology, and the epoch-making scientific advances that have been made in our time, one feels compelled to reach this conclusion once again.

And so, methinks, he who reads a history cares not much for the wisdom or folly of the writer (knowing well that the former is far less than his own, and the latter vastly greater), but hurries to know what the people did, and how they got on about it. And this I can tell, if anyone can, having been myself in the thick of it.

R. D. BLACKMORE—*Lorna Doone*

APPENDIX

W—Royal Westminster Ophthalmic Hospital
C—Central London Ophthalmic Hospital
C.R.—City Road Branch
H.H.—High Holborn Branch
† Continued in office after retiring age

Patrons

H.R.H. The Duke of York	1815–1827
Vacant	1827–1836
H.R.H. The Duchess of Kent	1836–1860
H.R.H. Princess Victoria, afterwards H.M. Queen Victoria	1836–1901
H.R.H. The Duke of Cambridge	1857–1904
H.R.H. The Prince of Wales, afterwards King Edward VII	1897–1909
H.R.H. The Princess of Wales, afterwards Queen Alexandra	1899–1925
H.R.H. The Duke of York, afterwards Prince of Wales, afterwards King George V	1899–1936
H.R.H. The Duchess of York, afterwards Princess of Wales, afterwards Queen Mary	1899–1953
H.M. King George VI	1936–1952
H.M. Queen Elizabeth II	1952 whom God preserve

Presidents

Sir Charles Price, Bart.	1804–1818
Mr William Mellish	1818–1838
Rt Hon. Earl Fitzwilliam	1838–1856
Mr William Cotton, D.C.L., F.R.S.	1857–1867
Sir John Lubbock, F.R.S., M.P. (afterwards Lord Avebury)	1867–1913
His Royal Highness Prince Arthur of Connaught, K.G.	1913 died 1938
Vacant	1939–1944
Mr Theodore W. Luling	1945 died 1955
No election since	

Chairmen of the Committee of Management

Mr Harry Sedgwick	1804–1818
Mr Ralph Price	1818–1830
Mr Stuart Donaldson	1831–1837
Rev. J. Russell, D.D.	1837–1857
Mr Richard Heathfield	1857–1859
Mr F. G. Sambrooke	1860–1871
Mr Philip Cazenove	1871–1879
Mr Charles Gordon	1879–1897
Mr H. P. Sturgis	1897–1921
Mr Theodore W. Luling	1921–1947

Renamed Board of Management 1947

The Rt Hon. The Lord Luke	1947–1956

Renamed Board of Governors 1948

Mr C. J. Malim	1956–1968
Mr Francis M. Cumberlege	1968–

Physicians

John Richard Farre	1805–1857
Frederick J. Farre	1837–1880
Robert Martin	1856–1884
Sir Stephen Mackenzie	1884–1905
James Taylor, C.B.E.	1898–1919
Sir Gordon M. Holmes, C.M.G., C.B.E., F.R.S.	1914–1927
W. J. Adie	1927–1934
W. Russell Brain, later Lord Brain	1930–1937
J. Purdon Martin	1934–1937
Denis Brinton	1937–1945
S. P. Meadows	1937–1967
W 1931 R. A. Hickling	1947–1949
C 1939 Simon Behrman	1947–1967 Locum to 1969
C. J. Gavey	1947–
F. Elliott	1948–1959
C. J. Earl	1959–
R. W. Ross Russell	1967–
W. Ian McDonald	1969–

Surgeons

J. Cunningham Saunders (Founder)	1804 died 1810
Benjamin Travers, F.R.S.	1810–1817

Sir William Lawrence, Bart., F.R.S.	1814–1826
Frederick Tyrell	1817 died 1843
John Scott	1826–1846
Gilbert Mackmurdo, F.R.S.	1830–1856
John Dalrymple, F.R.S.	1832–1849
James Dixon	1843–1868
George Critchett	1843–1877
Sir William Bowman, Bart., F.R.S.	1846–1876
Alfred Poland	1848–1861
H. H. Mackmurdo	1851–1852
John C. Wordsworth	1852–1883
John F. Streatfeild	1856 died 1886
J. W. Hulke, F.R.S.	1858–1890
George Lawson	1862–1891
Sir Jonathan Hutchinson, F.R.S.	1862–1878
John Couper	1866–1895
J. Soelberg Wells	1867 died 1880
Waren Tay	1877–1904
James E. Adams	1877–1884
Sir John Tweedy, LL.D.	1878–1900
Robert Lyell	1880 died 1882
Edward Nettleship, F.R.S.	1882–1898
R. Marcus Gunn	1883–1909
W. Lang	1884–1912
A. Quarry Silcock	1886 died 1904
J. B. Lawford, LL.D.	1890–1918
A. Stanford Morton	1891–1909
E. Treacher Collins	1895–1922
W. T. Holmes Spicer	1898–1920
Percy Flemming	1900–1919
J. Herbert Fisher	1900–1927
Sir Arnold Lawson, K.B.E.	1900–1914
C. Devereux Marshall	1900 died on active service 1918
Sir William T. Lister, K.C.M.G.	1904–1905 1919–1929
Sir John Herbert Parsons, C.B.E., F.R.S.	1905–1933
Claud Worth	1905–1921
W. Ilbert Hancock	1909 died 1910
George Coats	1909 died 1915
Malcolm L. Hepburn	1910–1926
A. Cyril Hudson	1913–1928
R. Foster Moore, O.B.E.	1914–1937
R. Affleck Greeves	1915–1938†

	F. A. Juler, C.V.O.	1918–1942†
	Charles B. Goulden, O.B.E.	1919–1939†
	B. T. Lang	1920 died 1928
	M. H. Whiting, O.B.E.	1921–1945†
	P. G. Doyne	1922–1946†
	Humphrey Neame	1926–1947
	Miss Ida C. Mann, C.B.E.	1927–1949
	Sir Stewart Duke-Elder, G.C.V.O., F.R.S.	1928–1936
	Rupert S. Scott	1928–1938
	R. C. Davenport	1930–1958
	H. B. Stallard	1933–1938 1947–1966
	Frank W. Law	1936–1963
	E. F. King	1937–1964
	J. H. Doggart	1938–1960
	C. Dee Shapland	1938–1964
	Harold Ridley	1938–1971
	Arthur Lister	1939–1970
	A. G. Cross	1947–1973
	A. G. Leigh	1947 died 1968
W 1923	C. L. Gimblett	1947–1956
C 1927	J. D. M. Cardell	1947–1961
W 1927	G. G. Penman	1947–1958
C 1928	F. T. Ridley	1947–1968
W 1936	E. Wolff	1947 died 1954
W 1936	T. Keith Lyle, C.B.E.	1947–1968
W 1936	J. G. Milner	1947–1956
C 1937	Sir Allen Goldsmith, K.C.V.O.	1947–1958
W 1938	A. S. Philps	1947 died 1956
W 1939	P. McG. Moffatt	1947 died 1963
	J. E. M. Ayoub	1950–1973
	S. J. H. Miller	1954–
	C. A. G. Cook, M.C., G.M.	1956–1973
	J. R. Hudson	1956–
	K. C. Wybar	1956–
	Redmond J. H. Smith	1961–
	D. P. Greaves	1961–
	P. D. Trevor-Roper	1961–
	D. Ainslie	1962–
	Professor Barrie Jones	1963–
	Lorimer G. Fison	1963–
	I. M. Duguid	1964–
	Barrie Jay	1968–

R. K. Blach	1969–
N. S. C. Rice	1969–
Peter Fells	1971–
M. A. Bedford	1972–
Professor David Hill	1973–
John Wright	1973–
Peter Wright	1973–

Curators and Pathologists

Charles Bader	1857–1867
Bowater Vernon	1867–1871
Edward Nettleship	1871–1873
T. C. Morgan	1873–1874
W. A. Brailey	1874–1882
W. J. Milles	1882–1884
J. B. Lawford	1884–1887
E. Treacher Collins	1887–1894
C. D. Marshall	1894–1899
W. T. Lister	1899–1901
J. H. Parsons	1901–1904
George Coats	1904–1909
A. C. Hudson	1909–1912
R. A. Greeves	1912–1915
F. A. Juler	1916–1917
C. A. Maghy	1917–1918
M. H. Whiting	1918–1919
H. Neame	1919–1923
R. S. Scott	1923–1928
H. B. Stallard	1928–1933
Frank W. Law	1933–1936
C. D. Shapland	1936–1938
	1939–1940
A. J. B. Goldsmith	1938–1939
A. G. Cross	1940–1947
C. Swan	1947–1948

Bacteriologists

	B. H. Wedd	1908–1909
	E. P. Minett	1909–1910
	S. H. Browning	1910–1943
	J. N. Cumings	1943–1946
C.R.	W. E. Armstrong	1946–1948
H.H.	E. H. Koerner	1947–1948

Dermatologist

Peter Borrie	1950–

Ear, Nose and Throat Surgeons

G. Seccombe Hett	1923–1929
Gilbert Howells	1929–1962
B. H. Pickard	1962–

Medical Officers to the X-Ray Departments

	Sir James Mackenzie Davidson	1898–1910
	Edward W. H. Shenton	1911–1912
	R. Higham Cooper	1912–1918
	Albert Bowie	1919 died 1939
	C. N. Pulvertaft	1940–1941
	M. Lederman	1941–1946
	R. S. Murray	1947–1961
H.H.	Douglas Gordon	1956–
C.R.	Glyn A. S. Lloyd	1962–

Radiotherapists

M. Lederman ("Consulting")	1948–1968
M. A. Bedford, Consultant Ophthalmic Surgeon in charge of the Radiotherapy Clinic	1972–

Anaesthetists

	Helen B. Alcock	1946–1969
	Sheila M. Anderson	1946–
	H. K. Ashworth	1946–1969
	Ivan G. Braddon	1946–
	E. Barnet Mallinson	1946 died 1965
	G. F. Panton	1946–1973
W	J. G. Bourne	1947–1948
C	Herbert Curtis	1947 died 1963
C	L. H. Lerman	1947–1971
W	B. G. B. Lucas	1947–1948
W	S. G. Shippard	1947–1971
C	O. L. Carden Sibley	1947–1948
W	Angus Smith	1947–
W	G. C. Steel	1947–1955
W	B. Sullivan	1947 died 1959

G. Barry Smith	1968–
Bruce Philpott	1968–1969
Doreen Birley	1969–
P. B. Hardwick	1969–1970
Doreen B. Pallot	1969–
J. R. Samuel	1971–
H. W. D. Denison-Davies	1971–

Dental Surgeons

Arthur E. Relph	1912–1915
R. M. Fickling	1915–1928
Stanley A. Riddett	1928–1930
John Winter	1930–1946 Dept. closed
Appointed Hon. Consulting Dental Surgeon	1946–1950
Re-appointed Consultant on re-establishment of Department	1950–1963 Dept. discontinued

Medical Officers to the Orthoptic Departments

	P. M. Duke-Elder	1931–1933
	M. A. Pugh	1933–1947
C.R.	J. H. Doggart	1947–1960
H.H.	T. Keith Lyle	1947–1968
C.R.	A. G. Cross	1960–1973
H.H.	K. C. Wybar	1968–
C.R.	Peter Fells	1973–

Medical Officers to the Physiotherapy Departments

	W. Stewart Duke-Elder	1927–1936
	Frank W. Law	1936–1959 Dept. closed
W 1929	P. Bauwens	1947–1966 Dept. closed

Medical Officers to the Department for Venereal Diseases

S. H. Browning	1920–1944
V. E. Lloyd	1944–1956
E. M. C. Dunlop	1964–

Deans of the Medical School

W. T. Holmes Spicer	1899–1920
M. L. Hepburn	1920–1926
C. B. Goulden	1926–1939
R. C. Davenport	1939–1959
T. Keith Lyle	1959–1967
A. G. Cross	1967–

Secretaries

Richard Battley	1804–1818
Matthew Heathfield	1818–1834
William Bircham	1835–1844
Robert Francis Dalrymple	1844–1846
F. A. Curling	1846–1856
Charles Gordelier	1856–1860
J. Mogford	1860–1872
Robert J. Newstead	1872–1897
Robert J. Bland	1897–1923
*Arthur J. M. Tarrant	1924–1957
J. P. Heming	1957–1964
A. F. Gray	1964–

* Title altered to "House Governor", 1947

Physicians of Moorfields who have served on the Council of the Royal College of Physicians

Frederick John Farre	1846–1848: 1866–1867: Censor 1841–1842, 1854: Treasurer 1868–1883: Vice-President 1885†
Robert Martin	1873: 1875–1876: Censor 1877–1878
Sir Stephen Mackenzie	1899–1901
James Taylor	1917–1919
Sir Gordon Holmes	1932–1934: Censor 1934–1935, 1937
Lord Brain	1947–1949: President 1950–1957
Denis Brinton	1956–1958
Richard A. Hickling	1960–1963

†President, Vice-President, Treasurer, and Censors are *ex-officio* members of Council

Surgeons of Moorfields who have served on the Council of the Royal College of Surgeons

Sir William Lawrence, Bart., F.R.S.	1828–1867 (Pres. 1846 and 1855)
Benjamin Travers, F.R.S.	1830–1858 (Pres. 1847 and 1856)
Frederick Tyrell	1838–1843
John Scott	1844–1846
Gilbert Mackmurdo, F.R.S.	1850–1869
John Dalrymple, F.R.S.	1851–1852
George Critchett	1871–1879
Sir Johnathan Hutchinson, F.R.S.	1879–1895 (Pres. 1889)
J. W. Hulke, F.R.S.	1881–1895 (Pres. 1893–1894)
George Lawson	1884–1892
Sir John Tweedy, LL.D.	1892–1907 (Pres. 1903–1905)
J. H. Fisher	1923–1931

Co-opted Members of Council, The Royal College of Surgeons

G. W. Black*	1945–1948
J. H. Doggart	1948–1953
A. B. Nutt	1953–1958
T. K. Lyle	1958–1963
A. G. Cross	1963–1968
J. R. Hudson	1968–

* Invited member 1945–1947

Representatives on the Joint Secretariat Committee of The Royal College of Surgeons

Of the Ophthalmological Society of the United Kingdom:

E. F. King	1947–1948
T. Keith Lyle	1948–1949
G. J. O. Bridgeman	1949–1950
A. G. Cross	1950–1951
Sir Allen Goldsmith	1951–1952
Frank Law	1952–

Of the Faculty of Ophthalmologists:

F. A. Williamson-Noble	1945
F. A. Juler	1945–1951
J. H. Doggart	1951–1962
J. R. Hudson	1962–1966
Kenneth C. Wybar	1966–1967
J. R. Hudson	1967–1970
Lorimer Fison	1970–

Residents—Moorfields and City Road

1854	Robert Henry Moon	1893	E. C. Fischer
1857	Charles Bader	1894	H. V. McKenzie
1860	T. H. Hawkins	1896	K. E. Chetwood-Aiken
1862	C. J. Workman	1896	D. N. Maclennan
1863	R. Wilson Willcox	1897	W. G. Byers
1864	Charles Moss	1898	W. E. Smith
1867	Francis Ewbank	1899	A. F. MacCallan
1870	T. C. Morgan	1901	W. S. Inman
1872	Frank Buller	1902	William Anderson
1874	C. W. Owen	1902	Colin A. Campbell
1875	A. S. Morton	1903	L. S. Miller
1875	R. J. Pye-Smith	1904	E. E. R. Sawrey
1876	R. Marcus Gunn	1904	Charles Goulden
1876	G. H. Burnham	1905	A. C. Hudson
1879	G. A. Berry	1906	Norman E. Gibbs
1880	W. J. Milles	1907	J. Stevenson Wilson
1880	W. A. Fitzgerald	1908	W. Ward
1882	M. J. Symons	1908	A. W. Weihen
1882	W. O. Maher	1909	H. C. Snell
1883	J. B. Lawford	1909	A. Beck Cluckie
1883	Ernest Hudson	1910	Leonard J. C. Mitchell
1884	E. Treacher Collins	1911	M. H. Whiting
1885	J. Gray	1912	G. F. C. Wallis
1886	J. R. Roberts	1912	W. G. Fraser
1887	C. H. Walker	1912	W. A. Anderson
1887	J. S. Hinnell	1913	J. P. Harrison
1888	H. T. Kelsall	1913	J. Fison
1889	D. Gunn	1914	P. Verdon
1889	D. J. Wood	1914	Ivor W. Joynt
1891	H. Gaiger	1915	Ivor L. Tuckett
1892	C. D. Marshall	1916	Clive M. Eadie
1892	E. Gault	1916	D. L. Shaw

1917	C. A. Maghy	1938	A. G. Leigh
1917	G. F. Rowcroft	1939	C. M. Heath
1917	M. E. Joll	1939	W. L. B. Burns
1918	R. Meyer	1939	V. B. Purvis
1918	M. Morton	1940	D. H. Douglas
1919	S. H. Miles	1941	M. Sterling Levis
1919	W. H. Simpson	1941	R. Dorrington Ward
1919	M. C. Gardner	1941	P. D. Trevor-Roper
1919	D. McMurray Dickson	1942	R. A. D. Crawford
1920	B. Graves	1942	S. P. Redmond
1920	E. F. Wilson	1943	J. R. C. Holmes
1921	O. G. Morgan	1943	P. Jardine
1921	M. Baranov	1944	J. M. Mallett
1922	S. T. Parker	1944	D. Ainslie
1922	T. Colley	1945	E. Lyons
1923	H. M. Armstrong	1945	C. C. Ring
1923	W. Burr	1946	T. F. Roche
1924	S. H. G. Humfrey	1946	D. G. Simpson
1925	W. M. Muirhead	1947	G. D. Elphick
1925	W. J. B. Riddell	1947	G. Fenwick
1926	C. H. Ackroyd	1947	E. C. Glover
1927	H. V. Coverdale	1947	J. R. Hudson
1927	F. W. Law	1948	D. P. Greaves
1927	W. E. Heath	1948	C. A. G. Cook
1928	J. Bruce Hamilton	1948	E. T. Meyer
1929	C. D. Shapland	1949	L. G. Fison
1929	L. B. Somerville-Large	1949	D. P. Choyce
1930	G. W. Black	1949	B. A. Ward
1930	E. F. King	1950	J. L. Bignell
1931	E. G. Recordon	1950	R. J. H. Smith
1931	C. Newlyn Smith	1950	J. C. Parr
1932	Frank Flynn	1951	R. F. Elliott
1932	T. M. O'Neill	1951	R. H. L. Ferguson
1933	N. H. L. Ridley	1951	M. J. Gilkes
1933	H. H. Skeoch	1951	A. J. Ogg
1934	A. Lister	1952	J. D. Brosnan
1934	T. J. Phillips	1952	S. W. N. Gibson
1935	A. H. Briggs	1952	J. Whitwell
1935	A. J. B. Goldsmith	1953	E. M. L. Evans
1936	E. C. Zorab	1953	B. R. Jones
1936	C. J. Blumenthal	1953	W. J. Levy
1937	A. G. Cross	1954	R. N. McCann
1937	G. H. Buck	1954	R. R. Collmann
1938	J. E. M. Ayoub	1954	J. Winstanley

1955	Miss T. M. Coyle	1964	H. C. Bentley
1955	C. B. Walker	1964	H. Cheng
1955	D. W. Hill	1964	P. J. Fenton
1956	C. W. Thornhill	1964	P. A. MacFaul
1956	L. J. Pigott	1964	A. S. Mushin
1956	S. B. Kapur	1965	H. V. Coop
1957	T. D. H. Gray	1965	U. Majzoub
1957	L. W. Poole	1965	A. B. Richards
1957	I. M. Duguid	1965	J. E. Wright
1958	R. F. Jones	1965	R. A. N. Welham
1958	J. E. Cairns	1965	J. L. K. Bankes
1958	N. L. Dallas	1965	A. J. Bron
1959	E. J. Arnott	1965	J. C. D. Hart
1959	G. M. Krolman	1965	D. J. du Temple
1959	Miss A. M. S. Connell	1966	C. N. Banks
1959	P. V. Rycroft	1966	P. J. Folca
1959	R. K. Blach	1966	D. Knight-Jones
1960	T. L. F. Averill	1966	R. McGuinness
1960	P. G. Watson	1966	J. R. Chesterton
1960	R. F. Fisher	1966	A. H. Chignell
1960	P. Hardy Smith	1966	D. L. Easty
1960	D. M. Watson	1966	J. Thomsitt
1960	A. Freedman	1967	N. A. P. Brown
1960	J. E. K. Galbraith	1967	R. E. Hartley
1961	M. A. Bedford	1967	R. J. Marsh
1961	M. L. Mulcahy	1967	H. P. Williams
1961	D. E. P. Jones	1967	F. H. Bors
1961	A. D. Fox	1967	M. F. Gundry
1962	A. Patterson	1967	D. A. Owen
1962	E. W. G. Davies	1967	J. R. Strong
1962	C. J. F. Maguire	1968	R. M. Brown
1962	N. S. C. Rice	1968	A. M. Hamilton
1963	B. Cobb	1968	I. M. Rabinowicz
1963	P. Fells	1968	W. Taylor
1963	M. J. Corrigan	1968	J. M. Cappin
1963	Miss M. T. Challis	1968	R. S. Clemett
1963	J. G. Henry	1968	W. J. Dinning
1963	P. N. Awdry	1968	I. H. S. Revie
1963	A. W. Gentles	1969	J. A. Bowbyes
1963	M. B. R. Mathalone	1969	P. K. Leaver
1963	I. Raiter	1969	J. R. Pyne
1964	J. B. Heinze	1969	S. H. Saunders
1964	H. Le Grice	1969	A. D. Holt-Wilson
1964	J. D. Scott	1969	J. I. McGill

1970	J. S. Shilling	1972	J. Keast-Butler
1970	P. C. Wellings	1972	D. McLeod
1970	R. A. Hitchings	1972	G. D. Sturrock
1970	I. S. Levy	1972	D. Lloyd Jones
1970	I. H. Chisholm	1973	R. H. B. Grey
1970	S. F. J. Pilley	1973	C. Townsend
1971	T. J. Halliwell	1973	G. H. Chester
1971	D. L. Hunter	1973	R. A. F. Whitelocke
1971	R. H. J. Darvell	1974	D. R. Michell
1971	M. G. Falcon	1974	N. J. A. Young
1971	A. J. Atkinson	1974	Mrs J. Carruthers
1971	A. D. McG. Steele	1974	M. C. W. Treplin
1972	P. L. R. Hein	1974	M. P. Quinlan
1972	A. T. Morris	1974	D. J. Spalton

Residents—High Holborn

1947	F. Clifton	1958	G. V. Catford
1947	K. W. B. Rostron	1958	J. H. S. Martin
1947	R. S. E. Brewton	1959	J. Anderson
1947	S. J. H. Miller	1959	G. W. Crock
1948	W. E. S. Bain	1959	B. S. Jay
1948	D. A. Langley	1960	Mrs M. C. Handscombe
1949	K. C. Wybar	1960	E. Cameron
1949	P. L. Baxter	1960	J. H. Kelsey
1950	G. Frampton	1961	J. D. Salmon
1950	M. L. Waugh	1961	Peter Wright
1951	J. Swartz	1962	P. J. H. Sellors
1951	W. S. Foulds	1962	N. A. Locket
1952	J. A. E. Primrose	1963	R. B. de Saram
1952	G. C. Swain	1963	B. Martin
1953	C. I. Phillips	1963	R. B. Harcourt
1953	C. G. Tulloh	1964	N. R. Galloway
1954	J. N. Ormrod	1964	M. D. Sanders
1954	T. G. O'Driscoll	1964	I. M. Rabinowicz
1955	R. D. Suckling	1965	C. M. Mailer
1955	G. G. Powell	1965	A. C. Bird
1956	S. J. Crews	1965	D. B. Archer
1956	C. M. Ruben	1965	A. Tomkin
1957	D. H. Coop	1966	T. J. ffytche
1957	J. D. Abrams	1966	J. J. Kanski
1957	C. R. Fenton	1967	M. S. Davies

1967	I. K. Lewkonia (Luke)	1970	P. D. Davies
1967	A. R. Elkington	1970	E. D. Dorrell
1967	D. V. Ingram	1971	D. A. R. McKay
1968	M. G. Glasspool	1971	D. S. I. Taylor
1968	A. G. Karseras	1971	J. A. Harding
1968	R. Daniel	1972	M. D. P. Crick
1969	F. P. G. Cheok	1972	J. R. O. Collin
1969	P. H. Bannister	1972	R. L. Coakes
1969	P. M. L. James	1973	A. R. Fielder
1969	D. A. Hadley	1973	D. T. H. Tarbuck
1970	R. P. Knowlden	1973	H. M. van Oldenborgh

INDEX

Figures in italics denote illustrations and, in the case of individuals, biographical notes.

299